THE
DISCOVERY
OF NATURE

by

ALBERT BETTEX

SIMON AND SCHUSTER

NEW YORK

Contents

'Go, my sons, sell your fields, your apparel and your rings. Burn your books, buy yourselves strong shoes, wander forth into the mountains, explore the valleys and the deserts, the beaches of the sea and the deepest abysses of the earth. Observe the characteristics of the animals, the differences between the plants, the various kinds of minerals and their special characteristics, and study the origin of everything in existence. Learn from the peasants the lore of heaven and earth and do not be ashamed. And finally: buy coal, build furnaces, observe and experiment tirelessly. In such wise and in no other will you come to the knowledge of things and of their nature.'

Petrus Severinus: Idea medicinae philosophicae, Basel, 1597

CHEMISTRY

Nothing is known to us about the men who first discovered the healing properties of camomile, recognized the value of the indigo plant for dyeing, built a wall of limestone or found grains of gold in the sand at the edge of a river. The earliest encounters of man the discoverer with the inexhaustible gifts of the material world which air, water and earth offered him, lie hidden in prehistoric times. In early historical times, when the mist begins to disperse, we find that in many parts of the world he already has some small command of practical chemical skill and knowledge. In the last centuries of the pre-Christian era, the peoples of the ancient Egyptian, east Asian and Greek cultures, taking as a basis this pre-scientific inheritance, erected upon it the framework of a knowledge of matter which depended not only upon research and experiment but also upon a search for religious cohesion. This was alchemy, which was to hold sway for two thousand years.

From these beginnings of alchemy until the present day, man has investigated matter over and over again, always drawing new conclusions. It was at first explained in terms of supernatural, spiritual forces, and later of invisible atomic systems which were thought to control it from within. The scientists whom we see from late antiquity to Paracelsus and Scheele and beyond, performing countless experiments, assessed the properties of matter and described them principally in qualitative terms, and stood in awe before the intangible forces which they found at work in their laboratories; from Lavoisier on, with ever more accurate tools, they conduct chiefly quantitative analyses: measuring changes with scales, thermometers, pressure gauges, electrical apparatus and so on, and expressing them in permanent neat formulae. At the end of the eighteenth century, the supposedly indivisible elements air, fire, water and earth, upon which the entire material world had been founded from the earliest times and which had long been doomed to defeat, crumbled under the sharpened perception of the scientist. In their place came a growing knowledge of what constitutes the earth surface from the highest mountain peaks to the most microscopically small crystal in the sand of the sea bed; of the nature of the gases which make up the air about us, and of the soluble substances concealed in water. Present-day chemists know ninety-two elements as the foundations of terrestrial matter (without counting the artificially constituted transuranic elements); they know hundreds of thousands of combinations of these elements, and are penetrating deeper and deeper into the innermost workings of chemical reactions.

Time and again, chemists have reached across the borders of their own subject and contributed with their findings to the illumination of natural events in other scientific disciplines: explaining the chemical forces in human and animal physiology, the processes of respiration and nutrition in plants, and the great cycle of matter from mineral to vegetable to animal and back again to mineral. In our century, they have provided the key to such deep mysteries as the chemical nature of chromosomes in cells, and in their industrial activities their enterprising experimentation is daily producing new materials. 'That which did not exist before is chemistry.'

The following pages will bring before the reader selected pictorial records of the history of this powerful science which has placed man in a rich, intelligent and diversified relationship to the whole material world. Justus von Liebig writes: 'The search for the causes of natural phenomena, the sources of plant and animal life, the origins of their food, the conditions required for their healthy development, and the changes by which we are affected owing to the physical nature of our bodies, are so appropriate to the human mind that those sciences which provide a satisfactory conclusion to this search exert more influence than any others upon the development of the mind. The perception of a new truth brings a man, as it were, a newly acquired sense, enabling him to observe and recognize many phenomena which remain unknown and obscure to others, as before they were to him.' He is convinced 'that chemistry offers one of the most powerful means of intellectual development, and that the study of it is useful not only insofar as it furthers the material interests of man, but also because it provides insight into the wonders of creation which surround us, and to which our existence, survival and development are intimately linked.'

The horizon becomes wider still when matter takes man back millions of years, through the history of its existence on earth and of its cosmic origins.

'IN THE BEGINNING GOD CREATED HEAVEN AND EARTH...'

The wood-carver had to introduce the written word to help him conjure up the power and setting of the act of creation. The earth and the vault of heaven, light ('Tag') and darkness ('Nacht'), water ('Meer'), land ('Erde') and the plant kingdom are all visible. According to the Book of Genesis this was the work of the first three days of creation, a part of that world which man was to explore and investigate tirelessly in the days to come. His research was to bring him to an understanding of the nucleus of the atom and of the most distant cluster of stars. For the believer this world owes its origin to a divine act of creation when all things had their beginning. Our artist portrays the invisible original cause as God, floating on the clouds and crowned with a divine halo. The God he shows us has not only called forth and blessed land and water; he has also invested His work with some of His own creative power. 'He ceases not to create and to nourish until the Day of Judgement', says Luther. 'Almighty God and Father, Creator of heaven and earth, Himself created the mountains and the valleys, the slopes and the rocky screes, the chasms and the seams, the sulphur and the mercury out of which grow ore and silver day by day.' This is the reply which came from the doctor, humanist and mineralogist Agricola from the depths of his native Saxon mountains. He was one of those explorers of nature who throughout time, each in his own way and in all reverence, became conscious of the traces of divinity in nature, finding them even in the inanimate matter of the earth's crust.

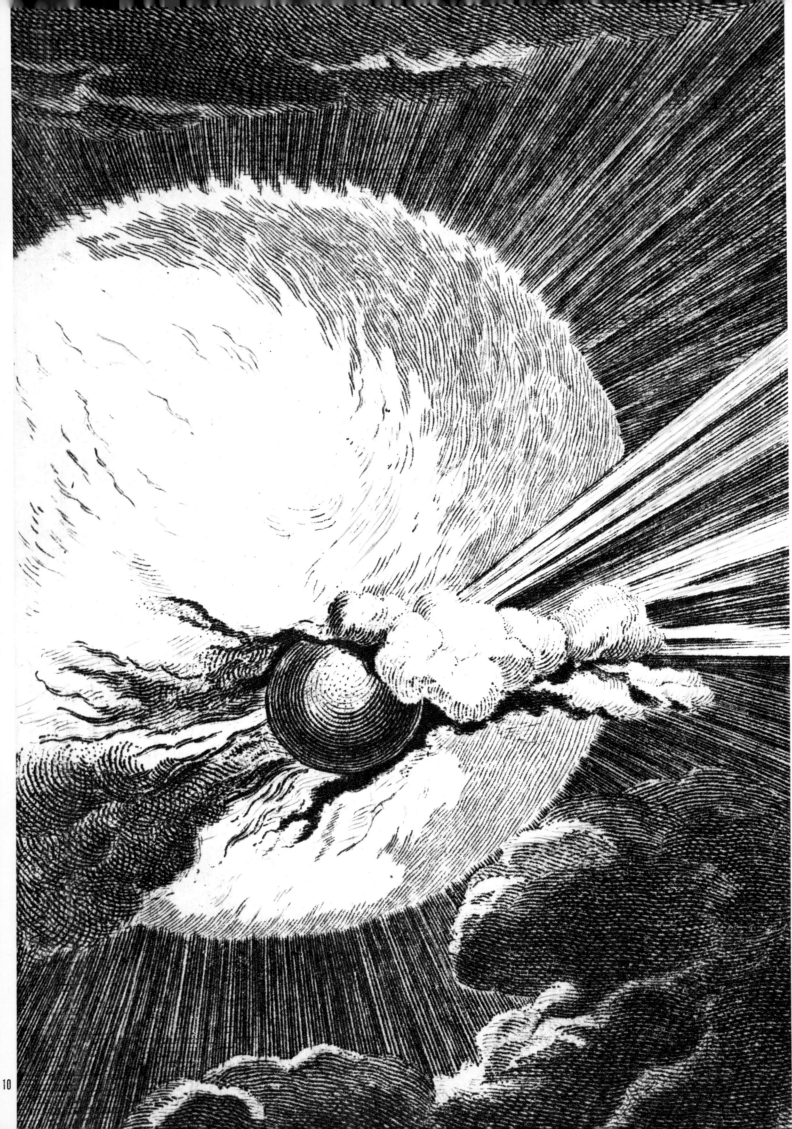

How the Planetary System originated according to Laplace and Kant

◀ A Cosmic Catastrophe creates New Worlds

'The science of the nature of the earth is connected with
that of heaven.' This sentence, written by Buffon about the
year 1745, lays down the bold view that earthly matter must
in the final analysis derive from cosmic matter. In the enlightened eighteenth century a few men well schooled in
mathematics drew up scientific explanations of the origin of
the world and these contained the two prototypes on which
all later cosmogonies are based. The picture on the left
gives an imaginative representation of Buffon's Theory of
Catastrophe; the highly condensed nucleus of a comet (in
those days comets were imagined to be of gigantic size)
burrows its way straight into the side of the sun, which
was thought to consist of glowing hot liquid, and with its
powerful thrust forces a part of the solar matter away into
space. This solar matter becomes condensed as it cools,
extinguishes itself and forms into slightly flattened spheres,
which come under the influence of gravity and begin to
move into parallel orbits in the same plane: these are the

planets. Therefore earthly matter consists also of solar
matter—and chemistry is thus remotely connected with
cosmogony. Some scientists, amongst whom was the English
astrophysicist James Jeans, developed the theory of catastrophe further in the nineteenth and twentieth centuries.
A cosmic pattern of another kind was produced by Pierre
Simon Laplace in 1796 (picture above). With the imagination
of a mathematician he saw in the darkness of the universe
a primeval nebula of glowing gas in rotation which stretched
far beyond the planetary system as it is known today. This
gas slowly cooled down, shrank and began to rotate faster
in accordance with the law of the conservation of angular
momentum. As a result nebular material detached itself at
the equator in concentric rotating rings. In each ring the
material became condensed into a glowing fluid structure
in the shape of a sphere: this was a planet. In the meantime
the nucleus of the primeval nebula which remained behind
formed the ball of the sun. Another nebular theory which
embraces the whole stellar system and approximates most
closely to present-day ideas was originated by Kant in 1755.

11

The Earth's Crust reveals its History

A few leading men who were studying the new science of geology late in the eighteenth century embodied in two well-known theories the answers to the bold question: 'What is the origin of the earth's crust?' One of them was the German mineralogist, Abraham Gottlob Werner. He assumed that chemical crystalline deposits like salts detached themselves from a primeval sea and together with finely disseminated substances like clay sank down to cover the sea-bed, the layers reposing one upon each other. This 'Neptunian' view was challenged by the 'Vulcanists' or 'Plutonists', headed by the Scot, James Hutton. Many scientists were aware of the veins and cracks in the interior of the earth and of those substances which clearly were in origin a form of fiery liquid which later solidified. All those who had dis-

covered this knew that fire and magma must have been the main substance forming the earth's crust. Werner's pupils, as a result of their studies of nature as a whole perceived the narrowness of their master's view—so did the Frenchman d'Aubuisson de Voisins. The above picture which comes from the second edition of his '*Traité de géognosie*' (1825–35) provides the evidence that the scientists were by then able to distinguish between sediments out of primeval seas and eruptive rocks. Near St-Etienne, between two jet-black coal-seams just the height of a man, lie the horizontal layers of slate which contain coal. But in the lower part of this 'Neptunian' sediment volcanic forces have intruded and left behind concretions of iron. At the top there is a 13 foot-thick layer of sandstone with petrified tree-trunks in it.

THE SMELTING OF GOLD IN ANCIENT EGYPT

For countless centuries before the beginnings of scientific chemistry prehistoric man learned to classify plants, dividing them into those which were poisonous and those which had healing properties; he was already practised in the skills of dyeing and brewing; he was beginning, too, to make use of the earth's mineral wealth. It is impossible to ascertain in what period this 'practical chemistry' was begun. But it is known for certain that, as soon as man became master of fire, the earth's crust began to render up to him its materials in full abundance. All of them, the minerals in the ores, the potter's clay, the mason's lime, yielded to his power as, with the help of fire, he mastered highly advanced chemical techniques, although he was still unable to explain them. Most of them were undoubtedly well-known by the beginning of the seven thousand years of the history of man which we are able to study with greater accuracy. We give four examples.

On preceding page: THE SECRET OF EGYPTIAN DYESTUFFS
Early civilized peoples obtained some of their dyestuffs and colouring materials, such as the blue of the indigo plant and the purple of the murex shell-fish, from the plant and animal kingdom; most of the colours used were, however, mineral dyes, found in the earth's crust. When the Egyptian painter depicted an act of homage like that in the top register of this bas-relief from the chambers of the temple at Kalabsha, he had a practical form of colour-chemistry to help him. This provided him with a limited number of mineral colours, which proved to be as immortal as the gods. These colours were mixed with water and then applied on top of white limewash. Later analyses have shown the red-brown colour to be iron oxide (red iron ore or burned yellow ochre); and the yellow has proved to be ochre—that is, feldspar which has effloresced and merged with iron compounds which are a frequent constituent of dyes. Blue was made artificially

IN A PARIS POTTERY OF THE EIGHTEENTH CENTURY CLAY IS BEING WORKED BY THE SAME METHODS AS IN ANCIENT TIMES

out of a mixture of materials: copper oxide was used as the source of this colour, and this was mixed with yellow into a pale olive-green.

Left: Gold has excited man throughout the ages as no other metal has done; it has awakened his basest greed and his purest delight; with its untarnishable lustre it has furnished him with a high symbol of purity and loyalty. As long ago as three thousand years before Christ the Egyptians were using slaves to extract gold-bearing minerals from the vast mines on the frontier of Nubia: this was the land of gold. The minerals were pulverized in mortars and stone mills, the mineral residue was washed out, and the gold was then fired in a crucible, melted down into a lump of placer gold and so refined into a state of purity. Shallow pans were used and these were placed in low smelting ovens. Lead and salt were added; the salt removed any silver residue from the gold by forming silver chloride with the residue;

this, together with the lead, went into the dross. Slaves stirred up the fire with bellows. After five days the crucible was taken off the fire and the gold was poured into small pots to cool down and solidify.

Above: Like gold, clay was also purified by washing out foreign bodies. The raw material, which is capable of swelling considerably in volume but is insoluble, is first thoroughly soaked and at (a) is being placed on a potter's wheel—which was already known to the ancient Egyptians. It is kept in motion by the feet and the clay is rounded into shape with the hands. At (b) small ovens, at (c) furnaces for chemists and at (d) clay pipes are being made. The final wonder is achieved in the glowing heat of the firing oven at the back; the material—which up till now has been so easy to fashion and mould—has the water forced out of it by the heat and is turned into the exact opposite: an article which is hard, non-porous and fireproof.

Alchemy

'Clever men once noticed that nature has caused the waters of several seas to have various substances dissolved in them and as a result of the drying effect of the warmth of the sun to discharge these in condensed form, and that in this way solid bodies originated.' This was stated by Agricola, the 'father of mineralogy', in 1530 in his book *De re metallica*. He coined the name 'succi concreti' for these deposits from the water; he meant thereby the salts, particularly the salt used for cooking, and correctly ascribed their discovery to that practical chemistry which taught men how to smelt metals, extract gold, and harden clay and enabled them to carry out important research into many substances in the sea and earth's crust thousands of years before the days of science. The ancient world already knew this method of extracting salt from the sunny Mediterranean where the coasts were seldom flooded by rain. A weir (C) regulates the influx of salt water to the low-lying coast-land. It flows into a system of ditches which intersect each other at right angles, washes against the shallow basins (E), into which it can be allowed to enter when the sluice-gates are raised. Here it evaporates gradually, the salt forms into crystals and augments as soon as more sea-water is let into the salt gardens for evaporation. Finally it is raked together, lifted out with shovels (G), put into jars, and sent all over the world in trading ships.

It was not until the time of scientific chemistry that salt proved to be one of the wonders of transformation in the making of a chemical compound: out of two poisonous substances, chlorine and sodium, originated that substance which day by day seasons the food of mankind throughout the world.

For almost two millennia the investigation of matter was governed by alchemy: that remarkable combination of human attitudes to the mysterious world of material things. Here we find the attitude of a scientist who works with furnaces, crucibles and alembics, and seeks to establish the properties of matter, combined with that of a mystic who is gripped by the presence of divine power, seeing it in every phenomenon from the stars down to the metals in the earth's surface. When once alchemy had been linked with the knowledge of the elements which was the product of Greek natural philosophy, it was here that the human mind emerged from the practical chemistry of earlier times to find in matter a great physical and metaphysical puzzle.

Alchemistic practices were in use in the last centuries of the pre-Christian era both in Egypt and in China. There, as in Europe, rumour spoke of a secret art which would enable man to transform base metals such as iron, tin or lead into the noble silver or gold. A certain Zosimos, living in about AD 300 near Alexandria, which at the end of the classical era served as the intellectual capital of three continents, has left us twenty-eight letters, written for teaching purposes, containing a disordered synthesis of what Babylonian astrologers, Egyptian alchemists, Greek natural philosophers and early Christian sages contributed to the solution of the problems of the material world. When, in the eighth and ninth centuries, great Islamic doctors like Jabir Ibn Hayyan emerged in the empire of the Caliphs, they took over the collective tradition of alchemistic knowledge and contributed to it their conclusions that all metals ultimately contained the postulated substances sulphur and mercury, and that it was possible to reconstitute a basic substance which would not only effect the transformation of base metals into gold, but also endow men with eternal youth and health. For centuries, the highest and boldest ambition of chemists was to discover this 'elixir', known also as the 'Philosopher's Stone'. It was in an Arabic formulation, translated into Latin, that the wisdom and folly of alchemy came to Europe in the middle of the twelfth century, and here it continued to determine the relationship of man to matter as late as the early eighteenth century. Popes and emperors, scholars and quacks practised it. Even Isaac Newton and the young Goethe fell under its spell.

One of the major contributions of the ancient Greeks to the study of matter was a theory on the basis of which material things were classified, in broad outline, up to the end of the middle ages. They found four basic, mysterious, irreducible forces at work everywhere in nature: warmth, cold, dryness and moisture, of which two appeared in visible form in each of the four elements. For in fire warmth and dryness were coupled; in water, cold and moisture; in air, warmth and moisture; in earth, cold and dryness. The whole visible world, in their view, was built up from these four elements, even if they were always differently proportioned in different substances. A small branch of new wood sufficed to prove it: on the cut surface, little drops of water appeared, showing that the element water was present in wood; steam rose if the wood was heated: therefore the element air was present; flames gave evidence of the presence of fire, and, since they left ashes behind them, the presence of earth was established. The four elements, however, seemed to them to point to the existence of a basic substance unperceptible to the senses: the *hyle* of Aristotle.

If the four elements were present in all substances, showing that all things in nature were related, was it not possible then to change any given substance into any other? For instance, to change the base metal lead into glorious gold, the image of God in the material world? If one altered the proportions of basic substances present in lead, it must be possible to elevate them to those of gold by unremitting chemical manipulation. According the mysterious teachings of the ancients, all metals were compounded from the principle of fire, which was found in sulphur, and the principle of moisture, which was found in mercury. The alchemists worked tirelessly to produce from wonderful syntheses of these two substances the 'philosopher's stone' which was to hold sway over metals and give man power over the processes of transformation in matter. The alchemist's belief in the transmutation of metals, in the transformation of lead, tin and other base substances into gold, rests upon these two concepts: the doctrine of the elements, and the vision of the philosopher's stone. If from time to time in the course of his work the alchemist actually produced shining golden-coloured metal, it may have been arsenic sulphate or a similar substance. Many a court alchemist suffered bitterly at the hands of a princely lord, greedy for gold. And alchemy brought many a trickster fame. Unknown to themselves, the alchemists found true gold of another kind in their laboratories. It lies partly in the knowledge they acquired of many new substances discovered and constituted by them. 'Before we could achieve the state of knowledge in which we find ourselves today in chemistry, it was necessary for thousands of men to work with all their energy to establish the permutations and combinations of relationship between all known substances, organic and inorganic; it was essential that fifteen hundred years' work should be done,' said Justus von Liebig.

For the alchemists themselves, the greatest good which grew from their concern with matter was a respect for the secrets of the material world, the like of which we seldom find after their time. The transformations of metals in the crucible were for them images of the purifications which they had to accomplish in their own souls. 'Copper does not stop or rest until it is changed into gold,' says the mystic Eckhart in the true tradition of alchemy.

The ethos of alchemy is always linked with a mystical philosophy nourished by a primeval inner consciousness. It is based upon a belief in the unity of the universe, in a divine principle which is effective both in this world and in the other, in the heavens as upon earth, and in matter itself. Thus, every metal and rock, every flame and all moisture is intimately related to the whole of nature, to man, and to the source of all being, and there is nothing, not even the tiniest pebble, in which no living force is at work.

For alchemists of distinction nature is a part of reality which has been exalted into a state of mystery (according to the poet Novalis). The artists who illustrated their works indicate the connection between earth, the cosmos and the primordial principle of the world with the help of symbolical figures, events and primeval signs; they set them in their landscapes, as a master of the seventeenth century, with his pious feeling for nature, has done here.

The earth's crust opens, and there appear in a dark cave figures representing the seven metals known by the alchemists: gold, silver, iron, quicksilver, copper, lead and tin. This ist the place where the metals were born. Here they are growing, having been called forth by the rays of the stars. The twinkle of the stars seems to have become intermingled with the lustre of the metals. In manuscripts of a period as early as the third century after Christ, these seven metals are associated respectively with the sun, the moon, and the planets visible to the eye, that is Mars (iron), Venus (copper), Mercury (quicksilver), Saturn (lead), and Jupiter (tin). Here late Babylonian beliefs in the divinity of the planets were becoming mingled with the views of Aristotle, of the later Albertus Magnus and others. Man lived in a world which was 'full of things related to each other'. Everywhere on earth and in heaven men were tracing out the things which corresponded and had 'sympathies' with each other: the glitter of gold recalled the brilliance of the sun; the shimmer of silver reminded men of the moonshine; the rugged iron reminded them of the god of war, the rolling quicksilver brought to mind Mercury, the swift messenger of the gods. The metals thus fitted harmoniously into the heavenly region and came to be included in it. But they were also associated with the four elements, for in all materials the alchemist saw essences arranged in differing mixtures of fire (above left), of air (above right), of earth and water (below).

But what is the meaning of the plaques in the hands of the figures sitting under the trees? The triangle pointing upwards was the sign for the light upward-moving elements, fire and air, whilst the triangle pointing downwards denoted the heavy elements, earth and water; the union of the two triangles in the six-pointed star was the sign of the universe, with which all things are associated. Another explanation is that the sign facing downwards represents the human body, and the one facing upwards signifies soul and spirit, and their union the totality of man, seen as the mirror of the whole world. There is an element of religion in this symbolical picture of the world; the haloes round the heads suggest it, so does the most perfect form of all, the circle; so also do the numerical relationships, and finally so does the fact that the sound of song is rising from out of the earth like the music of the spheres. The seven metals are singing...

The Emerald Table

The alchemists were convinced that their science began with a mythical Egyptian sage: Hermes Trismegistos, whom many identify with Thoth, revered on the Nile as the god of mathematics and science. He is supposed to have written the key sentences of his teachings on a small emerald table (emerald was the precious stone of Hermes as iron was the metal of Mars). According to legend the table was found in his grave. A version of his message in Latin was already known to the learned Albertus Magnus in the thirteenth century. A shorter version in Arabic was found by John Holmyard in 1923 in a treatise by the great Mohammedan alchemist and scholar, Jabir ibn Hayyan; he takes as his source Apollonius of Tyana, a neo-Pythagorean philosopher, magician and performer of miracles who lived at the time of Christ.

For the alchemist the table comprises the text of texts. In his *Amphitheatrum sapientiae aeternae* (1609) the alchemist and theosophist, Heinrich Khunrath, showed the legend chiselled into a vast rock as a message to all centuries: in Latin at the top, in German below. Flames of the spirit flare upwards out of it, and a spring, the symbol of life, wells up at the side. Churches, as the seats of prayer and meditation, appear round about as if it were a place of pilgrimage. The magnificent introductory sentence declares the mystical unity of the universe, of the spirit which rules it and of earthly things. 'That which is above is like to that which is below, and that which is below is like to that which is above, to accomplish the miracles of one thing.' In the dark sentences which follow one can deduce, according to J. Holmyard, the foremost expert of modern times on alchemy, that the universal soul or spirit permeating both macrocosm and microcosm implies the possibility of transmutation. Sun and moon point the way to gold and silver, and perhaps also to sulphur and quicksilver. In these was to be found the secret of the philosopher's stone, which was a manifestation of that spirit which bound all things together.

THE ALCHEMIST ON HIS KNEES

In a high hall there stands, to the right, an alchemist's workshop with everything that is necessary for the performance of the act of purification, that is, transmutation. In the bottles and flasks on the shelf there are enigmatic substances like *hyle*, the prime substance of Aristotle, azoth (the 'philosopher's mercury'); then there is sulphur (on the right, next to the azoth) and quicksilver (☿)—forces of the philosopher's stone. Whilst the pillars in front of the hearth on the right are called 'Ratio' and 'Experientia'—reason and experience—on the left in front of the long row of folio volumes a tent has been set up containing pictures for meditation and the Bible: it is inscribed with the name of Jehovah in Hebrew characters. Like the materials in the glow of the Athanor furnace (front, right), so the soul of the alchemist must be purified down to its very depths, for only he who is possessed of divine grace can succeed in the great work. On the table lie a lute, a viola and an open sheet of music: a reference to the great world harmony, with which the pure adept knows he is at one. It is this world harmony which, as the text on the table-cloth says, 'scares away sadness and evil spirits' as it resounds from earthly instruments. This is one of the curious plates in Khunrath's *Amphitheatrum sapientiae aeternae*.

23

ENCHANTED LANDSCAPES OUT OF THE 'ATALANTA FUGIENS' OF THE ALCHEMIST MICHAEL MAIER

On preceding page: A PAGE OUT OF THE MOST BEAUTIFUL AL-CHEMISTIC MANUSCRIPT OF ALL, '*Splendor Solis*' (from the copy in the British Museum). The text of this German manuscript which bears the date 1582 was ascribed, quite wrongly, to a certain blustering globe-trotter and charlatan by the name of Salomon Trismosin. The twenty-two pictures are pure alchemistic poetry. Here too one recognizes a motive of purification and rebirth, depicted within a frame decorated with flower and animal ornaments in the Renaissance style. Everything that is imperfect and burdened with guilt goes down like the old king in the sea, and a new purer life issues forth, here in the form of a young king—just as in the alchemist's oven purified gold issues forth out of impure materials. The landscape is interwoven with all the magic of symbolism: next to the old tree which has been cut down the new one is turning green as it grows: next to the morning sun as it rises over the dark clouds the morning-star sends down its rays: a white dove has glided down on to the golden ball held by the young ruler.

The doctor of philosophy and medicine, Michael Maier, from Holstein, a friend of the Order of Rosicrucians, is amongst those alchemists who rose to the very highest ranks of society. We find him after 1608 as physician in ordinary to Rudolf II in Prague. The Emperor's palace had laboratories and libraries and became a stronghold of alchemy. Maier looked deeper into books than into retorts, and he brought to his writings, which were partly profound and partly abstruse, a book-knowledge which was rich in mysteries. One of his treatises, called *The Fleeing Atalanta* (1618), still has great charm today, thanks to its fifty symbolical etchings. These may have originated from the workshop of Matthäus Merian the Elder. Above, left: the 'ubiquity' of the philosopher's stone is portrayed. In some mysterious way, so it is supposed, the stone is everywhere to be found, but it can only be recognized by the deserving: it is there for the poor as for the rich, on every road, on the mountains, in the air and in the water. 'One finds it in the open country, in the village and in the town' according to a passage in the alchemistic treatise *Gloria Mundi* of 1526. 'It is in everything which God created. Maids throw it on to the street. Children play with it.' But men pay no attention to the key of knowledge which God hands to them everywhere...

In the picture above right, coral serves similarly as a symbol of the substance which effects transmutation, taking the place of the philosopher's stone. Just as the 'stone' becomes gradually hard and reddens on the alchemist's purifying hearth, so does coral in the warm waters of the south when a cold breeze from the north sweeps over them, according to alchemistic views.

The middle picture portrays with a like boldness and mystery four fire balls suspended over a shining river: the lowest one is that of Vulcan, then come those of Mercury and the moon, and finally that of Apollo and the sun. The adept is exhorted not to forget, as he works, the enigmatic picture which so enticingly invites the mind to penetrate into the deeper mysteries of nature. 'May these balls of fire guide your hands in your art' is the accompanying text.

Volgen Die Caracter Der Alchemey

									Label
☉									Golt
☽									Silber
									Eisen und stael
									Queck silber
									Zien
♄									Bley
									Eisen Rost
									Kupper
									Schwefel
									Vitriol
									Salpeter
									Alaun
									Grünspan
									Saltz

FROM THE WORKSHOP WHERE THE ALCHEMIST CARRIES OUT HIS RESEARCH

Left: A SIGN-TABLE OF THE SIXTEENTH CENTURY

In the late Middle Ages secret signs appear more and more often in the alchemists' manuscripts. They used them whenever they wished to refer to certain substances: they did this partly out of sheer addiction to mysticism, partly as a defence against the uninitiated. By degrees these signs multiplied until they could be counted by hundreds. Our table shows an attempt to collect a number of them. All seven metals have the astronomic planetary signs; in the case of gold and silver something of the shape of the sun and the moon which these two metals represent has been incorporated into the signs. Sometimes one recognizes a sign of the zodiac, and sometimes a letter (the f of ferrum in the sign for iron rust = 'Eisen-Rost') or the salt sign, the first in the saltpetre ('Salpeter') row. The secret seemed to be preserved best where geometric forms, letters and planetary signs were entwined into coils.

Above: Through the centuries we see alongside the alchemist who tended more towards mystical speculation the man who busied himself on the soot-covered hearth. His equipment was already known in the days of ancient Greece and India. In the archaic still shown here, the flask containing the distilling solution is joined at the top to a device called the alembic; this has a pipe in it which drains the material after condensation into a receptacle. The walled-up oven was fired by coal or charcoal. Metal plates were sunk into it, and sand or ashes were poured on to them to damp down the heat. The vessels were then placed in this so-called sand-bath. The smoke escaped through openings which could be regulated. Many alchemists succeeded in purifying far more materials than the seven metals. The 'Latin pseudo-Geber' for instance, an unknown practitioner of the thirteenth century, had an amazing understanding of the methods of extracting important mineral acids, particularly sulphuric acid.

Iatrochemistry

The Discovery of Phosphorus

Phosphorus was discovered by a Hamburg merchant by the name of Brand, who, wishing to rid himself of financial worries, tried to make gold as an alchemist. The alchemists believed that traces of primary matter were to be found in human excreta, and in 1669 Brand spent many hours distilling large quantities of urine. He thus produced one of the most remarkable substances known to chemistry: a powder which gives out in the dark a continuous soft whitish light. Brand sold the secret of his phosphorus to Daniel Kraft, a physician who took the wonderful substance from one princely court to another, and from one annual fair to the next. In London Boyle tried, without success, to buy the prescription from him. In 1678 the philosopher Leibniz arranged for Brand to come to Hanover for a short time. A poem in which the mysterious silent glowing of the phosphorus becomes the image of the inwardly blissful soul demonstrates how deeply engaged the philosopher was in the work of the alchemist.

In the year 1771, the painter Joseph Wright of Derby completed a painting: *The Discovery of Phosphorus* (left). With the fantasy of the early romantic period the painter vividly recreates the act of discovery, and in so doing conjures up the lost world of alchemy. In a Gothic vault which houses an alchemist's laboratory it is about midnight and rays of light from three different sources merge. From outside come the rays of the full moon, inside there is candlelight; this lights up the faces of two amazed assistants who stand rooted to the spot. For a miracle is being performed in the silence of that room: light, of a kind which seems supernatural, begins to shine more and more brightly from the round retort in which a liquid, vaporized in an athanor and purified, is concentrating itself anew. It is the birth of a new and radiant element. The old alchemist, his face lined from countless years of research, kneels down to venerate the great secret. (Mezzotint by William Pether after the original painting.)

In the sixteenth century, the study of matter entered a new sphere, under the impetus of an idea which derives from one of the most powerful figures in the history of science. Anyone who today walks through the forest of glass tubes to be found in the gleaming white laboratory of a major pharmaceutical firm is looking upon the latest products of the so-called iatrochemistry of that period. The aim was no longer the refinement of metal, but the healing of nature through nature: that is, the healing of the sick human body through the powers of those substances which the doctor, now turned chemist, knew. Not that the ancients did not know the healing properties of substances from all three realms of nature, such as plant juices, animal fat, sulphur or antimony. A glance at the 'Materia medica' of Dioscorides (*see* p. 148) is enough to show that this was not so. But in iatrochemistry, the newly and joyfully discovered chemical concept of the human organism was combined with new methods of treatment. Adherents of the older attitudes prevalent at the time felt themselves to be threatened by this new intellectual alliance as it was manifested in the work of such a challengingly original mind as that of Paracelsus (or van Helmont or Glauber). Thus, some universities defended themselves forcibly against the new doctrine. On the other hand, on St. John's Day 1527 in Basle Paracelsus, the leading spirit of iatrochemistry, publicly burned a book in which the hated theories of Galen and Avicenna were set out.

For fifteen hundred years, the teaching of doctors in Europe had depended upon the doctrines of Galen. Their central point is the so-called medicine of the humours, according to which the human body is governed by four humours, each corresponding to one of the four types of temperament. These are the sanguine, blood, which incorporates the forces of warmth and moisture; the phlegmatic, phlegm, incorporating cold and moisture; the melancholic, black gall, incorporating cold and dryness, and the choleric, yellow gall, incorporating warmth and dryness. In a healthy man, these humours should be balanced. But at the sick man's bed-side the doctor, consulting his manual, had to discover which humour was disturbing the balance: perhaps yellow gall in the case of jaundice, blood in a high fever or phlegm in the case of a cold. The struggle was conducted largely by means of blood-letting, purgation and the remedies of the herbalist. Theriac was in great demand as a vehicle for as many as a hundred drugs: amongst them perhaps one which happened to be precisely what the sick organism required. Individual drugs were chosen to suit the humours: feverish illnesses were fought with cooling medicines and cold agues with warming ones such as pepper or bitter almonds.

Iatrochemistry removed man from this rigid, stereotyped régime, and enabled him to resume the personal identity he had lost, as a person whose organic structure was the seat of many and subtle chemical processes which could by no means be explained in terms of four humours. When this system was disturbed by illness, chemical medicaments were introduced through its chemical centre, the stomach: largely purified extracts, in carefully graduated quantities and combinations, corresponding precisely to the specific character of the illness in question. Thus iatrochemistry brought about the downfall of the universal electuary and was the beginning of a new investigation of the material world in search of the hidden beneficial, healing properties not only of plants, but principally of mineral acids, of metal salts, and of alkalis. It was these products which were to rectify an excess or deficiency of any substance in the sick body, or by nourishing it or purifying it in other ways to restore it to a harmonious relationship with the remainder of the world.

The iatrochemists added considerably to man's knowledge about matter, and especially about pharmaceutical substances. Paracelsus used preparations of substances dangerous in themselves, such as antimony and the arsenical acids, and investigated the compounds of metals in endless small-scale experiments. A seventeenth-century Dutchman, Johann Baptist van Helmont, based his selfless work in medicine on Paracelsus' views. The last great follower of Paracelsus, Johann Rudolf Glauber, died in Amsterdam in 1668. He was a self-taught man who travelled widely, and a most able practical chemist. He lived on the sale of the preparations made in his laboratory. He studied in depth the reactions of salts released from metals on other substances, achieved subtle gradations of strength in mineral acids, simplified the methods of obtaining hydrochloric acid which served as medicament and natrium sulphate, used as a laxative, the salt which still bears his name.

Their opponents claimed that the iatrochemists killed more men than the weapons of the Thirty Years' War. Yet even if this false claim were allowed, they would not have disposed of the fact that in a hundred and fifty years the new pharmacists had conquered a great deal of new ground in chemistry. The same spirit drove them as that which in Paracelsus' time sent Magellan and da Gama out into unknown seas. But they were driven also by the spirit of the alchemists, and so the iatrochemists accommodated the facts they discovered by empirical methods within the accepted unity of heaven and earth. Even inorganic matter was, in their view, full of mysterious living forces. When they saw yellowish-green solutions turning suddenly to dark blue in their alembics or brown gas pouring suddenly from a heated mass, they interpreted these as manifestations of a life-force or a hypothetical basic matter common to all substances. Paracelsus added a third principle to those of the combustible, embodied in sulphur, and the liquid, embodied in mercury, which in the alchemists' view governed the material world. This was the concept of the incombustible, embodied in the form of salt or ash. Many iatrochemists were astrologists. Paracelsus believed his three principles of mercury, sulphur and salt to be as closely interwoven in a basic substance as the Trinity in God. In the minds of the iatrochemists, the spirit of pansophism (see p. 362) is still bound up with the desire for empirical discovery.

FROM THE PLANT TO THE DRUG

Adam Lonicerus (Lonitzer), city physician at Frankfurt-am-Main, had this woodcut made for his 'Herbal' of 1578: it is a picture full of information. Above, the woman herbalist is fetching the officinal herb from the wood; on the right, the gardener is clearing a fitting space in the garden for this indigenous plant next to the highly cultivated foreign ones. In the middle, it comes into the hands of science and becomes a subject for discussion by the learned scholars in their long fur-trimmed coats. Then the hour of sacrifice strikes for the plant: it must now deliver up to mankind its healing substances. On the left, there is the kind of activity in progress which one sees in a chemist's dispensary. The city doctor of Strasbourg, Hieronymus Brunschwig, a predecessor of Lonitzer, described the transformation which is taking place here in these pensive words: 'It must be understood that distillation is simply the separation of coarse from delicate matter; the conversion of things fragile or destructible into things indestructible, of things material into things non-material, of bodily things into spiritual things; and the preservation of the incorporeal as if it were corporeal.' The distilling equipment stands in rows on shelves which are heated from below and allows the liquid to drop into small receptacles after scalding the plants. The woman is preparing the herbs. Finally (top left) the doctor examines the patient's urine at the sick-bed prior to prescribing the drug. An edition of Lonitzer's comprehensive herb-book appeared as late as 1783. Herbals have always been among the works most in demand, ever since the invention of printing. They stood like bibles of physical fitness alongside the Book of Books on the shelves in many houses. As a memorial to Lonicerus the doctor, Linnaeus gave the name *Lonicera* to a genus of plants to which honeysuckle belongs.

In pictures of the sixteenth century doctors usually appear dressed in fur-trimmed robes. This ceremonial dress seems to have raised them to the status of a kind of nobility and given them a place alongside the nobility by birth. Sometimes in such pictures there is a folio volume displayed in an equally ceremonial way—the complete sacrosanct works of the Greek doctor Galen or of the Arab Avicenna. It was from these works that students of medicine built up their concepts of the human body until the end of the Middle Ages.

The woodcut on the left is quite different. One of the greatest doctors, Theophrastus Bombastus of Hohenheim, stands bare-headed and at his ease in the open air; he seems closer to the mountains and the woods than to the academic wisdom of books. His heavily pleated tunic is a protest against the ceremonial robes—the wandering doctor Paracelsus was all his life impetuously independent, and from this he derived his powerful ability as others did from their domestic seclusion. 'Rest is better than unrest, but unrest is more productive than rest', he said.

The inward driving force of this restless wanderer, who always carried a sword with him, was a passionate yearning for direct experience of life, of mankind, of nature, and of the supernatural world. We see him 'growing up amongst the fir-cones' near Einsiedeln in Switzerland, as the son of a poor doctor, but then soon moving from university to university in his thirst for knowledge. We can trace him later as a mining chemist, field surgeon, doctor, professor, alchemist to the nobility, sectarian preacher and beggar, journeying from London to the Balkans, from Naples to Tübingen, from Basle to Salzburg. He was acquainted, as the picture suggests, with the mansions of the nobility as well as with the hovels of the poor, and he learned more from popular medicine during his dealings with peasants and midwives than from the inflexible scholarship of Galen. 'I marvel at the way in which you know me down to my very depths, though you have only seen me once': that is how Erasmus of Rotterdam expressed his gratitude to him.

But new ground was broken in the history of medicine and chemistry when he abandoned both academic and popular medicine to venture into a new field. 'Do not make gold, make medicine!' was his call to the alchemists. At the sick-bed he had seen in men 'the alchemist within', that is to say the power of chemical substances in the sick body and in the healing 'arcana'. In every man, in every human organ a special spiritual force (which he called Archaeus) was at work, which transformed food into flesh and blood. Whenever illness forced its way into this order of things like an enemy Archaeus, it had to be fought with specific herbal or mineral Archaei which were suited to the organs suffering pain. He saw that one single material could contain very different healing substances—the idea of the isolation of the effective substance had been born. What is more, Paracelsus made poisons into healing forces when he raised dosage to a separate art *within* the doctor's art. 'I separate that which is not an arcanum from that which is, and then give to the arcanum its right dose.' In this way he fought, for instance, the 'tartar diseases' such as rheumatism, arthritis and gout which were considered incurable. He did so by treating with natural, mainly mineral drugs the chemical causes of the illness which had been stored in the body: these were presumed to be salts taken in with the food but not excreted.

On the right, three of Paracelsus' prescriptions for powders to treat concretions in the urine.

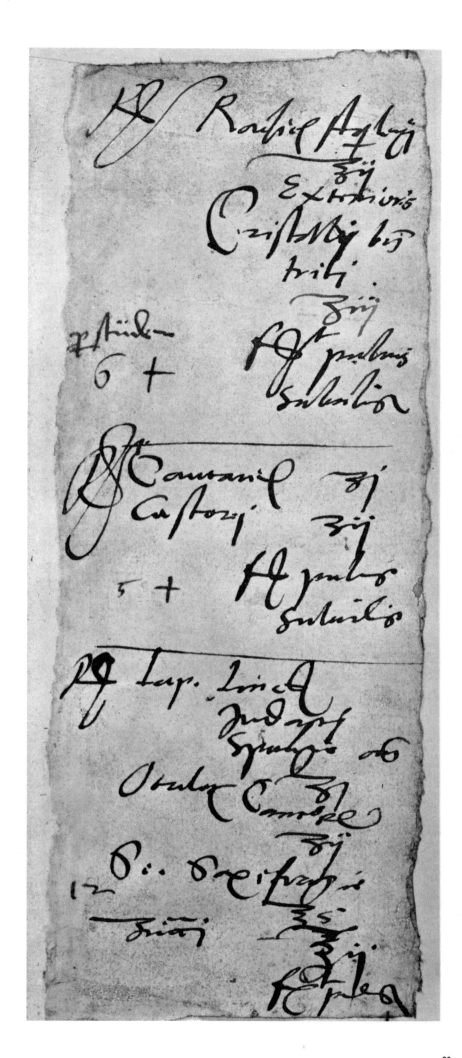

THE DREAM LABORATORY OF ANDREAS LIBAVIUS

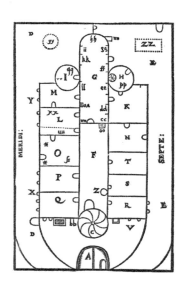

Andreas Libavius (or Libau), doctor, chemist, poet laureate of Jena university and director of secondary schools in Rothenburg and Coburg, was a scholar with the encyclopaedist's passion for collecting. He collected and arranged the already quite extensive chemical knowledge of his time in a handbook entitled *Alchymia* (1597). It is the first of its kind and whilst it included the theoretical hypotheses of the past and of the author's day, it did not neglect the practical handling of chemical substances. It is precisely in this field that his book contains something remarkable: the plan of a Utopian chemical institute, which goes far beyond the laboratories of the alchemists or apothecaries, or of those at the mines such as existed at that time. It is a building for the experimenter and research worker of the future, but a gold-maker's furnace (pp) in a secret laboratory (H), to which one climbs by a narrow spiral staircase, indicates at the same time Libau's liking for alchemy. A long area with apparatus for distilling (hh), for upward distillation (ff), for analytical weighing (ee), for crystallizing (O), for the work of the chemical apothecary, and so on, is reserved for chemistry. A little porch built into the east door (A) gives access to the house.

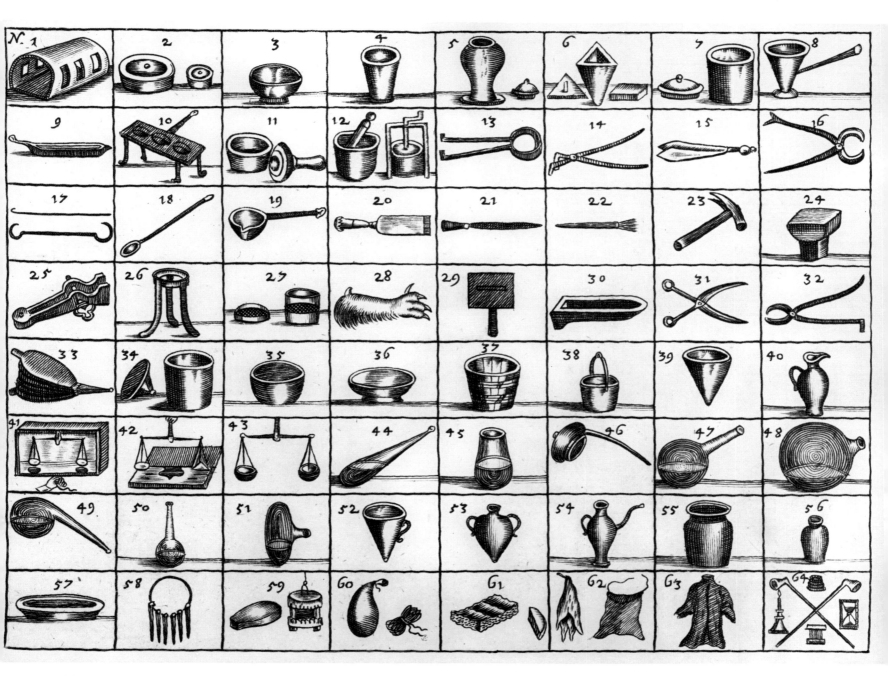

THE 'PORTABLE LABORATORY' OF JOHANN JOACHIM BECHER (1680)

Becher was one of the last Paracelsists, a doctor whose mind roamed restlessly through all the branches of knowledge, and also a man of the world who, whilst in the service of the Bavarian state, worked out and helped to execute comprehensive plans for the establishment of trade and industry in the sense of mercantilism. He was responsible for the first beginnings of the phlogiston theory (*see* p. 37). The borders between alchemy and the empirical chemical analysis of the future cut right through his complex personality. This is reflected in his 'portable laboratory'. Next to the old alchemist's household equipment appear objects which foreshadow a future art of chemical analysis taking into account not only the quality of substances but still more their quantitative relationships. The scales (41) is to become an instrument which will make it possible to penetrate into the most hidden secrets. (1) is a muffle, (4) to (6) are crucibles, (10) is a mould for making castings, (18) an iron spoon, (25) a vice, (26) a tripod, (27) sieves, (28) a hare's foot for mixing together the powders, (29) an eye-guard against the fire, (39) a filtering bag, (44) a separating flask, (46) a head of a still, (49) a retort, (50) a phial, (51) 'a philosphers's egg for sublimation', (58) testing needles for gold and silver, (59) testing stones, (60) pig's bladders, (61) cork and wax, (62) a hand-towel and apron, (63) a working overall, (64) an hour-glass, a candle, a roll of tobacco and pipes, and below some theriac to prevent poisoning whilst at work.

Here some grand act must be in the course of execution. Round the middle of the picture, arranged in order, is everything required for the art of alchemy—as if a great task almost transcending its powers were being attempted. Below on the right the apparatus of the alchemistic laboratory has been set up. The alchemist is holding the retort, an implement of transmutation, against his heart in an attitude of conjuration. Below on the left, clothes have been washed in the open air—this is a symbolical act of purification—and drops of rain, the unpolluted water of heaven, are being collected. Above, in a secluded, rocky mountain region the kneeling adept prays for the blessing of the One God, whose name, Jehovah, is inscribed on the tent. Ergon and Parergon,

the main creative act and the subsidiary one are both to be blessed—the preparatory act performed by the alchemist and the main act itself: the creation of an artificial man. Sun and moon lend their powers to the creature which is coming into being in the glass ball.

Alchemistic symbols can often be explained in many different ways. But here the artist can hardly have been thinking of the glorification of gold-making, but rather of one of the most audacious dreams of magic and science: the creation in the retort of a homunculus with wonderful qualities. This creation of 'nature through art' was ascribed to some magicians of ancient times but also to the theosophist Robert Fludd and to the great guardian of secret knowledge, Paracelsus.

The Elements: ancient and modern Theory
I Air and Fire

'Methinks the chymists, in their searches after truth, are not unlike the Navigators of Solomon's Tarshish Fleet, who brought home from their long and tedious Voyages, not only Gold and Silver and Ivory, but Apes and Peacocks too.' In 1661, with this impudent attack, the young Irish nobleman, Robert Boyle (*see* p. 90) challenged the 'apes' and 'peacocks', that is the alchemy and iatrochemistry of his time. He fought not against their practical discoveries but against their delight in over-hasty, unproven theories. Boyle rejected the three principles: sulphur, mercury and salt. In their place, he introduced critical judgement into chemistry, assessing discoveries only in terms of constructive human comprehension. This method of attack, set out in his book *The Sceptical Chymist,* vitiated against one of the principal supports of alchemy: the ancient Greek doctrine of the elements air, fire, earth and water, forces which were thought to be represented in every body (*see* pp. 17 ff.). Boyle analysed countless substances into their component parts, finding none of the 'principles' in them, but formulating a new concept of the elements more consistent than the old with the discoveries he had made. He classified as elements only entirely homogeneous bodies such as gold and silver: 'certain Primitive and Simple, or perfectly unmingled bodies, which not being made of any other bodies or of one another...' So the new concept was at least outlined, and a new aim established. The chemistry of the future must set out to discover the totality of 'true' elements. A century later, Lavoisier improved the definition with his claim that an element was a substance which could not be further analysed by chemical means.

In spite of his scepticism, Boyle introduced a 'principle' into chemistry. In the natural philosophy of the time, Joachim Jungius and Pierre Gassendi had rediscovered the atoms of Democritus. Matter was seen as a playground for tiny, indivisible particles. The almost incredible number of differently formed solid masses, and the elements themselves, resulted from variations in the size and combinations of these particles. Boyle was aware of the danger that excessively narrow views might be substituted for the too far-reaching interpretations of the alchemists, and he avoided it. He recognized, for example, the fact that the theory of atomic systems was not far-reaching enough to account for the life of human and animal bodies. Indeed, the organization and movement of atoms in matter were to him as much a mirror of God's majesty as were the movements of the stars in the heavens to Newton or Kant.

Outside Boyle's immediate circle of friends, this powerful impetus towards a purely experimental and critical chemistry gained ground only slowly. Again in the eighteenth century, there came from Germany a theory which assumed the presence of an unmeasurable, hypothetical force in every body. This theory, the phlogiston theory of Georg Ernst Stahl, Professor of Medicine at Halle-an-der-Saale, conquered the whole scientific world. It was a large-scale attempt to provide a complete explanation of the process of burning, whether by fire, or as a result of the oxidation of metals, or of respiration. When a substance burned, it was said, the inherently combustible element of it, phlogiston, was released. The substance known today as the oxides of metals were seen as burnt out shells from which the combustible element was gone. On the other hand, some substances rich in phlogiston, like charcoal, could communicate their flame to others.

Towards the end of the eighteenth century, a group of scientists all of whom supported the phlogiston theory (Black, Cavendish, Scheele, Priestley and so on) stumbled upon compounds in air, the precise analysis of which was to destroy the old concept of air as a single element, and would eventually destroy the phlogiston theory itself. They opened up for chemistry the hitherto neglected sphere of gases. They had chosen the most difficult of all the elements: volatile, fleeting, invisible and intangible. What they called air seemed protean in its changes: at one moment the animals taking part in their experiments were breathing in a substance under their bell-glass which brought them increased liveliness: at the next they were dead. The different kinds of gas could lie hidden, unrecognizable and bound, in acids, in alkalis, in stones and metals. A flame, a metal, another acid could force them to wake and make their appearance. New apparatus had to be evolved: bell jars and pneumatic troughs: glass cages from which there was no escape. The presence of a gas would be known, and important conclusions drawn from the rise or fall of the level of water under a bell jar, from the change of colour in a piece of litmus paper, from a glowing wire or a coloured flame. But this was above all the beginning of the era of weighing in chemistry. Following the example of Lavoisier and Black, scientists performing experiments in which burning played a part weighed the initial substances and the products and compared their weights with minute care.

These scientists were slow to realize that the centuries-old legend of air the element was dying under their hands. Lavoisier, himself originally a believer in phlogiston, was the first to place chemistry on a valid theoretical basis, firmly opposed to the phlogiston theory. Measuring and weighing, he proved that when heat was generated no phlogiston was produced by the substance heated, but in fact the oxygen present in air combined with the substance itself as the warmth, and indeed light, was produced, just as it combined with the blood and released warmth in breathing. In all chemical transformations, however, the quantity of matter in existence after the operation remains the same as before. Amongst other things, Lavoisier reformulated the law of conservation of matter. Matter does not come from nothing, and is not lost.

A hundred and twenty years after Boyle's *Sceptical Chymist,* the great French scientist, with his genius for order and clarity, had established the elemental status of the gases nitrogen, oxygen and hydrogen discovered by his contemporaries, and of phosphorus, sulphur and many metals. He had shown the way chemistry was to go in the following century. It had to become a science of precise quantitative analysis. Its task was to refine and purify its own concept of the elements, discovering new basic substances and penetrating yet more deeply into the infinitely wide field of research offered by the mixing of elements and the relationships between them.

THE ELEMENT AIR

An immense atmospheric space stretches high above the earth. The parts of the earth where there is only ocean below and sky above were found by the Swiss painter Johann Jakob Ulrich to be the places in which the 'elemental' force of this atmospheric space can be grasped best. In the language handed down through the last two thousand years the German scholar Konrad of Megenberg of the late Middle Ages explained how primeval landscapes of this kind came about: above everything rules the element fire with its light and warmth, underneath as the second lightest element is air, at the bottom lie water and earth. Goethe was so deeply moved by the play of cloud formations in this atmospheric space that in 1820 he kept a daily record of the clouds for six weeks, in order 'to apprehend it all with his own eyes'; whilst doing so he paid the highest tribute to the English metereologist Luke Howard, who in 1803 gave names to these volatile formations: cirrus, cumulus (shown in Ulrich's picture), nimbus and stratus.

In the late seventeenth century came the physicists and they weighed what appeared to be without weight, the air. Today we know that the air covering the earth must weigh about five trillion kilograms. Then came the chemists and did something which since prehistoric times had been regarded as impossible: they analysed the element air and showed it to be a mixture of gases. In their wake came the biologists who explained the process which enabled plants, animals and men to breathe. Others followed who saw the empty air suddenly swarming with bacteria and fungus spores. Finally, the twentieth century sent its rockets up hundreds of miles to examine the uppermost atmosphere and solve the puzzle: where does the atmosphere end and space begin?

The English physician John Mayow, a follower of Boyle, came near to the secret of air by observing the process of combustion. He isolated the air under a pear-shaped glass jar, which he placed upside down in a bowl of water (top right). A burning candle, placed inside it, went out after a short interval and meanwhile the water rose slightly. Part of the air had evidently been used up, and the remainder was no use for the burning process, for when Mayow tried to set camphor alight from outside with a burning glass, he failed. Experiments with mice produced the same results: the part of the air which made breathing and combustion possible was removed. What was left (later called nitrogen) seemed to have precisely the opposite effect. Mayow assumed that with combustion, as with breathing, 'saltpetre spirit' in the air maintained the burning flame; similarly in the case of breathing it was this which made the dark 'used up' venous blood bright red. He was close to the truth. Saltpetre is rich in oxygen!

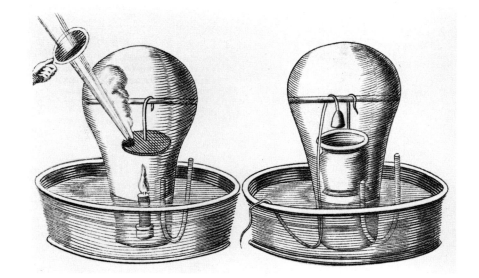

More than a century after Mayow, the glass ball standing isolated in a bowl of water, in which phosphorus could be set alight from outside with a burning glass, became the symbol for the new chemistry. Corbould's allegorical picture (left) shows how this chemistry with its quantitative measurements and its division of the air into oxygen and nitrogen is already turning towards the future. The goddess of science, holding the globe, is turning gently away from the old alchemist, who dreams the dream of the philosopher's stone.

The new gas chemists had a second apparatus for their research: the pneumatic trough (centre right) developed by Stephen Hales *(see* p. 154). He led the gas which was to be examined through the siphon-like curved pipe (r–r) into a vessel hanging from a wire (a–b); this vessel was completely filled with water and then plunged upside down into a bowl of water (x–x). The air pressure prevented the water from running out, but the water inside the vessel was gradually forced downwards as the gas, now trapped, collected at the top.

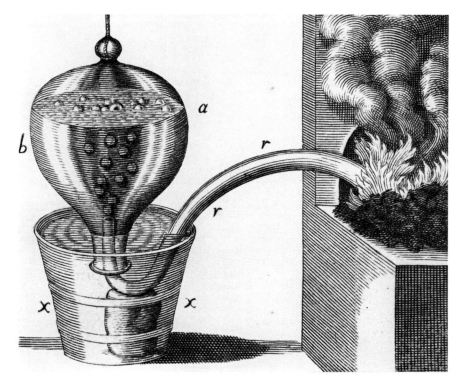

Torbern Bergman, the Swedish chemist, evolved an elegant method of generating carbon dioxide (bottom right). The bottle is filled with distilled water together with a considerable amount of calcium carbonate, then at (L) a funnel which can be closed with a rod (P) and at (A) a pipe curved into the shape of an S are cemented in so that they are airtight. When sulphuric acid is allowed to pass through the funnel and drop gently into the water, the carbon dioxide present in the calcium carbonate is released and rises through the pipe into the glass (H–G) which has been filled with water and hung upside down. When all the water has been forced down into the trough (N–M), the jar is taken out quickly and stood with the opening facing upwards. Carbon dioxide is heavier than air. A candle (E) which has been immersed in it goes out. Thus the experiment explains why the carbon dioxide which lies invisible at the bottom of certain caves can be dangerous to small dogs but not to a man walking upright.

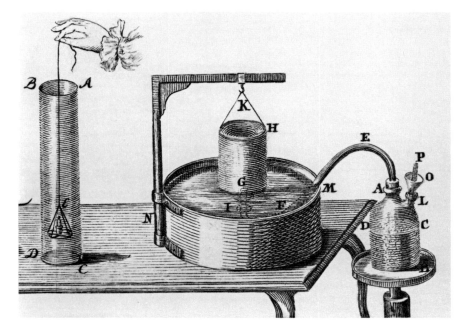

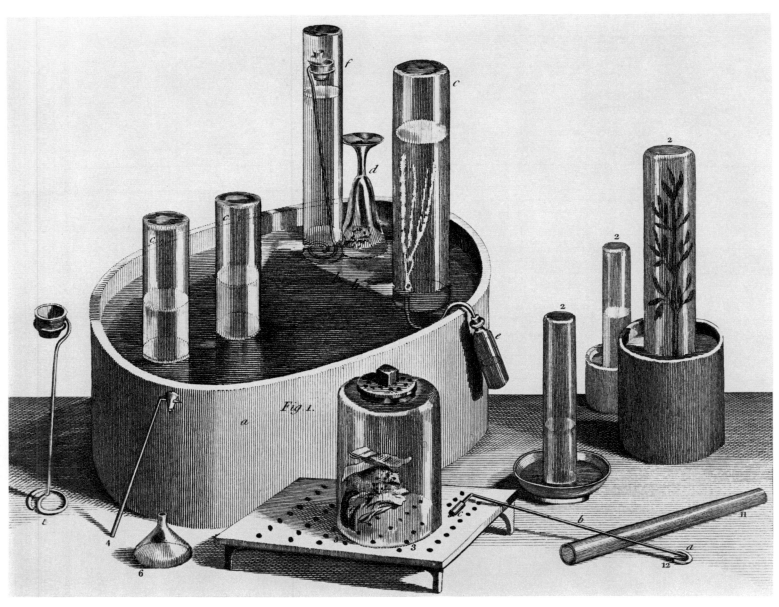

JOSEPH PRIESTLEY'S APPARATUS

In the same epoch in which men in balloons rose freely into the air for the first time, chemistry brought to an end the ancient conceptions about the indivisibility of the element air. Suddenly there is talk in scientific writings of air composed of sea and vitriolic acids, of fixed, of combustible, of mephitic, of dephlogisticated air, of fiery and of putrefied air. In the year 1772 the Swedish apothecary, Wilhelm Scheele, discovered 'furnace gas', oxygen. As fate would have it, Joseph Priestley anticipated him with the publication of the same discovery. This preacher, physicist, librarian, language teacher and self-taught chemist announced in 1774 that new ground was being broken in chemistry, comparable only to what happened in physics when Newton formulated the theory of gravity. An inventor of genius, he improved the pneumatic trough (a) by using mercury as the confining liquid. The cylindrical glasses, in which he collected the gases, served at the same time as measuring instruments.

He was able without danger to guide the gases which had been generated in the small bottle (e) out of the heated fluid into the water in the glass vessel through the perforated stopper and a flexible hose. As a prison for mice he used the broad glass cylinder (3), which he used to clean with strips of paper. With such primitive apparatus Priestley produced for the first time sulphur dioxide, hydrochloric acid, nitrous oxide, ammonia gas and others, and investigated their behaviour, combining them with countless other substances. With much reluctance he had, as a result of his own experiments, to concede that the 'opinion impressed so deeply on our souls that air was indivisible elemental matter' was untenable. On 1st August 1774 he isolated oxygen out of heated red mercuric oxide (f) and recognized as a result of many tests the remarkable reviving power of this sort of 'air'. 'Up to now only two mice and I myself have had the advantage of breathing it,' he wrote.

THE STORMING OF PRIESTLEY'S HOUSE ON 14th JULY 1791

Probing his way tentatively, he noticed in experiments with plants (2) that the non-breathable carbon dioxide could be breathed by green plants in the daylight (*see* p. 176).

Above: 'I consider my settlement at Birmingham as the happiest event in my life,' wrote Priestley in the year 1787 as he looked back on seven years of zealous activity as preacher and research worker in that town. Just four years later the event took place which is depicted here. Priestley disapproved of monarchies 'which brought up their subjects to passive obedience'. On 14th July he was celebrating the second anniversary of the storming of the Bastille with friends of the same views when a screaming mob, goaded on by monarchistic and Anglican enemies of the republican and enlightened theologian, attacked first the chapel belonging to his community and then Priestley's home with axes, set fire to them and reduced them to ruins. The household equipment together with the books, manuscripts and all

the apparatus which had enabled him to perform so many successful experiments, were hurled out of the windows. No one stopped the orgy of destruction. Priestley had to flee to London under a false name. His lively discussions with James Watt, Dr. Withering and others were for ever over. His challenging tenacity had already lost this contentious man much sympathy. This tenacity of Priestley's and his sturdy enthusiasm for his scientific work were both rooted in a stoic imperturbability. He had an unassailable faith in the reasoning power which God gave to man so that he should perform some useful function on this earth, as in fact Priestley did throughout his life with his writings and research. In 1794, aged sixty-one, he emigrated to the land of the future, America. Even in the year before his death, long after Lavoisier had disproved the phlogiston theory, there appeared from the pen of this high-minded obdurate man a final treatise: 'The Doctrine of Phlogiston Established'.

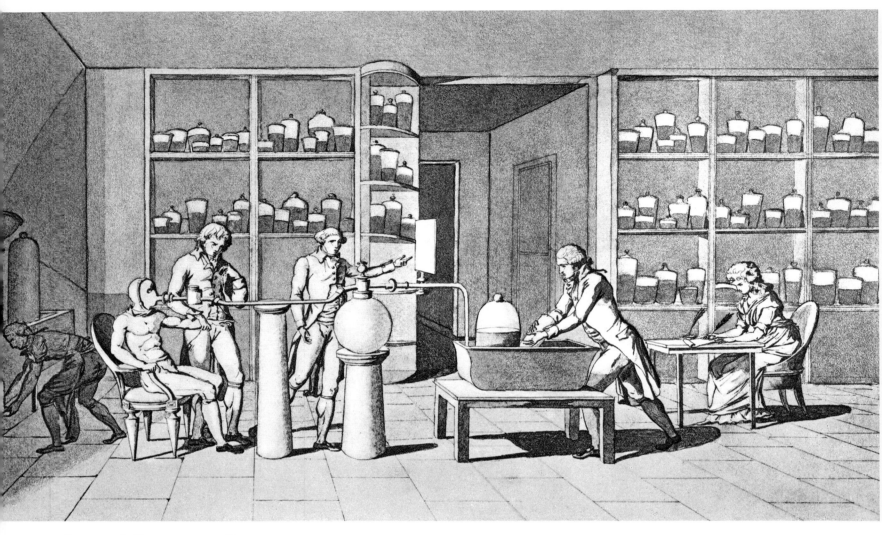

LAVOISIER'S EXPERIMENTS IN RESPIRATION

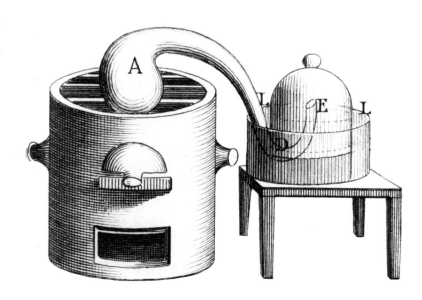

The man in the fashionable tail-coat who in these pictures is directing five assistants from the background, giving them his instructions in a complicated experiment with the elegance of an orchestral conductor, is Antoine Laurent Lavoisier. The income he derived from his position as *fermier général des impôts* enabled him to follow his vocation with lavishness. The revolutionary observations of Black, Priestley, Cavendish and others in the field of 'air types' and the false interpretations they derived from them through the phlogiston theory were his starting point. The distinction of having observed as yet unknown 'types' of air and the behaviour of animals and plants in them fell to others, but the clear-sighted Lavoisier, after long years of work, went beyond this stage, partly by outstripping their experiments with his own famous improved apparatus, but mainly—since he had originally also been a phlogistician himself—by establishing a concise and convincing set of explanations for combustion, calcination and respiration.

His laboratory in the Paris arsenal became the best equipped and the most famous in Europe. Enormous quantities of acids, salts, bases, and metals stood in glass holders awaiting experiments. He collected gases in enlarged copper-lined pneumatic troughs; he used an electrical machine (far right) for transforming into water, as Cavendish did, hydrogen and oxygen gas with an electric spark in a vessel out of which the air had first been pumped; with Laplace he invented a calorimeter which measured the temperature of

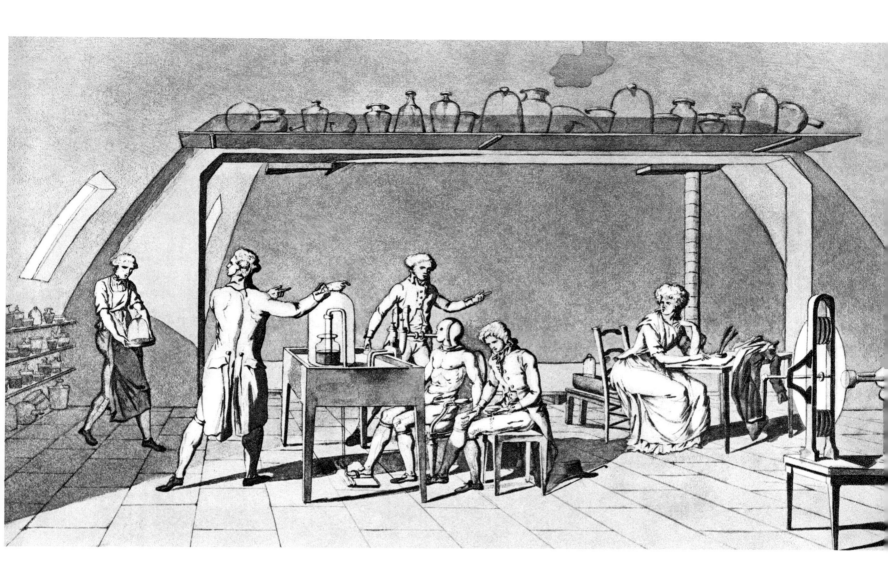

bodies with the help of melted ice. One room was devoted entirely to precision balances. 'Exact' was his favourite word. With the balances he refuted the phlogiston theory.

A shining example of his exactitude is the classical experiment for the decomposition and re-composition of air (below left). A glass retort containing four ounces of liquid mercury is placed on an oven. The pipe of the retort (E) empties its contents under a bell-glass. Mercury is used as the confining liquid in the vessel (LL). For twelve days a fire kept the mercury in the retort at vaporizing temperature. Gradually it turned into a firm red material—calcined mercury oxide, saturated with oxygen. The air which had been in the retort and under the bell-glass at the beginning of the experiment had lessened by about one fifth; the mercury had risen in the bell-glass to a corresponding extent. The red mercury 'calz' weighed 45 grains. In the air which remained a candle went out immediately. Lavoisier put the 45 grains into the retort of a similar apparatus, heated them and saw that the red mass transformed itself back into liquid oxygen-free mercury. It weighed 41½ grains. A fixed quantity of oxygen had been dissipated in which a candle burned brightly. It was precisely that fifth part which had been taken out of the air in the calcination. If one combined the released 'burnable' fifth, the oxygen, with the non-combustible four–fifths of the air, ordinary air was re-created. Lavoisier proved definitively that oxygen was a separable part of the mixture of nitrogen and oxygen of which all air is composed.

There was nothing to indicate any trace of phlogiston. The illustration is from Lavoisier's *Traité élémentaire de chimie*.

In 1789 the laboratories in the arsenal became a centre where the respiration studies of Mayow and others were thought out to their conclusion in a coordinated manner. Complicated apparatus stood ready to weigh the inhaled and exhaled air, to isolate it, to measure its temperature and so on. The records were kept as usual by Lavoisier's wife, a gifted draughtswoman, who is to be seen in both these pictures. An airtight mask was fixed on to the face of the person on whom the experiment was to be made—this was the chemist Séguin—a tube led the exhaled air into the pneumatic trough. Respiration showed itself to be, as Mayow and others had already supposed, a combustion process. The oxygen combined, probably in the lungs, with the venous blood, and in this way warmth was created. The exhaled air no longer contained the amount of inhaled oxygen, but it did contain carbon dioxide which had been drawn out of the body, mixed with water vapour. The blood had to distribute the oxygen gained throughout the body.

During the revolution the well-to-do Lavoisier was executed, having been falsely charged. It was a senseless act, though true to the ideology of the revolution. On 8th May 1794 the head which had contributed the decisive method of thinking to modern chemistry fell under the guillotine. 'The republic does not require scholars,' said Coffinhal, the vice-president of the revolutionary tribunal.

ROMAN LIME-KILNS IN THE SEVENTEENTH CENTURY

Lime, like iron and clay, is one of the most important of those substances in the earth's crust which men learnt to use in the earliest times with help of fire. The raw material in the form of limestone, marble, chalk, and so on, stands heaped up into whole mountains in the countryside. Wherever lime holds together people's houses or the walls of their towns, and covers them over with its protective wash, it brings to mind the distant quarries from which it originates. But the raw material appears in a transformed state. In the lime-kiln it turns into a white, brittle, porous mass called 'quicklime'; it is then mixed with sand and water into a mortar and pressed between the building stones, where it stiffens into that hard insoluble cement which even today lends stability to many buildings of the ancient Romans. The

Romans were masters of construction with lime. From their city, in which Sébastien Bourdon painted a successor of the Roman lime-kiln (above), this art spread throughout Europe. In the time of the painter a large number of lime-kilns stood at the entrance to the city on the Via Appia. Among the landmarks alongside this road was the crenellated tower of Caecilia Metella's grave. Enormous blocks were removed from its walls and ground into small pieces; they then found their way as raw material into the lime-kilns. On the right at the edge of the picture the painter has brought into his scene the Castello Sant' Angelo which is in fact situated far away. On the left behind the roof support can be seen the subdued glow of the oven. Horses and donkeys bear away in baskets to the building sites the end product, the bright quicklime.

In those days no one knew as yet what lime really was or what chemical secret lay hidden in this remarkable process which transforms hard heavy limestone from the earth's crust into the much lighter quicklime with its strong tendency to attract to itself other substances, and then changes it back again into the hard slaked lime used in the walls. The solution was found in 1775 by a young Scottish scientist, Joseph Black. With a passion for experimenting more ardent than that of Priestley and an analytical mind which Lavoisier could have taken as an example, he made a clear distinction between the mild and the caustic alkalis. Later on, Black established with the help of acids that limestone in its normal state was saturated with 'fixed air' i.e. carbon dioxide. As soon as the water and this 'fixed air' were eliminated in the lime-kiln, there appeared the caustic properties of the 'burned lime' or quicklime (CaO). This avidly attracted to itself water, animal matter and, above all, carbon dioxide. As the water once again slowly left this combination, there remained behind the original hard product, limestone ($CaCo_3$), with which the process started.

Black suggested technical improvements for lime-kilns. What the lime-burners had been doing for a long time had now become scientifically intelligible: eliminating as thoroughly as possible the carbon dioxide from the limestone—which had to be as pure as possible—in order to obtain a quicklime with caustic properties. A work of C.-R. Fourcroy de Ramecourt, *L'art du chaufournier,* appeared in 1766 and showed the readers of those days among other things how lime was fired in the Champagne (right). The heat was kept in by giving the lime-kiln a circular ground-plan and bending it into a vault at the top. The walls consisted of bricks and mortar. The structure was sunk in the earth right up to the top brim; in this way it was protected against any sudden cooling off and disintegration. How was the 'fixed air' eliminated? By breaking the stones down into small pieces and arranging the layers loosely. For the heat from the fire had to draw the large quantities of carbon dioxide quickly upwards as they were generated. Passages were made in the stone mass so that a strong draught could operate; wooden stakes (S) were inserted into it and then into holes which had been made in the separating arch (R). As soon as the stakes were burned up, the draught began to work with threefold force. The art of the lime-burner consists in raising the heat very gradually in this miniature fiery furnace, in distributing it to every side and in maintaining the intensest glow as evenly and as long as possible. He regulated it with the help of the aperture which was connected with a tunnel leading through the hill; furthermore he could vary the amount of earth with which he covered the stone mass. In the fire area a bundle of twigs (P) has been placed in layers on a grate of beams (O). Later the fire consumed the wooden supporting posts (M) as well and went on burning on the stone hearth (I), where it could be stoked from outside. After about twenty-four hours the burned lime was ready to be taken out.

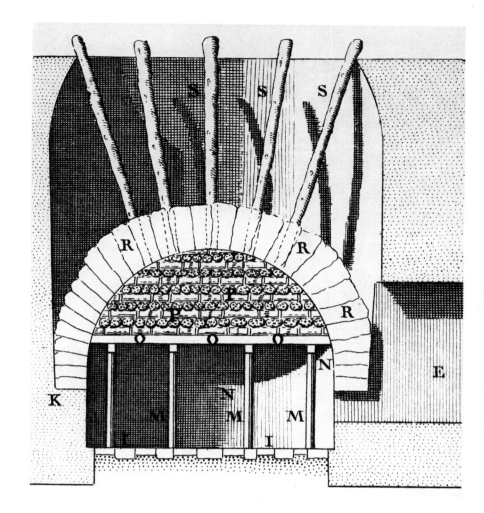

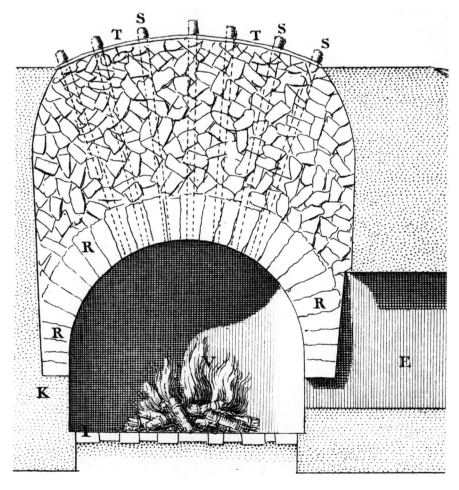

The Elements: ancient and modern Theory
II Water and Earth

By the end of the eighteenth century it was widely recognized that air and water were not elements. The word 'earth' had long ago become a kind of collective concept for 'earths', but fire was still classed as an element—and a puzzling and inexplicable one. Even Lavoisier, who had shown that there was no 'fire substance' phlogiston, still considered light and warmth to be 'principles' or forces existing within all matter, which became apparent in the combustion processes; Berzelius held the same view half a century later. Today a flame is known to be made up of highly heated gases and glowing particles which are vigorously whirled upwards.

It was during the time when views about the concepts 'air' and 'water' were beginning to waver that the ascents of Vesuvius by Sir William Hamilton took place—excursions into one of the oldest domains of the element fire. The wealthy Scot was from 1764 until 1800 the British Ambassador at the court of Naples; as a side-line he made studies in archaeology and vulcanology. In four years he climbed Vesuvius twenty-two times—and not only at times when it was safe. The painter Peter Fabris made book illustrations for him, which Hamilton used in his campaign against the Neptunists. Hamilton, being a convinced Vulcanist, regarded fire as the decisive force in the formation of the earth's crust. One of these pictures (left) records a night scene on 11th May 1771. The side of Vesuvius has split open and a stream of lava is pouring towards the village of Resina. The molten masses are piling up in a ravine, forming a vertical wall of fire 50 to 60 feet high out of the red hot lumps of lava. The viscous stream carries on its back vast quantities of scoria. The ground trembles, the air is hot and full of smoke and of the thunderous noise from the lumps of lava as they collide. Hamilton has invited to the scene the Sicilian ruler and his wife (right). Did he choose to pay this visit at night because he wanted his guests to experience the primeval force of the fiery element at its mightiest?

The fact that water itself is a compound of different basic substances became accepted about the year 1800. In the sixteenth century it was already possible for scientists to produce one of them: 'combustible air' (hydrogen gas) by means of the action of metal on hydrochloric acid. In 1761 the French chemist, Macquer, saw that when he held a porcelain cup over a flame made by burning this gas, water appeared on it. But he did not understand the process. On the contrary, even he continued to hold that water was a chemically irreducible substance. Five years later, however, the mystery of water was illuminated on a country estate near London. Here lived Henry Cavendish, withdrawn, shy of his fellow-men: according to Biot 'the richest scholar and perhaps the most scholarly rich man ever'. Lovingly, he investigated nature in his laboratory and his observatory, and for a long time kept his important discoveries to himself. It was he who first described hydrogen precisely in the year 1766, but he thought it was pure phlogiston. In 1772, he separated nitrogen from air, and it was he, too, who discovered the composition of water, by heating 'combustible air' (hydrogen) with oxygen in a closed test tube under electric sparks. The product of his experiment was a quantity of water which weighed precisely the same as the gases used. Through the chemist, Charles Blagden, Lavoisier learned of these experiments. It fell to his part to provide the true explanation and at the same time to furnish the conclusive empirical proof of the fact that water is composed of one part of oxygen to two parts of hydrogen.

The 'element' water, like the 'element' air, was closely connected with the new discovery of a number of basic substances made in the vicinity of 1800. They were made at least partly as a result of the new technique of electrolysis (*see* p. 54), which brought to men like Davy and Faraday new insight into the properties of matter. Water nevertheless was and remained a powerful natural force in the world. In the laboratory, almost unnoticed, a humble servant, it was used merely to clean apparatus before and after experiments, and as the ever-present invisible substance in which others must be dissolved before they could become capable of chemical activity: '*Corpora non agunt nisi liquida...*'

'Everything we make and do, create or discover seems to me insignificant in comparison with what the farmer may be able to achieve. The progress he makes alleviates the needs and worries of man, so releasing him to enjoy the good and beautiful things which art and science provide for him.' This vision of a future man freed from the bonds of hunger by improved cultivation of the land, was sketched in 1862 by the great chemist Justus von Liebig. This vision incorporated all the wisdom acquired in his long years of investigation into agricultural soil, and the agricultural crops nourished by it. The concept of earth as an element had long become untenable in the face of the substances which had been found in earth with its abundance and diversity of stone, soil and mineral content. Mere eyesight showed increasingly clearly that earth as a whole was a mineral deposit rich beyond measure, a wonderful treasure-house of chemical elements, compounds and mixtures, of amorphous and crystalline substances. The new geology and chemistry united to substitute this picture for that of the indivisible element proclaimed by earlier ages. Between 1790 and 1830, geologists produced one unknown mineral after another from the inexhaustible depths of the earth. In Asia, America and Africa, new lands were opened up as time went by, adding to the research field of mineral chemistry. One of the last chemists who were able to command a knowledge of all forms of matter was Jöns Jakob Berzelius, who discovered the elements cerium, selenium and thorium, and isolated silicon, which is present in countless types of stone.

For Liebig, however, the discovery that the very uppermost thin layer of soil contained most minutely distributed quantities of important chemical materials was of the greatest possible significance. Scientists had already shown that plant leaves in their breathing assimilated carbonic acid from the sunny atmosphere (*see* p. 176). Similarly, the roots derived from their soil bed the substances which were also essential for the production of sugar, starch and fat in the store-houses of the plant itself. Liebig specified exactly what was essential for this process. In his major work, *Organic Chemistry in its Application to Agriculture and Physiology,* countless tables are provided to determine the matter: true weapons, these, against hunger. Time and again, they refer to the minerals calcium, potassium, phosphorus, nitrogen, and the trace elements iron, magnesium, sulphur and chlorine. A master of organic analysis, Liebig found them in the ashes of burnt plants. Against heavy opposition, he called upon farmers and governments to guard in all circumstances against encroachment upon agricultural land, the most valuable capital asset a nation could possess. This was indeed a form of capital which could be increased, now that it was known which mineral substances were removed from the soil by a particular type of plant, for these could be restored to it in the form of artificial chemical manures. Thus, a wise combination of crop rotation with natural and artificial manures could bring about the miracle by which soil was not exhausted: the earth no longer became poor and sterile. Rather, the image of nature as the giver of life and food was to be seen reflected in fields of waving corn and prolific potato crops. Paracelsus' follower Glauber and later Duhamel du Monceau and Carl S. Sprengel had indeed suggested the use of chemical fertilizers, and Liebig's were at first completely unsuccessful. Nevertheless, it was Liebig who first put agricultural chemistry and the use of fertilizers in farming onto a practical scientific basis. So it was that chemistry became a force in the world's struggle against hunger.

THE ELEMENT WATER

'Three-quarters of the earth's surface is covered with water, three-quarters of the bodies of plants and animals are filled with it,' said the chemist Paul Karrer. The water cycle, the descent of water from the clouds in the sky to the earth and its ascent back again into the air, is one of the most magnificent spectacles in nature. And whilst in the outside world water appears in the form of rain showers, springs, rivers, seas, lakes and pools, it performs its greatest work silently within living creatures. It is in the roots, stalks, branches and leaves of plants, in the protoplasm of the cells and in the ducts which carry the humours throughout the animal body—that continually flowing substance which releases and re-absorbs so many other substances. There are some which nourish the body, others which build it up, and others again which heal it. It is the water in the body which cleans away and removes products which cause decay; in fact it is only with the help of water in combination with air that the living process is made possible. It is a living-space in itself, the oldest on earth, and its host of inhabitants ranges from the gigantic whales and sea-plants down to the minute world of the invisible unicellular protozoa. In this picture by the Swiss painter Biedermann a waterfall pours over rocks which are dead, but within the area to the left and right where the spray reaches, life is blossoming.

THE WATER CYCLE ACCORDING TO ATHANASIUS KIRCHER (1664)

Long before scientific chemistry existed, Greek philosophers were asking how rivers and oceans came to have their inexhaustible supplies of water. They did not believe those who were content to regard rain and snow as the great providers of water. Did not the soil, the plants, and the domain of air absorb rain water in such large quantities that there was hardly any left to supply the springs? And why did rivers go on flowing even when no rain had fallen for several weeks? Aristotle taught that most of the water on earth did not come from above, but rose up from the depths, and for more than fifteen centuries the world listened to him. The opinions which prevailed during these years are shown in the picture above; they were strengthened by a conviction deriving from the faith and piety of the Middle Ages. After all, Solomon the Preacher had described the water cycle once and for all in one sentence: 'All the rivers run into the sea, yet the sea is not full; unto the place whither the rivers come, thither they go again.' Doubtless whirlpools in the sea led people to suppose that these were places where water was being sucked down through openings in the earth. The downward pressure of the sea with which was associated a kind of upward suction force from the mountains caused the sea water to pass through underground channels (coloured dark) right up to points under the mountain peaks. In ancient times it was also assumed that steam vapours which rose from the depths of the earth cooled down in the mountains and then formed extensive reserves of water underground. A similar deduction was made by the learned Jesuit father Athanasius Kircher from the existence of warm springs. In his picture water gathers in caves before it flows down once again into the sea to complete the cycle under a most emphatically rain-free sky (light coloured channels).

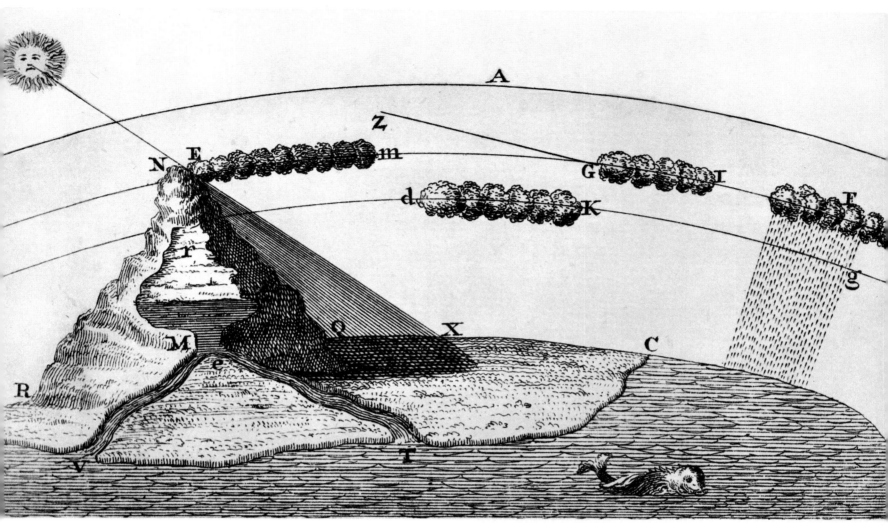

THE WATER CYCLE ACCORDING TO STEPHEN SWITZER (1729)

The first man to submit the old explanations to sound scientific criticism was Bernard Palissy, a Huguenot of refreshing courage and common sense. In his *Discours admirables de la nature des eaux et fontaines* (1580) he developed his observations about solid matter and the earth's waters in the form of discussions between two allegorical figures 'Practice' and 'Theory'; and it is characteristic of him that 'Practice' always recognizes the truth. He demonstrated clearly by comparative measurements and calculations that rain and snow water were the principal suppliers of water to the rivers and seas. A century later the physicist and meteorologist Edmé Mariotte gave a clearer exposition of this kind of water cycle, including even the origin of the raindrops in the clouds. The Englishman Stephen Switzer, from whom the above picture derives, based his theories on the work of Mariotte and the astronomer Edmund Halley.

The feather-light water vapour rises under the inducement of the sun's warmth through thinner and thinner air until it arrives at a layer of cooler air where it condenses into steam and clouds (F, G). The cloud sends down rain-water (g). Mountains are a special kind of rain-makers; the wind blowing on the sides which have been warmed by the sun carries the vaporized water lightly upwards, whilst the coolness on the side of the mountain in shadow assists the condensation into rain (left). But the falling rain, in so far as it is not immediately turned back into vapour, seeps into the ground and collects in the feed chambers (r) inside the earth. (The connection between the geological strata and the underground water channels was recognized in 1715 by the Italian, Antonio Vallisnieri.) The chambers empty themselves into the springs, and the water flows back to the sea (V, T); here the vast cycle is beginning anew.

FARADAY IN HIS LABORATORY IN THE ROYAL INSTITUTION (WATERCOLOUR BY HARRIET MOORE, 1852)

The Royal Institution, founded by Count Rumford in 1800, was a kind of superior private academy for the natural sciences. But lectures were given there for the layman too and the influence of the Institution was thus spread throughout London's population. Michael Faraday stands at the head of its many famous members. Many years before he himself succeeded in performing his epoch-making experiments in the spacious laboratory there, he had eagerly copied out many lectures in that same building: he was a poverty-stricken young bookbinder, almost a Dickensian figure. The famous **Humphry Davy** had observed here the 'most astonishing changes' caused by the current from the recently invented voltaic piles in chemical compounds, when these were dissolved in fluids. He had been the first to separate the light metals potassium and sodium from their oxides by electrolysis; he did the same with alkaline earth metals like calcium and magnesium after unimaginable technical difficulties. One day Faraday, who was a member of his audience, handed him a clean and perfectly bound copy of a lecture. Davy boldly accepted this as if it were an examination certificate and brought the self-taught student into the laboratory of the Institution as his assistant in 1813.

Faraday worked in conjunction with the Institution as laboratory director and lecturer for several decades. Between 1831 and 1840, working ardently in the experimental room (left), he developed a new method of current generation, which became the basis for the whole of modern heavy current technology (*see* p. 137). But judging by the installation in the picture, this was also a place where electrolysis was performed. The jars on the shelves are full of countless acids, salts, earths and metal oxides. Faraday broke them all down into constituent parts in thousands of experiments, using the power of electric current. We see on the right the apparatus which supplied it and measured it: on the table on the right next to a bright glass sphere is a Leyden jar, to the left of the sphere, also under glass, a galvanometer. On the floor is a machine for frictional electricity. The vast voltaic piles of the Royal Institution are not shown. Faraday divided the substances which could be decomposed from those which could not, giving the now common name 'electrodes' (the anode and the cathode) to the two poles he introduced into the substances to be decomposed. But he went further than this; having discovered the fact that atoms possess a positive and negative electric charge, he made this the basis for the theory of the migration of 'ions' and went on to establish that the products of decomposition are formed in quantities which correspond to their chemical equivalent weight.

Right: RITTER SEEKS THE BEST METHOD OF ELECTROLYZING WATER

We have shown how much new ground was broken by masters of electrolysis like Davy and Faraday. The accompanying sketches take us back to the beginnings of this kind of analysis around the year 1800. Independently of Ash, Nicholson and Carlisle who were the first to break water down into oxygen and hydrogen with the help of electricity, the German physicist and romantic natural philosopher, Johann Wilhelm Ritter, who translated Volta's works and discovered ultra-violet rays, found his own new technique of breaking down substances. He began with an ordinary glass tube filled with water (top, in the middle). Through the corks fitted to each end of the glass tube a piece of gold wire was passed, which was then connected with the source of current. Immediately small gas bubbles began to rise from the wires. To collect these properly was an impossibility. Therefore Ritter built the second apparatus (bottom). Two gold wires were again inserted into corks and led into water through the side of a marble container. In order to collect the gases, which were being given off from the water by the current, he used two glass test-tubes filled with water which he plunged into the container from above. Ritter placed two glasses in the marble vessel in case the wires should shed 'gold oxide'. For sixteen hours he allowed electricity to flow through the water. At the end, one of the test-tubes was more than half filled with hydrogen, the other was less than half filled with oxygen. But Ritter doubted whether the water had really been decomposed. So he separated the gold wires completely and then tried to insert them at the same time into two different parts of the water which had been entirely separated from one another. This was possible with a V-shaped glass (centre). He used concentrated sulphuric acid as a means of separating the water in the two legs of the glass. He achieved a more radical separation with the U-shaped apparatus (top, on either side). In both cases oxygen built up on one wire and hydrogen on the other, but never both on the same wire. Because the same water had been transformed into different gases at the same time, Ritter came to the false conclusion that water could not be broken down electrolytically. He had forgotten to enquire into the nature of electricity, which works differently at the anode and the cathode. With the two kinds of apparatus shown below, however, he had created basic technical patterns which outlived his false conclusions right up to present times.

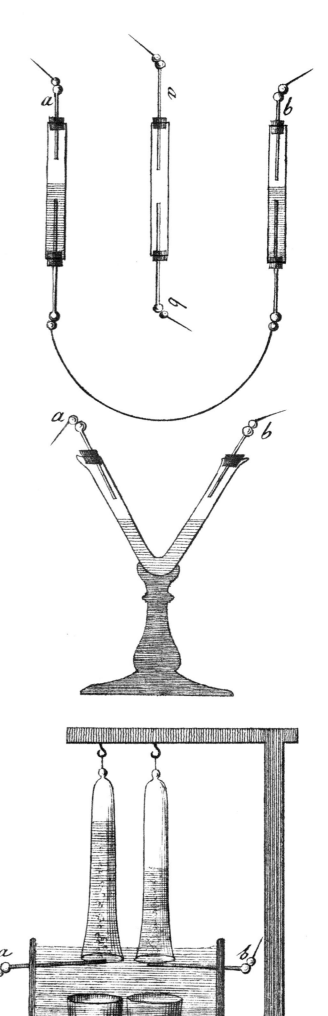

THE ELEMENT EARTH

'Organic life has to develop in the outermost crust of the earth under the influence of the sun. The Great Master-builder therefore gave this crust the capacity to attract and hold fast all those elements which provide food for the plants and so for the animals as well, and He did so in such a way that not even the smallest part is lost.' In these words Justus von Liebig described that province of reality whose mysteries he solved as did no other. The province in question is the relationship between the soil containing the nutrients and the plants (*see* p. 50). The splendour of the earth in summer with its fields of corn heavy with ears, which the Swiss painter Robert Zünd found so overwhelming (above), was explained scientifically by Liebig. He taught how these harvests could be maintained and increased. To give an example: the substances removed from the soil which

provided nutrients for the corn must be replaced by potash, phosphoric acid salts, and ammonia with its wealth of nitrogen.

Left: LIEBIG IN HIS MUNICH LABORATORY IN 1866

Corn stalks lie on the ground ready to be transformed into ashes. The most important aid in such investigations of complicated organic substances was the potash apparatus invented by Liebig (not very clearly depicted), made of five glass bulbs. The scientist's forefinger is pointing to it. Twenty-six years after the publication of his main work, the early illustrated papers circulated this picture to their readers. It was the epoch when the agricultural reformer was received like a prince at court in Paris, London and Munich.

THE RESPIRATORY CYCLE IN THE WIDE OPEN SPACES

On preceding pages: THE MAIN WORKROOM IN LIEBIG'S LABORATORY AT GIESSEN (1842)

The picture on pages 58–59 recalls the place where Liebig during twenty-eight years of endeavour made the decisive discoveries of his research work. In Paris, in the laboratories of a Gay-Lussac, a Thénard or a Chevreul, he had found out in 1822–23 the true nature of large-scale chemical analysis, in which one used eyes, hands and clear-sighted logic. He had also seen there that the greatest tasks of the century in chemistry lay in the sphere of organic chemistry which was now coming into being as the medium for the investigation of animal and plant matter. In Giessen a world-famous workroom for this new chemistry was set up under the twenty-five-year-old lecturer. Here Liebig, with the help of his highly refined apparatus, began to trace the composition of the oil of bitter almonds, and many organic acids, aldehydes, chloral, etc. In the laboratory the bearded Mexican Ortigosa stands on the left, with the famous potash apparatus

in his hand. Behind him a colleague is taking the reading of gas volume in a graduator, the man next to him is observing the condensation in a glass flask. Behind Famulus Aubel, who is stirring something in a mortar, a chemical problem is being discussed, at the table on the right a distillation process is being carried out. On the extreme right two young chemists are studying a reaction in a test-tube. The man in the top hat is August Wilhelm Hofmann, later a master of benzene and aniline chemistry.

Above: In many of the great investigators of nature there is a hidden Paracelsus, who will not be satisfied with isolated discoveries, but probes into nature as a whole. This was the case with Justus von Liebig. The pull towards this kind of investigation is seen at its best in his representation of the great respiratory cycle, in which he was able to take account of the work of Priestley, Lavoisier, the botanists (*see* p. 176) and others.

He started with something which seemed incomprehensible: the fact that gigantic green plants can live in sea-water; for

THE RESPIRATORY CYCLE IN A SMALL CONFINED SPACE

instance the up to 164-yard long giant seaweed! Down below in the sea its stalk grips firmly on to a piece of rock. Close under the surface of tropical seas its leaves hang like draperies of fern. Why can plants of this kind live, when they are cut off from the air and are totally unable to draw food from the rock? Because the chemical conditions under which sea plants and animals live are basically the same as those of the living beings above them in the air. In sea-water carbon dioxide, ammonia and other necessary nutritive salts are released. The sun as it shines on the sea supplies the required light energy for the assimilation of carbon dioxide. In this way the sea plant extracts from the carbon dioxide contained in its medium of life the carbon which together with other substances builds up the compounds essential to life; and like the land plant it divides off the oxygen. This increases the supply of air dissolved in the water and provides the breathing element for mussels, cockles and the small fish which live in the tangles of seaweed. They absorb oxygen and when they exhale return carbon dioxide resulting from

the combustion process in their organism. So we learn from the respiratory cycle in the sea how 'the lives of plants and animals are interconnected in a wonderfully simple way'.

Above: Liebig had seen at the house of Robert Warington, the founder of the Chemical Society, an astonishing novelty: a fresh-water aquarium. In this his host, by placing together a few goldfish and the waterplant *Vallisneria,* had created a partnership which supported life and respiration. Thus the English, proceeding along the lines indicated by Ingen-housz (*see* p. 176), demonstrated one of the most important phenomena in nature. From this time onwards Liebig, during his lectures on this subject in Munich, used to stand a large vessel on the testing table containing water plants, fish and cockles. The aquarium became one of the favourite articles of furniture in the bourgeois drawing-room. The aquarium shown in our picture, reproduced from the *Gartenlaube,* a German periodical (1873), exhibits life in the air and in the water simultaneously and so provides two examples of the respiratory cycle.

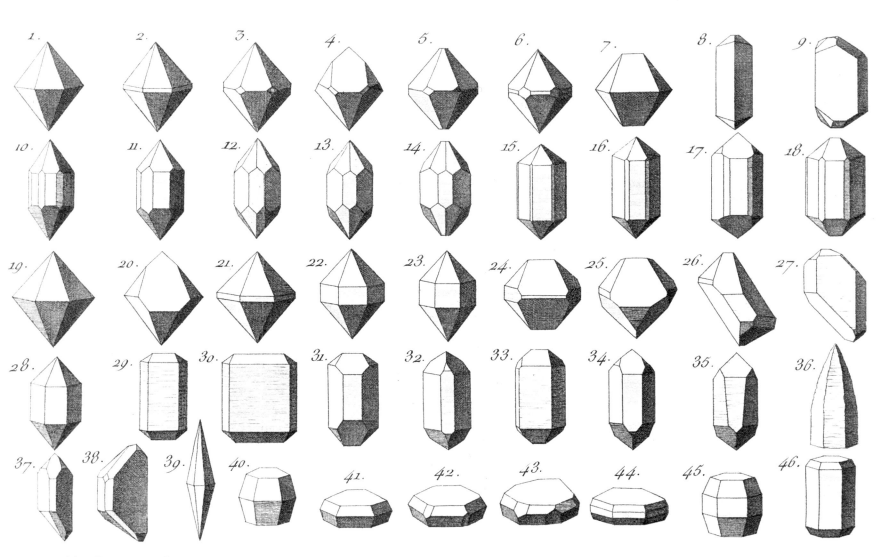

THE DOMAIN OF CRYSTALS

Following the lead of Agricola, the new crystallography began to classify crystals according to size, lustre, colour, and so on. There were already some thirty systems when Romé de l'Isle published his *Cristallographie* in 1763. He used geometry and mathematics in his approach to the 'geometry of nature' in crystals, as Haüy called it, with its inexhaustible variety; he counted the edges, measured the angles with delicate compasses, and defined the shape of the surfaces of countless crystals. He followed the Dane Nicolaus Steno who in 1669 discovered the law of constant angle ratios, but Romé de l'Isle was the first to classify crystals systematically according to their basic shapes and variants of these. So (see picture above) he derives over forty variants, made up almost entirely of six-sided prisms, from a hexagonal dodecahedron with twelve triangular surfaces. 10 is an elongated version of 6; in 11–18 this shape gradually changes; 19 is related to 1 but with different angles; 20–26 are variants of it.

When Abbé René-Just Haüy, the real founder of modern crystallography, one day dropped a crystal which broke into pieces, he discovered that from the surface of crystals right into the inside all the small particles of matter were arranged symmetrically. With the help of a structural diagram (bottom right) he elucidated the law of diminution, according to which certain shapes can be defined as having a regular level by level decrease in the number of particles composing them. He succeeded in perceiving in outline the long-sought 'Proteus hidden from discovery by its changing shapes'; he had found his way very close to the grating-like structures we know today as *raumgitter* (*see* p. 144).

The English scientist James Sowerby also used, among other things, Haüy's crystallography as his guide in his magnificently illustrated *British Mineralogy* (1804). The picture on the left shows the rust-brown heavy globular structure of red iron ore (Fe_2O_3), which contains radial fibrous crystalline forms in the shape of small rods.

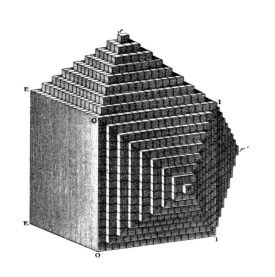

In the two pictures on this page, the Middle Ages are seen in contrast with the late nineteenth century. During the period when the first cathedrals were being built, many of the ancient stories about the miraculous origin of minerals were adopted, particularly from the work of Pliny the Elder, the Roman admiral and naturalist who met his death when Vesuvius erupted in AD 79. Among these was the tale about the large crystals which grew inside the bodies of animals. Precious stones were considered to have powers of healing and helping men in various ways. It is not surprising therefore that the picture of crystals (above) appears in a herbal, the *Hortus sanitatis* (1491). The woman who is seen drawing the crystal Alectorius out of a capon, is performing an act of magic, it being considered undeniably true that it conferred radiant beauty on its bearer.

Today we know that crystals are precipitated out of solutions or molten masses in the inside of the earth and that they grow by extracting nutritive substances from the medium surrounding them. In the lava from the volcanic island of Santorin in the Aegean Sea (left) there are here and there small gas bubbles from the fiery area inside the earth where it originated. The Frenchman, Ferdinand Fouqué, carried out extensive research in the years 1866, 1867 and 1875 in this Eldorado of crystallography. He was a master in the art of examining crystals with the microscope and he did so under polarized light. And so, when enlarged 120 times, it became possible to see the long whitish and striated rectangles of labradorite, a kind of feldspar—one of the countless compounds of silicon. Silicon exists in almost every rock except lime and hardens it. It is this substance which Berzelius had tried to isolate with incredible patience. A few particles of iron ore can be seen, coloured dark. To the left, gathered together in a mass near the edge, there is a swarm of minute augite crystals, a dust far smaller than anything visible to the naked eye, and yet each speck has its angle constant, its grating-like structure and its chemical substance.

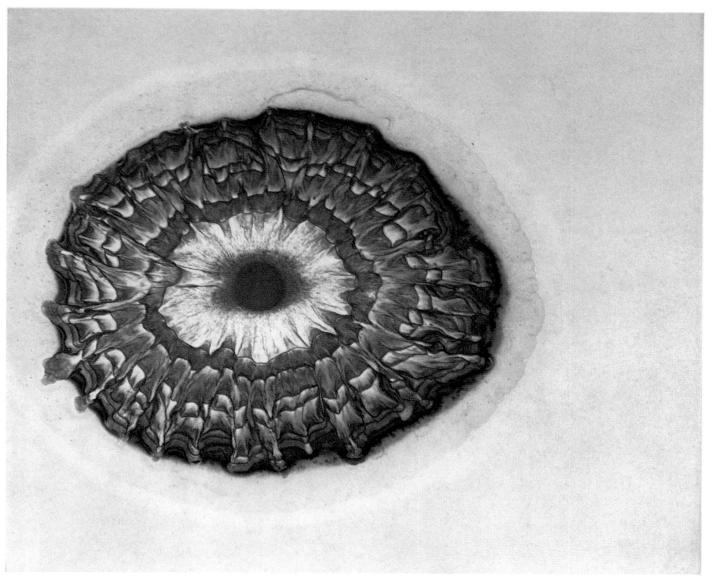

'The Formative Impulse in Substances' at Work

In 1850 and 1855 the chemist Friedlieb Ferdinand Runge brought on to the market two highly remarkable books which had sheets of blotting-paper clipped inside, and cut back a little at one edge like the one above. He poured drops of certain solutions carefully on to the middle of a piece of blotting-paper which lay stretched on a string net, and then watched how coloured images of unusual beauty immediately appeared, wherever the solution sank into the absorbent paper. The same substances always produced the same magic images, shapes and colours. 'I call this power the formative impulse and I regard it as the prototype of the living force which is active in plants and animals.' That is the language of qualitative chemistry, which records phenomena and reflects on hidden forces. We see this kind of chemistry appearing again and again, even at the time when the other chemistry had begun to predominate—the chemistry which weighs and measures, and calculates atomic mechanisms. Runge recognized the traces of sulphuric acid from manganous oxide in the brown veining, and of sulphuric acid from copper monoxide in the greenish edgings. He did not know that from this art of reading the writing of substances on filter paper there would develop a new technique of analysis, chromatography; it was inaugurated in 1903 by the Russian botanist Tswett.

Runge, who found for the first time substances like red madder, atropine and caffeine, suffered the bitter fate of the unrecognized discoverer. After his years as lecturer in Berlin and Breslau he worked from 1831 to 1852 as technical director of a firm of manufacturing chemists in Oranienburg. This small concern could easily have become the largest in Germany, if the value had been properly assessed of the things which Runge, with his brilliant knowledge of natural dyestuffs, extracted by distillation from the almost worthless waste product of gas-works, coal-tar: aniline and phenol, the basic materials for the most beautiful artificial dyes. In the year 1833 he publicly announced his discoveries. The commercial director of the concern, who was opposed to creative 'technological individuals', and besides saw his sacred profits threatened by competition from aniline, paid no attention. Runge lost heart. It was the Englishman W. H. Perkin who produced a violet dyestuff out of aniline on which men of vision based a whole new chemical industry.

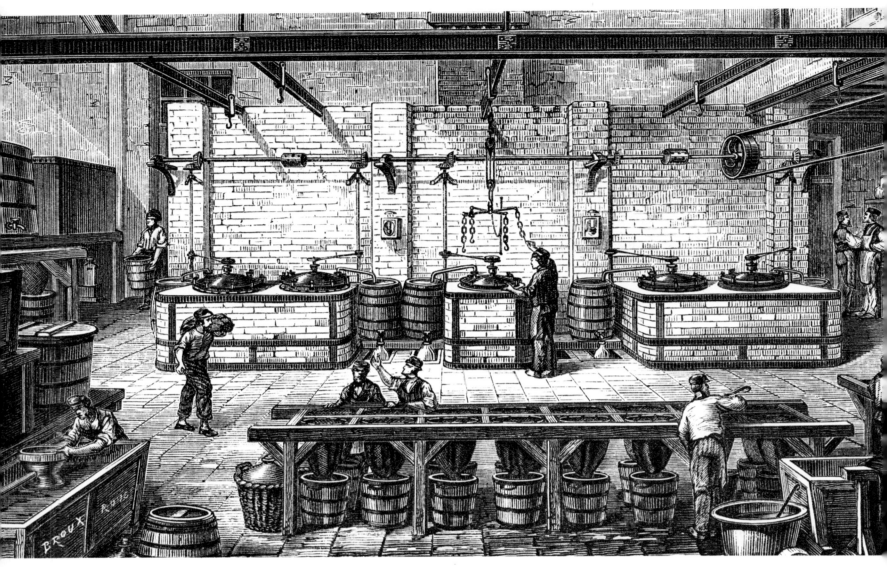

AN INDUSTRIAL CHEMISTRY WORKSHOP ABOUT 1865

In the chemical works which developed extensively in the late nineteenth century after modest beginnings, we find the handy equipment of the chemical laboratory appearing in a gigantically enlarged form. The small mortar became a stone-crushing machine, the retort turned into a huge boiler. This trend is seen in this drab workshop in the factory of Poirier & Chappat at Saint-Denis, where the artificial dye-stuff aniline blue was manufactured in two stages. In the first, rosaniline is heated in five pressure boilers, called auto-claves; it is distilled several times with surplus aniline and a little benzoic acid up to a temperature of 170 degrees C., under heavy hermetically sealed covers. They can be seen in the brick kilns in the background. The escaping aniline and water vapours are led off through water-cooled barrels into vessels. In the second stage the insoluble aniline blue is extracted out of the distillate in the trough on the left under the influence of diluted sulphuric acid. Finally, the green iridescent crystals are collected in filters (foreground). The manufacture of coal-tar dyes was one of many aspiring chemical industries. Swarms of chemists and armies of workpeople were employed in them. Industrial chemistry has had a far-reaching influence on human existence. It has created alongside natural substances a second world of matter, without which the feeding, clothing and health services of the growing world population would be unthinkable. It has utilized the results of several centuries of chemical research: its factories have in the meantime turned into important research centres in their own right.

Mathematical Chemistry

John Dalton, son of a poor English weaver, came to Manchester at the age of twenty-seven as a private tutor. His real life was lived in his study and in the laboratory of the local Literary and Philosophical Society. His *New System of Chemical Philosophy* (1808) would have been forgotten if it had not contained one or two almost incidental sentences about the atom, a roughly constructed table of atomic weights and a few sketches of atomic shapes. These brought the humble young man international fame, for they are the beginning of modern chemistry's atomic theory: 'Now it is one great object of this work, to shew the importance and advantage of ascertaining the relative weights of the ultimate particles, both of simple and compound bodies, the number of simple elementary particles which constitute one compound particle, and the number of less compound particles which enter into the formation of one more compound particle.'

This was the whole revolutionary programme. As many as four hundred years before Christ, Leucippus and his disciple Democritus had spoken of these invisible ultimate particles of every substance, and named them the 'indivisibles', for 'indivisible' is the meaning of Greek *atomos* which gives our word *atom*. Boyle, Gassendi, Newton and many others had also postulated minute particles as the units from which the whole of creation was composed. According to Dalton, however, the atoms of different elements were not only different from one another in size and weight, but each element was made up of atoms of a kind peculiar to itself alone. In 1797, J.L. Proust had shown that the basic weight relationship of elements in a chemical compound was immutable. Dalton added to this 'Law of Simple Proportions' his own 'Law of Multiple Proportions', according to which elements could combine with one another in more than one proportion, provided that the proportions consisted of whole numbers.

Dalton had established facts of this kind chiefly by observing the process of dissolution of gases in liquids. The law of proportions illuminated to some extent the mystery of chemical reactions; it also provided the key to the purely mathematical determination of the relative weights of the atoms of a substance: that is, their weight calculated on the basis of the assumption that hydrogen had the value one. By measuring the actual weight of elements in compounds, and comparing them, scientists put themselves in a better position to estimate the relative weights of atoms. Compounds were seen to be groups of atoms of elemental substances put together in specified numbers according to a set pattern. If every type of atom were represented by a separate symbol, all the elements other than carbon and all their most important compounds—the quintessence of chemistry—could be written down on two sheets of paper (*see* p. 70). In 1811, a brilliant mathematician, a lawyer who became a self-taught chemist, Amadeo Avogadro, introduced the illuminating concept of the molecule: the smallest group of atoms capable of determining the identity of a substance. He also put forward a method of establishing molecular weight from the concentration of a gas. However, it was left to his belligerent compatriot Stanislao Cannizzaro to bring about acceptance of this totally neglected theory about the year 1860.

From 1860 onwards, chemistry was in command of its language of formulae and its atomic and molecular theories. But there was one substance in nature which refused to be accommodated in this tidy scheme: carbon. Both before and during our own time, chemistry was dedicated largely to the investigation of so-called organic matter in man, plants and animals. So the chemist was continually brought up against the inexhaustible capacity of carbon for the formation of compounds. Friedrich August Kekulé von Stradonitz brought to light this striking capacity of the carbon atom, together with its unique capacity for combining the same group of atoms consisting of carbon and hydrogen in different regular structures, and, if they were not saturated, for developing into long and complicated chains. He gave to organic chemistry structural sketches (amongst them the famous *benzene ring*) which provided a bird's-eye view of the superabundance of possible carbon compounds (*see* p. 71). To the many triumphs of organic chemistry belong the synthesis of vitamins, hormones and antibiotics, which have come to be such important helpers of mankind.

One of the highest aims of science is to uncover the inner organization of nature. Thus, after 1850, more and more scientists devoted themselves to the task of ranking the round sixty elements then known according to their atomic weight. In this process, they observed that certain properties of the basic substances seemed to recur from time to time—as in a house in which rooms standing one above the other are all constructed alike because their principal supports are common to them all.

The significance of this fact was shown by Dimitri Mendeleyev from Tobolsk, who taught in Petersburg: the Linnaeus of chemistry. In 1869, he drew up a table showing the organization of elements which, with additions and alterations, remains valid up to the present. Taking hydrogen, the lightest substance, as his first, he set them side by side like cards in a game of patience, beginning a new row every time he found one which showed a recurrence of properties already found. The horizontal rows showed steadily increasing atomic weights and valency, the vertical rows contained chemically related substances: for example, the alkaline metals (*see* p. 72). There were gaps in this system: where, it was to be assumed, elements as yet undiscovered would take their place. Mendeleyev, unlike Lothar Meyer who had reached the same conclusions independently, was bold enough to anticipate the properties of unknown elements in terms of their relationship to their neighbours in the system. He was later justified by the discovery of substances which in fact correspond to his descriptions: for instance, gallium and germanium.

In later years, Mendeleyev turned from the abstract quantitative chemistry of tables to the whole natural complex of nature in its relation to man. He lived to see the remarkable years 1896 and 1898 in which Henri Becquerel dicovered the radioactivity of uranium and the Curies the element radium. These were the first steps into a new era. The content of the atom had become the principal research subject of physics (*see* p. 140). Hesitatingly, chemistry began to follow.

Opposite: JOHN DALTON COLLECTS MARSH GAS

Marsh gas (methane), a light hydrocarbon gas, originates from the decaying remains of plants and animals when air is cut off; it often rises from swampy stagnant water. It is beside just such an algous pool near Manchester that we see Dalton stirring up the muddy bottom with a stick; a farmer's boy catches the gas bubbles in a broad glass jar as they rise. A saucer is used to prevent the odourless and colourless gas from escaping. Every pool is a paradise for naturalists and children. The boy on the left has been attracted there by the prospect of catching sticklebacks. Dalton, the private tutor who had the reputation in the town of being a crazy eccentric, is moved by thoughts which are to make history. He was to build up (as the Italian Avogadro did later) his modern atomic theory largely on the basis of his observation of gases. (Detail of a painting by Ford Madox Brown in Manchester Town Hall.)

John Dalton collects marsh gas

Overleaf, left: DALTON'S SYMBOLS FOR CHEMICAL SUBSTANCES

Dalton invented a system of signs to illustrate his theories. In the rows at the top there are eighteen of his symbols for elements, from left to right: oxygen, hydrogen, nitrogen, carbon, sulphur, phosphorus, gold, platinum, silver, calcium, magnesium, barium, strontium, aluminium and so on. The rest of the signs represent 'compound atoms' (like Amadeo Avrogadro, we now use the clearer term molecules) and also more complicated combinations; the large, cross-shaped figure is the symbol for alum. The signs include those for aluminium, sulphur, oxygen and potassium (centre) for which today's formula reads: $KAl(SO_4)_2$. Below, there is an attempt to show by rays emitted from the atoms of certain gases (for example carbon monoxide and carbon dioxide) the space which the atoms of gases create around themselves. It was Berzelius who simplified the language of chemistry and replaced Dalton's symbols by one or two of the first letters of the Latin names of the elements and indicated by figures the number of atoms of an element in a particular molecule. Since it was later agreed that the signs for each element should indicate at the same time the atomic weight of the substance, chemistry now had at its disposal a language which was understood without translation from Alaska to Tasmania. In the late Middle Ages we can count about 3,900 chemical signs—today there are 103. The difference between these two figures indicates the prodigious progress made over five hundred years.

Overleaf, right: A MODEL OF A GIANT MOLECULE (COPPER-PHTHALO-CYANINE) AS SEEN BY AN ARTIST (1953)

In the molecule of this blue artificial dyestuff each of the strange sparkling forms corresponds to an atom. Their arrangement in a giant molecule follows the teaching of Kekulé. In the centre is a copper atom. All round this are eight groups of carbon and nitrogen atoms, each group having a dark space in the middle; on the outer four corners four hexagon rings (like Kekulé's benzene ring) grow outwards. They consist of hydrogen atoms (indicated by the white rays pointing outwards) and carbon atoms. The formula reads: $C_{32}H_{16}N_8Cu$. This highly complicated design is in fact a representation in one picture of the wonderful discovery made by Kekulé in the year 1858 known as 'valency'. This binding force works according to given laws in each kind of atom and determines its impulse to combine or not to combine with other atoms. (Drawing by Professor Hans Haffenrichter.)

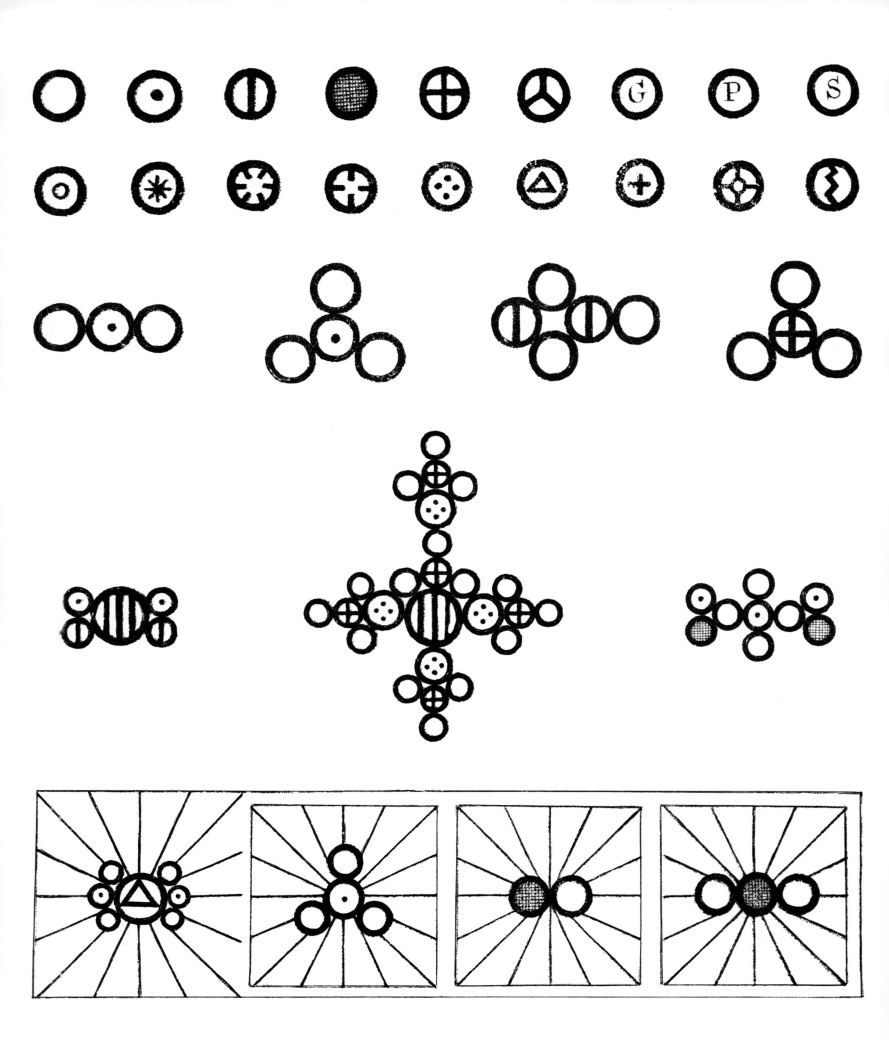

A woodcut by Hans Weiditz in Petrarch's *Mirror of Consolation* (German edition of 1532) depicts man as living in close union with the material forces of nature (top right). In those days they were thought simply to consist of the four indivisible elements. Thus our *Anthropos* is holding in his right hand the flaming ball of fire, in his left the head of a wind-god; his feet rest on two spheres: the left-hand one, which is floating, has the force of the element water contained in it, that on the right contains the force of the element earth. This is an allegory with a medical theme; it was supposed to convey that the human body remains healthy as long as the forces of the elements balance each other within it and friendly stars stand over it. Even those who have long ago substituted the ninety-two new elements (below) for the four old ones, may regard this picture as having greater significance than simply a representation of the truth as it was seen at that period. The body and soul of man at all periods have been closely linked with the world of matter, says the message. What does more to create the life within him than the four elements, which stream through him—the air which he breathes, the warmth of fire in the organic combustion processes, the water which carries substances from organ to organ, the minerals of the earth which in changed forms

he ingests with his nutrition? And moreover: now, as ever, man makes his direct emotional contacts with the beauty and power of matter mainly through the four primeval elements—when he listens to the foaming water, the roaring wind, the crackling fire or the silent earth heavy with its mineral forces.

Bottom, left: The English physicist and chemist William Crookes, who had discovered the element thallium by means of spectrum analysis, suggested in 1888 in the journal *Chemical News* that Mendelejeff's periodic system of the elements should be demonstrated three-dimensionally in curves in a figure of eight. He expected that by these means it would be easier to see how the elements form themselves into groups in accordance with inherent laws. Thus the electro-positive elements came to be placed at the back of the spiral, and the negative ones in the front. Crookes kept to the table of the periodic system which had been improved in 1880. According to this the row begins with the element hydrogen (H, atomic weight 1.0080) and ends with the heaviest: uranium (U, atomic weight 238.07). With this arrangement of disks (signifying elements) placed vertically one below the other, natural relationships appear which provide important information: thus under F, where the iron (Fe), palladium (Pd) and platinum families come close together—all are grey-coloured metals which are difficult to smelt but which easily form salts in certain solutions. Light disks indicate the famous gaps in the system. A later hand added in the middle of the model the signs for some of the rare inert gases (He = helium, Ar = argon, and so on). They are placed there where the curves cut across each other and reduce themselves to a zero point, the right place for elements without valency, which like 'rarities of noble birth' refuse to combine with others. The latest research has, however, shown that they are not so noble or so aloof as had been thought.

When the physicists of our century recognized that the atom was not an a-tom, not 'a-tomos', not indivisible, but a compound structure, it required only a few re-groupings to assimilate the periodic system to the new theory. It was not the atomic weight but the number of protons contained in the nucleus or the number of electrons spinning round the nucleus which was the deciding force in the atom, and this number rose as one proceeded from hydrogen to uranium in much the same way as the atomic weights increased between the same two extremes.

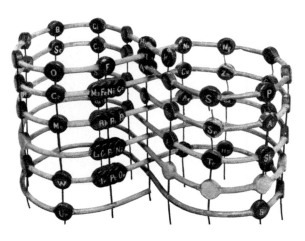

PHYSICS

Even so-called inanimate nature surrounds us with an abundance of 'life': of visible and invisible movements in the realms of air, water and solids, of mysterious energies. The number of different compartments into which physics came to be divided with time reflects the abundance of these phenomena.

Planets rotate round the sun. Has the force which keeps them on their path through outer space anything to do with the path followed by a ball thrown upwards by a child? Mechanics provided the answer to such questions. Is there any connection between the rolling of thunder and the inaudible chirruping of an insect in the grass? These were the questions asked of acoustics, the science of sound. Why do we rub our hands in the cold winter air, and has this anything to do with the power which drives the pistons of a steam engine up and down? This is the province of the physics of heat. Are the colours of the rainbow connected with the seven coloured stripes cast by a glass prism upon white paper? Such considerations were aroused by the phenomena of light in the minds of the observant masters of optics. Are the same forces at work in the shapes formed by iron filings in the vicinity of a magnet as in the polar lights? Is lightning in the sky related to the crackling sparks in an electric machine? Such were the problems which faced the sciences of magnetism and electricity. Has the gentle glow of fluorescent figures on a wrist-watch anything to do with the sun's powerful energy? These are the questions which faced modern atomic physics.

Since the seventeenth century, physics has moved away from perceptible and measurable phenomena such as a burning candle or a moving magnetic needle into a fourth dimension: a world of immaterial forces, to wave movements in a hypothetical ether, to fields of force which are to be found everywhere on earth and even within the atom itself. It created for itself a highly refined form of mathematics designed to express the greatest truths in the smallest space. Newton's law of gravity, which explains the interplay of forces in the solar system, could have been written on the shaft of the pen of its propounder.

In the late nineteenth century a number of dicoveries were made which brought the sub-compartments of physics closer together. Scientists looked for constants in nature: for basic forces to which light and warmth, electricity and magnetism could be traced back. The most rational of all the sciences became mysterious again.

Mechanics

'In the beginning was mechanics': so said Max von Laue. Wedges, levers, pulleys and wheels served as helpmates in the burden of human toil long before the existence of scientific mechanics. Most of the early civilizations came to possess a similar store of pre-scientific experience in their dealings with the same inanimate objects which prompted the Greeks to formulate early scientific mechanics. For in this realm too the Greeks showed their genius for transposing natural events into intellectual concepts. The heritage left by Euclid, Archimedes and Hero includes the earliest major achievements of the young science.

Not until the time of Stevin, Galileo and their kind, did mechanics come to be a passionate preoccupation of great minds, when the impetus of the renaissance period induced men to look at the world with their own eyes, and explain it in terms of their own logic and, even in mechanical phenomena, opened up new continents. A bold race of physicists together established a new form of observation of nature and cleverly thought-out experiments, and set down their conclusions in mathematically formulated laws. The period from Galileo to Descartes and Newton saw triumphs of an astonishingly refined mode of quantitative thought. The whole physical world, including light and sound, seemed to possess structures which worked mechanically and could be expressed in figures; they were closely bound up in a cosmos of physical laws and of number.

The path of mechanics turned very gradually from the domain of visible things to what Helmholtz termed the levers, ropes and pulleys which work behind the scenes of outer reality, controlling events, as it were, from back stage. The most important discovery of this kind was the theory of the conservation of energy, which had extremely far-reaching implications.

The mode of thinking of this science had illuminated many phenomena of inanimate objects, from the fall of objects to the movement of the stars, leaving no problems unsolved and no contradictions. It served as a model on all sides. Could the body of an animal or a plant not be regarded as a purely mechanical thing? Were the circulation of the blood or the flight of birds not 'mechanical'? More and more, attempts were made to submit all forms of life to the axioms of mechanics and its mathematical processes. 'Let us make bold to say that man is a machine,' said La Mettrie in 1748. In the second half of the nineteenth century, this mechanization of the world at large found widespread acceptance, shortly before the investigation of the atom by physicists laid bare an area of purely physical truth in the very citadel, as it were, of physics, before which mechanistic thought was compelled to retreat.

If physics seemed sometimes to take flight into a fourth dimension of pure number, it seemed all the more tangible for that in the practical spheres in which technicians applied its laws. Modern civilization, with its transcontinental railway trains, its transoceanic wireless communication, its atomic power stations, and its fear of nuclear bombs is built upon the foundations laid down by physics.

PRACTICAL MECHANICS IN OLD BABYLON ▶

The Babylonians were very skilful mechanics. They already knew of five simple machines: the lever, the wheel, the roller, the wedge, and the screw. No less than four of them can be seen in the relief plate (right). A stone block with the image of a man-headed bull on it has been floated down the Tigris, whose waves are shown at the top on the right, to Nineveh where it has been laid on a sleigh-like vehicle. Wooden pegs jut out at the front and the back on the long sides. It is there that the thick ropes are fastened, on which the hordes of prisoners of war have to pull as they bring their great load inland. Four simple machines are introduced like benevolent spirits: lever, wedge, roller and wheel. The group of prisoners, driven on by blows from the overseer's stick, continues ceaselessly to lay rollers in front of the sleigh and remove them from behind; in this way the friction is reduced. Two assistants have put a wedge under a long beam which acts as a lever. The arm of this lever provides a point of support on which men are heaving with all their weight so as to propel the vehicle. And with that miraculous thing, the wheel (above, right), twice the load can be moved with half the effort used by one man working with ropes and beams. Nowhere in Mesopotamia do we find a scientific system of physics which might have formulated the laws of the lever. The Greeks were the first to propound and enunciate such a law which is: the leverage length between the force applied and the fulcrum should bear roughly the same relation to that between the fulcrum and the load, as the load bears to the force applied.

Overleaf, left: 'DO NOT DISTURB MY CIRCLES!'

The first man to unite physics and mathematics in the grand style was Archimedes of Syracuse. He is remembered as a thinker who utterly forgot everything else as he applied himself to his mathematical problems. This is how he is depicted in a mosaic found in Herculaneum. For two years the town of Syracuse under its ruler Hieron had defied the besieging Romans. When they finally entered the town in 212 BC, he was sitting, oblivious to all around, deeply engaged in new problems. His apparatus consists of the abacus, a low rectangular box, the bottom of which was covered with a fine layer of sand which had been smoothed out flat. It was on this that the mathematician drew his spirals, parabolas and circles, which could thus easily be rubbed out. A Roman soldier is ordering him to surrender. The answer is a resolute no. His legendary words: 'Do not disturb my circles' have become proverbial.

'Do not disturb my Circles' (p. 74)

Right: Signs drawn by the Hand of Man

The renowned Roman architect Vitruvius tells in one of his ten books *De Architectura* of how one day a Greek ship in which the philosopher Aristippus, a pupil of Socrates, was sailing with some companions, was wrecked near the island of Rhodes and sank. The travellers survived the shipwreck and succeeded in reaching land. They were wandering along the lonely seashore when suddenly the philosopher discovered geometrical figures drawn in the sand. 'Let us be of good heart, for I see the signs of man,' he is supposed to have exclaimed. In 1792 the English illustrator Burghers gave the incident deeper significance when, unconcerned about chronological accuracy, he drew in the drifting sand two geometric designs: a curve like the one Archimedes had

designed to calculate the area of spirals, and an ellipse, made by slicing a cone. It was the relationship of this ellipse to the circle enclosing it which the great mathematician had tried to turn into a geometric law. The travelling companions are standing in front of the two signs, both of which derive from that aim in Greek thought which made history: to discover universal truths, and to record them in a timeless form. Mathematical principles and geometrical figures seem more than anything else to exemplify such timelessness. 'Geometry is the knowledge of eternal being,' Plato had said. In this sense Euclid had come to write his elements of geometry in Alexandria, and Archimedes, stimulated by Euclid, had come to apply himself to his investigations of the quadrature of the parabola, and the volume of spheres and cylinders.

ARCHIMEDES AND HYDROSTATICS

The Greeks brought to light the mathematics hidden in the behaviour of solid and liquid bodies at rest and recorded their theories in formulae which had a timeless application. Such activities were also a powerful incentive to the enquiring mind of Archimedes. He formulated the laws of the lever. He tried to establish a law for determining the position of the centre of gravity. He found methods of establishing the relative densities of solid substances. A well-known anecdote tells how in applying these laws he obtained the conviction of a goldsmith for fraud. The goldsmith had been commissioned to make a wreath for King Hieron out of an exactly measured quantity of gold. The wreath when it was delivered had the correct weight, but the suspicion arose that the craftsman had substituted an inferior metal—silver—for part of the gold. The omniscient Archimedes was to be the judge. He himself examined the material used, in this way: he took a lump of gold and a lump of silver, each weighing exactly the same as the wreath, but their volume was unequal because of their unequal specific gravity. He compared them by immersing them one after the other in a vessel full to the brim with water; he then measured the water which overflowed in each case. When, after filling up the vessel for the third time, he put the gold wreath into it, it turned out that it caused more water to overflow than the lump of gold and less than the lump of silver. Therefore the 'golden' wreath must have contained some silver since this displaces more water. In our late medieval woodcut the lumps have turned into balls, the wreath has become a crown, and instead of the articles he used Archimedes himself is seen in the bath-tub. The artist wanted to bring yet another anecdote into the picture: the happy solution of the difficult problem is said to have come to relieve Archimedes' depression as he was in his bath. He is supposed to have been so overcome with joy that he ran through the town, naked as he was, shouting his famous word 'Eureka'—'I have found it'. The word has echoed through the centuries.

About the year 300 BC a new seat of important scientific research began to flourish: the academy of Alexandria, a foundation of the far-sighted kings of the House of the Ptolemies. The leading men were no longer philosophers, but empiricists, men of creative ability who were masters in one particular branch of knowledge: the geometrician Euclid, the astronomer Aristarchus, who was the first to dare to regard the sun and not the earth as the centre of the world, the doctor Erasistratos, the discoverer of the nervous system, the geographer and cosmographer Ptolemy and many others. It is assumed that Archimedes studied here as technologist and mathematician; it was also here in about 100 BC that Hero lived, the greatest practical genius of all the scientists of the ancient world. He invented the three automatic machines shown on the right.

Top: An automatic temple door. Its hinges are extended into the space under the temple in the form of two round rods which end in pin-points at the bottom and so revolve easily. A heavy lead sphere on the right (shown too low in this drawing) closes the wings of the door by its weight. If a sacrificial fire is lit on the hollow altar (left), the heated air expands in the altar's sealed copper body and finds its way downwards through a pipe into a metal sphere, which is half filled with water. There is no way out for the heated air which continues to stream in from above, and so the water is forced downwards and then through a U-shaped siphon into an empty bucket; this is connected with the hinge-extensions by a double chain over a small roller. The chain is slung round the hinge extensions in such a way that the doors open when the bucket, as a result of its increased weight, begins to pull on them. If the sacrificial fire goes out, the counterweight of the lead sphere on the right will shut the door again, because the cooler air in the altar now contracts, and brings back the water from the bucket into the metal sphere as a result, so Hero thought, of a reverse pneumatic reaction.

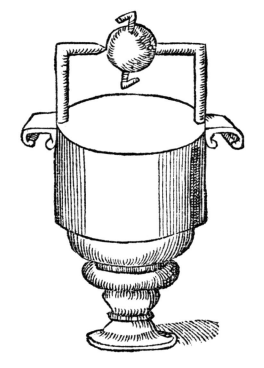

Centre: The well-known aeolipile. A cauldron is filled with water and placed on a stand. On the top is a hermetically sealed lid. To one side of it a rod bent into a right angle is soldered on: one of the supports for a small thick-walled rotatable hollow sphere; the opposite support consists of an air-tight pipe which is led into the cauldron whilst the other end is led into the hollow sphere. When the cauldron is heated, steam is built up and this can only escape by the pipe on the right. It reaches the hollow sphere—where it seems to be confined for the second time. But here there are two ways out, for in the sphere bent tubes have been inserted at the top and bottom; the ends of these jets face in different directions. When the steam escapes through these tubes, the hollow sphere begins to revolve ever faster as a result of the retro-action. The first steam-engine, which in addition worked according to the principle of jet propulsion, had been created.

Bottom: An automatic machine for holy water. Inside there is a rod carrying a balancing arm. The right end of the arm is flattened into a disk and catches the coins as they fall while the left end of the arm is attached to a little lid by a thin chain. This lid fits exactly on to a tiny can which stands at the bottom of a cylinder filled with holy water. A pipe leads out of the cylinder to the outside. As the can-lid is heavier than the disk for the coins, it normally keeps the can closed, so that no water can flow out. If a coin is dropped, the lever arm with the little tray sinks and the lid is lifted: holy water flows out, but only until the coin slides off the tipped-up tray and so causes the balances to return to their position of rest. Evidently the illustrator has imagined that the balances are tipped to the left when in the position of rest.

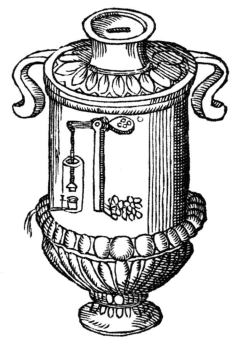

Anyone who reads the descriptions of Hero's pneumatic and automatic machines, which are works of art in themselves, imagines he is looking into a toyshop: he will see magic cans, beakers out of which, like Tantalus, one could not drink, automatic water machines, wind organs, magic drinking horns, automatic theatres—undoubtedly the world of this Greek was full of such things as conjuring tricks and curiosities. But it was also a world which was made conscious of the mechanical properties of objects, seen by a mathematician and physicist who was sharp-witted, observant and imaginative and did not hesitate to explain his experiments in atomic terms. Even when he 'only' discovered how the suction of a vacuum or the expansion of air when heated or the weight of a coin could be used as a driving force for small machines, these were, all the same, miniature triumphs of man the explorer over miniature forces within miniature objects; they differed only in scale, not in essence, from the monumental triumphs of modern technologists. The value of the works of men like Archimedes or Hero was enthusiastically recognized by popes of the late Middle Ages like Nicholas V (who had the writings of both translated) and well-known inventors of the Renaissance like Stevin, Galileo and Leonardo da Vinci. For them, those two were equal in importance to the great poets and philosophers of antiquity.

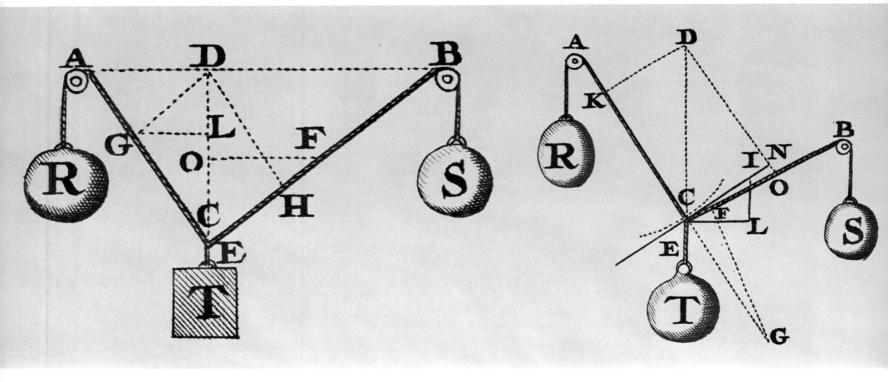

THE LEGACY OF SIMON STEVIN TO THE SYMBOL LANGUAGE OF STATICS

Greek mechanics had contented itself with observing forces of a simple kind, like those in the work of the lever. The laws which resulted from this established the behaviour of bodies in undynamic, uncomplicated cases. But was there not also, perhaps, a law of mechanics encompassed by the movement of a rowing boat which the oarsman rows across a river with powerful strokes perpendicular to the current, but which is carried to the other bank in an oblique line owing to the opposing force of the current? Even these elemental situations, in which two forces act upon a body from different directions, were left by the ancient world to a future science of force relationships with all their complications. It was a Dutchman, Simon Stevin, who, in the last decades of the sixteenth century, carried the mechanics of Archimedes a decisive stage further. As chief supervisor of land and water engineering projects in the Netherlands he was a man of practical experience. With the help of block and tackle he was able to illustrate far more clearly than his great teacher that length of rope and force are inversely proportional. He discovered the laws which determine the behaviour of bodies on an inclined plane, introduced calculation by decimal fractions and broke also new ground by writing his works not in Latin, the normal academic language, but in his own beloved Dutch, thus giving them an atmosphere of freshness. Above all he created, at least

in outline, a representational figure for physics, that of the parallelogram of forces—a discovery of no lesser importance than the lever laws of the Syracusan or Galileo's laws of falling bodies. Newton finally elucidated what Stevin had begun. The parallelogram of forces enabled man to ascertain the direction and strength of the resultant force, when forces coming from different directions act upon the same body: he thus explained the oblique course of the boat across the river. Mathematics proved to be inadequate, at that time, for the formulation of things which had this kind of complication: so mechanical processes were shown in the form of geometric figures, as the French scholar Nicolas of Oresme had already done. The venerable yet clumsy attempts by Stevin (*see* p. 100) were superseded, and very soon we find everywhere in works on mechanics the parallelogram of forces modified in the most varied ways, as here in the two figures from Borelli's *De motu animalium* (1680). Over rollers assumed to be weightless, 'immaterial' cords lead which indicate the direction of the motive force; these—two of them working in opposite directions (R, S) and the one resulting from them which acts upwards (C, D), and corresponds to the load (T)— are represented by weights, whilst the parallelogram of forces is built up around the line of the resultant force. The figure on the right represents the silent struggle of the forces in a yet more complicated case.

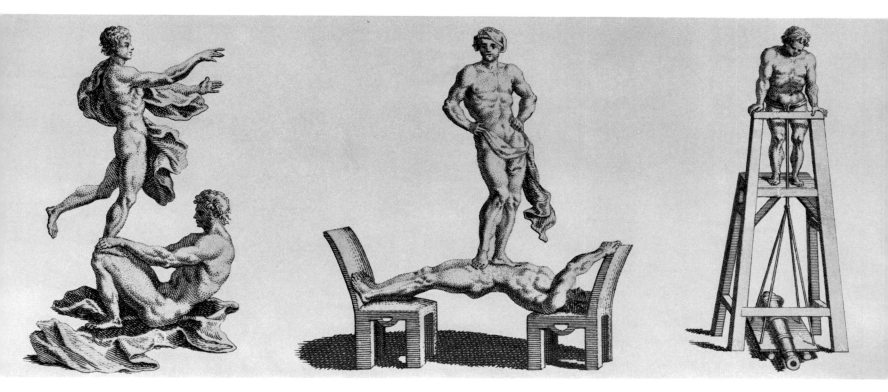

HERCULES AND PHYSICS

Stevin, with the eye of a physicist, observed not only objects but also man. He came to the help of the toiling load-carrier by showing him how the physical effort was made easier when the centre of gravity of the load was in the right position, in harmony with the lever system of the body. The human body which was tall and upright and yet at the same time moved so easily out of its perpendicular position was, for physicists since Stevin's day, a much favoured medium for the demonstration of statics. Amongst the phenomena they studied were the performances given by many a lion-like Hercules in the side-shows of the fairs. John Theophilus Desaguliers, a Huguenot living in London, who worked as a demonstrator for the Royal Society and was highly esteemed by Newton, was one of those who made such studies. The man on the scaffolding on the right is bearing the full weight of a gun-barrel. As soon as the rollers are taken away from under the platform on which the gun is resting, the weight of the load is distributed between the flats of his hands and the soles of his feet; the weight is best distributed when the point of application of the load on the body is placed as near as possible to the centre between these four supports. The two figures on the left are demonstrating under the most difficult of conditions the fact that the equilibrium is best when the man on the ground places the soles of his feet as exactly as he can below the centre of gravity of his partner who is balancing on his knee. In the middle picture an athlete is stiffening his body to act like a load-carrying bridge. The two chairs have been tied so that they cannot move; he can thus arch himself on them with feet, head and arms and at the same time rest his shoulders on one of them like a bridge on a powerful support.

The more this new science of bodies subject to dynamic movement came into its own alongside the traditional statics, the stronger became the will to know more of these forces. 'There is hardly a natural process of any kind which does not involve mechanical operations'—this is how Helmholtz summed up his views nearly two hundred years later. Was not every animal that ran, flew or swam a living demonstration of the laws of statics and dynamics? For instance the flying or landing bird? In Italy a branch of zoology and medicine sprung up which was closely allied to physics and was given the name of iatromathematics; its founder and most creative mind, Giovanni Alfonso Borelli, went so far as to set an iatromathematical God over the world: 'Since the scientific understanding of all these things (the flight of birds, the swimming of fishes and so on) is based mainly on geometry, it will be right to suppose that God used geometry in the creation of animal organisms, for this is the only science which enables man to read and understand God's handwriting in the animal world.'

Galileo Galilei and classical Mechanics

In the year 1586 the 'creator of modern Rome', Pope Sixtus V, decided to move a 92 foot-high stone obelisk which weighed nearly 240 tons and had been brought to Rome from Egypt in the time of Caligula. It was to be transported 275 yards and re-erected in the square in front of St Peter's Cathedral which was then in the process of being built. The architect Domenico Fontana from Melide was given the responsibility of directing the operations. He had not much more at his disposal than the time-honoured simple machines of the ancient Babylonians and the laws of statics which had so far been discovered. Fontana, using an army of nine-hundred workmen and seventy-four horses, thought the operation out to the last detail and turned it into a sumptuously produced drama of renaissance technology. On either side of the obelisk he erected a tower, made up of four strong 98 foot-high composite wooden beams placed vertically; these were propped up on three sides by a supporting structure of sloping beams which were strengthened in many places. At the top a network of stout beams was laid from one tower to the other; from these were suspended on ropes the pulley-blocks with their sets of wrought-iron pulleys which had to lift the obelisk and then lay it on a kind of rolling platform. The double tower was in due course re-erected at the new site. The obelisk was wrapped in rush matting and packed into a framework of beams for protection; this covering alone weighed nearly twenty-eight tons. Fontana had calculated exactly the thickness and length of hempen rope required to lower and then lift the colossal load. Each coil of rope was wound upon a capstan firmly anchored in the ground; men and horses toiled at these under the control of a supervisor. The ropes were led round rollers and up to the pulley-blocks in the tower frames, which themselves were secured by eight heavy ropes. The technical skill lay in distributing the enormous weight of the obelisk, the covering and the tackle amongst the innumerable ropes in such a way that they all took an equal strain, and in directing the effort of men and animals at forty capstans with 160 levers exactly in accordance with the rhythm required. A blast on the trumpet brought the mass of well-trained workers into action; a bell signal was used to call a halt. The many onlookers behind the fences were forbidden on pain of death to make any noise. Our picture shows a section of an early phase in the operation, when the obelisk, still in its old position and supported in the middle by an oblique movable prop, was being lowered on to the rolling platform.

In 1586, the year in which the Egyptian obelisk was transported to Rome, to the amazement of its citizens, a twenty-one-year-old Florentine, Galileo Galilei, was writing his first work, on the hydrostatic balance. He was the son of a musician of the minor nobility. The study of the work of Euclid and Archimedes had first roused him to a realization of his calling. No one should hope, he said then, to discover anything approaching the work of Archimedes. He himself was nevertheless to do so, but it was in the works of his old age, the Dialogue on the two chief Systems of the World (1632) and the Discourses *concerning two new Sciences* (1638) that he was first able to set out the harvests of astronomical facts, which had ripened in the course of the years (*see* pp. 314 ff.), and, more important, of insight into physical phenomena. His laws were not aphorisms derived from the theories of a theoretical man. Devoted observation of nature was the mainspring of his science: to improve the life and technical skill of man his aim. So he formulated a theory of statics for the benefit of builders who needed to know the laws which could determine what weight could be carried by beams and scaffolding. With his improvement of the telescope, he brought the moon and stars closer to the human observer than any other scientists before Huygens; he discovered the phenomenon of acoustic resonance, and his greatest discoveries too, the laws governing free-falling objects and projectiles, were closely linked with practical experiment. It was no accident that the beginning of the *Discorsi* takes place in the Florentine arsenal which became a place of discovery for Galileo. In his own words, 'It seems to me that here a wide field of speculation is opened up for thinkers: especially in the domain of mechanics'.

In physics too, however, Galileo had developed a new mode of thought, which was to serve as a foundation for the future. Without this, it would not have been possible to construct either the bathyscaphe which enables men to return in complete safety from the depths of the sea to the surface, or the rocket capsule in which they return equally safely from space to earth. Galileo reached a proper understanding of the function of observation in the process of physical discovery, of logical abstract reflection and confirmatory experiments. In this way alone, he held, could science open up areas 'which had previously been closed to speculative minds'. His critical attitude was directed against those who, like Aristotle, drew premature conclusions from inadequate observation and without experimental proof. 'Did Aristotle ever establish by experiment the alleged fact that when two stones are dropped, one of which is ten times heavier than the other, they do not reach the ground at the same time?' he asked. Stevin had already proved the contrary by experiment, discrediting the conviction of centuries. It was precisely in the proof of disputed cases like this that Galileo's method achieved mastery. True, the scientist had to contemplate the full range of natural phenomena, but it was necessary for the mind to follow artificial methods in order to isolate a specific collection of these phenomena and to deduce from them the law of nature on which they were based. After that, he had to consider how the relevant law could be established in the experiment: in an ideal situation of his contriving. Only then could it be so expressed in mathematical terms or geometrical figures that it came to include the future as well as past behaviour of objects, thus serving as a basis for prophecy. Every time a stone fell, a ball was thrown or a dart shot, it served in some measure to confirm the strict quantitative law of nature laid down by the physicists.

It was a measure of the boldness of Galileo's mind that he insisted on establishing the existence of an underlying law precisely where it seemed impossible: in the variable dynamic movements which abound in nature. That he offered an entirely new scientific approach to a very old subject was made plain in the *Discorsi*: new insofar as he showed that the projectile course and the rate of fall of objects obeyed immutable laws (*see* p. 100). Even Galileo, however, did not emancipate himself completely and in every respect from the 'old' science, nor indeed from the hated Aristotle, a we see in his attempts to formulate the forces at work in falling objects with the help of the old theory of impetus.

All the passion for research, the love of experiment, the inclination towards wide perspectives, which are to be found in the work of Galileo, Huygens, Newton and other leading figures of modern classical mechanics were already in evidence in that of Leonardo da Vinci. His notebooks, difficult as they are to read in his mirror writing, conceal an abundance of observations on mechanics, optics, and the chemical, technical and anatomical worlds; rich, intuitive, chaotic fragments, without the force of systematic cohesion, they remained almost totally without historical influence, for his writings were not published until the nineteenth century.

The horizon of the creators of classical mechanics was wide. Fascinated by the mysterious rising, falling and resting of terrestrial objects and the rotation of the heavenly bodies, they had all received noble conceptions of mechanical movements as their inheritance from Copernicus and Kepler. Galileo, Huygens and Newton made important astronomical discoveries. Huygens, who was the first to observe the separate ring system encircling Saturn, discovered the physical laws governing pendulum movements, the transfer of force between objects meeting each other, and the outward spread of light (*see* p. 100).

Newton pursued this line of thought to its conclusion in one of the greatest intellectual achievements of all time when he succeeded not only in formulating a coherent system to include all the phenomena hitherto regarded as the province of mechanics, hydro- and aero-dynamics, but also in explaining the mechanics of all terrestrial and cosmic bodies in terms of a few unified general forces. In order to express them mathematically, he was forced to create a new and more refined form of calculation which evolved independently of a similar calculus invented by the philosopher Leibniz. In this way, epoch-making new tools of the greatest importance were evolved for the renewed mathematical investigation of terrestrial and cosmic physics. The mathematicians of the seventeenth and eighteenth centuries, among them Jacques and Jean Bernoulli and Leonhard Euler, continued to build upon these foundations.

An Unusual Setting for a Legend

The Eureka-call of Archimedes; Columbus' challenge—who can stand an egg on end without its falling?; the kettle, which is supposed to have given James Watt his ideas for improving the steam-engine; the leaning tower of Pisa, allegedly the scene of Galileo's experiment with free-falling bodies—such are the legends woven round many of the leading explorers of nature; this they have in common with the kings of early history. And there is a royal thread running through one of the three well-known stories about Galileo. The old man was brought before the tribunal of the Inquisition and forced to withdraw his defence of the Copernican theory of the universe. 'Nevertheless it does move!' the accused is said to have called out at the end of the hearing, stamping his foot. The legendary words from this trial which was by no means legendary have never been forgotten by posterity. At the beginning of Galileo's career, when he was studying medicine at Pisa, a chandelier which was swinging to and fro in the cathedral is supposed to have given him the idea of measuring the duration of each swinging movement against his pulse. It turned out that the time of swing remained the same even when the arc of swing was reduced. The first of Galileo's pendulum laws had been discovered. Again, he is said to have proved in another experiment how bodies can behave in a startling way: this was when he let drop from the top of the leaning tower of Pisa two objects differing in weight, a leaden ball and a wooden one. They both landed on the ground at the same time, thus contradicting both the presumptions of laymen and the pronouncements of highly esteemed scholars. The three stories are not fully authenticated, although Galileo's pupil Viviani told the last two, and Galileo, when he lived in Pisa as a mathematician from 1589 to 1592, did in fact undertake experiments with falling bodies. From this point, however, it was still a long way to the elaboration of the law of falling bodies.

The three legends have survived to the present day, because they allow us to see genius in a most graphic way, and for another reason, too: they reflect in the most concise form through Galileo's example three elemental faculties the explorer must exercise: he must observe thoughtfully, experiment boldly, and fight for the truths he has discovered. So it is perhaps right that this unique tower of Pisa, whose name is connected by legend with the work of a unique natural philosopher, should appear in this book.

GALILEO'S MOST RENOWNED EXPERIMENT

This picture, painted in 1841, carries us back to an experiment Galileo is alleged to have made during his time as lecturer at Pisa. To the left and right are men of ill-will: the blasé Prince Giovanni de' Medici (Galileo had shown a dredging-machine invented by the prince to be unusable), and Galileo's scientific opponents. These were leading men of the universities, who are bending over the sacrosanct book of Aristotle, where it is written in black and white that, according to the rules of gravity, bodies of unequal weight fall with different speeds. Galileo (the tallest figure left of centre in the picture, surrounded by a group of students) had boldly stated the opposite view, namely that a grain of sand, provided it met with no resistance, would fall as fast as a millstone. Physics showed him to be right. His weapon was a method to which he had devoted constant thought. It combined observation of nature, critical logical deduction of the natural laws, and to crown it all and give it the seal of proof: experiment. The painter G. Martelli has placed the most important object in the middle of the picture: a little ball, which rolls downwards in a sloping groove. With this Galileo provided the proof for a law which governs countless phenomena in nature: the behaviour of all bodies as they fall to the earth. This law of falling bodies (*see* p. 100) is based on the assumption that the falling body meets with no resistance on its fall. The experiment had to represent this ideal situation as closely as possible. The speed of a free fall was fast and difficult to measure, so in order to slow it down and enable him to examine it more minutely, Galileo checked the fall by using an inclined plane, on which the basic conditions remained in principle the same. It was not of course possible to make a grain of sand or a millstone roll down this slope, or groove, but very well-polished balls of different materials could be used, and in order to reduce the friction as much as possible, the groove was lined with smooth parchment. The same balls, when hung on fine threads of the same length served also to help prove certain laws of the pendulum, for the swing of a body on the thread was nothing but a special form of free fall. In particular, by allowing the balls to run down the groove faster and faster, Galileo observed the rules governing the acceleration in the speed of falling bodies. The measurement of very small units of time caused endless difficulties—a unit of the order of a second only appeared in physics after Huygens had invented the pendulum clock in 1658. Galileo had to content himself with measuring the time taken by the rolling ball against the amount of water flowing out of a bucket in a fine stream or against the pendulum: sometimes, too, he used the oldest of all methods of measuring very short units of time: the human pulse. For it is this that the kneeling monk is demonstrating. In the eighteenth century the philosopher Immanuel Kant went so far as to extol this demonstration as the prototype of the physical experiment.

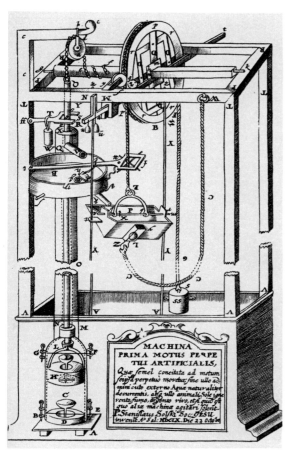
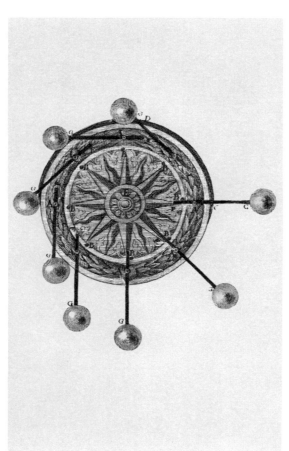
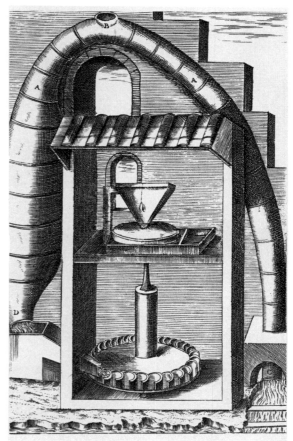

The Perpetuum Mobile

The realm of those who through the centuries have persistently believed in the perpetuum mobile (and still believe in it) borders on religion, on the land of Cockaigne, and on physics. In the thirteenth century there appeared in a sketch-book of the architect Villard de Honnecourt the earliest drawing of a machine which was designed to go on running for ever by its own power. A baroque variant (above, centre) demonstrates the simple conception: a wheel with an uneven number of weights fastened to its periphery like movable pendulums, is carried round continuously by the ever-falling weights. The eye of the devout man of the Middle Ages saw a religious meaning in this: the perpetuum imitates the perpetual rotation of the heavenly bodies; it is a symbol of the perfection of God.

Attempts were made to induce motion of this kind by chemical transformations and magnetic forces; but the instruments most frequently used were the pulley, the roller and the weights from the mechanic's workshop. A Polish Jesuit father, Stanislaus Solski, demonstrated a hydraulic machine (left) before his king in 1609. With its subtle combination of pumps, pulleys, rollers, valves, taps and hanging water-containers, it created a great sensation.

Vittorio Zonca, the city architect of Padua, had read in the writings of Hero of Alexandria that, with the help of the two arms of a siphon, water could be led across from one vessel to another. Zonca suggested in 1607 that a mill could be driven by an enlarged siphon (right). The two arms of a copper tube had their openings C and D closed (C was lowered into a stream) and water was allowed to flow in through the opening B until the pipe was full to the top. If this were then closed down and made air-tight, and if at the same time the points C and D were opened up, the force of the water as it rushed down the wider arm of the pipe AD sucked after it the water in the arm AC. This continuous circular flow of water then caused the horizontal paddle wheel, which drove the mill, to turn with great force.

The bold inventors had overlooked the resistance caused by friction and other mechanical obstructions, which can only be overcome by the application of renewed power. A further proof of the impossibility of the perpetuum mobile was furnished about 1850 by scientists who had discovered the law of the conservation of energy.

Perpetua mobilia are still being thought out by musing dreamers. Arago said in 1802 that it was always in spring-time that the best projects originated. A man-made, continuously turning wheel seems to have the magic of a piece of immortality in a mortal world and exerts a powerful attraction on many, or perhaps it is the dream of making something work without any effort in order to get money out of nothing. Victor Hugo discovered the only true solution of the problem: 'Science seeks a perpetuum mobile. It has found it: it is science itself.'

The burgomaster of Magdeburg, Otto von Guericke, tried with the help of a wooden barrel and a brass pump to solve two problems which had occupied thoughtful minds for many centuries. Was the conception of the vacuum, which prevailed in the ancient world and in the Middle Ages, right? According to this, as the whole universe was understood to be somehow filled with substances, there was no state of nothingness in the spaces between the stars: indeed it was assumed that a *horror vacui,* a strong abhorrence of vacuum, pervaded the whole world. He sought the answer by seeing whether a complete vacuum could be created in miniature on earth.

Torricelli, a pupil of Galileo, had in the year 1643 poured mercury into a glass tube which was closed at the bottom; when it was quite full, he turned it upside down, keeping the open end closed with his finger, and stood it in a bowl full of mercury. The silvery column had gone down by a small amount and had then stood still; the space at the top of the glass tube must have been completely empty, for no air could have made its way in. Where then was the *horror vacui?* (The instrument, a forerunner of the barometer, is shown in the picture on page 89.) But Guericke, experimenting two years before Torricelli, was determined to refute beyond all doubt the theory that there was no vacuum in nature. His pneumatic experiments were those of a pioneer probing into a wholly unknown branch of research. First he filled a barrel to the top with water (top, left). If it were carefully pumped out, the space left could not contain air. Two men tried with all their strength to pull out the handle of the pump, but they only tore the whole pump, handle, cylinder and all, away from the barrel. The fastenings were then strengthened, and this time at least part of the water was pumped out. Air immediately sizzled through all the cracks into the barrel with great force. The law of the *horror vacui* seemed to have triumphed, much to the chagrin of the experimenters. After another failure Guericke changed the material and shape of the vessel which was to be pumped out (centre). This time the air was pumped direct from the vessel. Two helpers seemed to be on the point of succeeding when the two hemispheres crumpled up with a loud bang 'just like a linen cloth being crushed between the fingers'. For the first time the force of air pressure had been encountered in an experiment. It was only with a new and better-constructed sphere that it became possible to resist the force of the air pressure from outside.

Guericke had proved more clearly than Torricelli that man could create 'nothingness' artificially. God had set His cosmos in nothingness, in an empty space of which the physicist's vacuum provided a trace. Guericke also established with some accuracy the weight of the apparently weightless air by weighing the receiver before and after it had been pumped out. He also attached to the pumped-out sphere a square glass vessel filled with air. When he opened the connecting cock, the air was sucked into the sphere with great force and the atmospheric pressure often broke the glass vessel (bottom).

BLAISE PASCAL HAS THE AIR PRESSURE MEASURED

The 4,800 foot-high mountain, Puy de Dôme in the Auvergne, was the scene in 1648 of one of the most famous experiments in the history of physics. It was organized by Blaise Pascal, the co-formulator of the theory of probability, who was a physicist and later author of mystical writings. He decided to complete, with the column of mercury, the experiments which had been interrupted by the early death of Torricelli. His aim was to carry them on to the point where he would have definite proof that air pressure and not a *horror vacui* forced the column upwards. If it were correct, thought Pascal, that air exercized pressure, then this pressure, like that in a column of water, must drop the higher one climbed; and correspondingly the mercury must fall in the tube, as the pressure on the mercury reservoir dropped. Pascal lived at that time in Rouen. So he asked his brother-in-law Perier, who lived in Clermont-Ferrand, to climb the near-by Puy de Dôme with a barometer and observe the behaviour of the mercury column throughout the ascent and descent. Perier made a start on 19th September by assembling at the lowest point in his town two sets of apparatus of the kind used by Torricelli. The mercury stood at exactly the same level in each of them. He marked the height on the tubes and left one of them in the charge of a friend. He packed the other one carefully into a case and began the climb with a few companions. On the summit the level of the mercury was checked five times at various points. Each time the level turned out to be about three inches lower than it had been at the foot of the mountain. During the descent, about halfway down, the group again took measurements and noted that the mercury column had risen again. When in the evening the barometer was compared with the one which had been left in the valley, the mercury in both of them stood once more at exactly the same level. It had thus been proved that the air-pressure had dropped regularly as they went higher. The theory of the *horror vacui* had been refuted by a factual experiment and it was soon to be discovered also that wind and storms had something to do with differences in pressure.

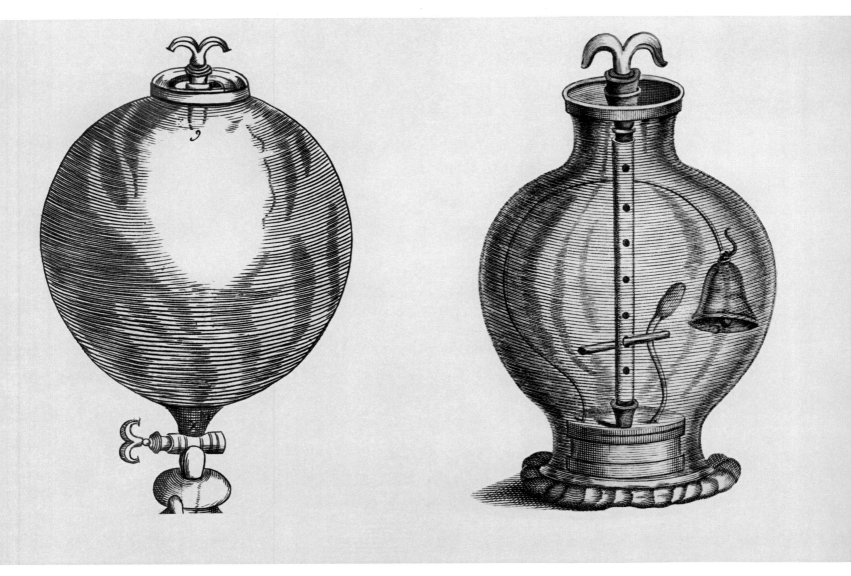

ROBERT BOYLE'S AIR PUMPS

Robert Boyle was the seventh son of the Earl of Cork, who owned vast properties in Ireland. So no doors were closed to the inquisitive young man with his wide interests. Europe stood open before him as he set off with his private tutor on the usual Grand Tour. He had free access to the scholarly circles of his own country, he could obtain any book he required, and on his estate in Dorset and later in London he set up his 'Elysium', which was a laboratory full of apparatus and attended by secretaries and assistants, to whose number Robert Hooke belonged for a time. He refused all offers of high position in State and Church so that he would be freer to live in London in aristocratic Pall Mall under the protection of his sister Katherine who was equally gifted. When Katherine died, Robert who had for long been an invalid followed her to the grave one week later. He devoted his life to two aims: to make natural science more scientific and to preach a form of Christianity which was tolerant and delighted in nature. The countless experiments he mounted showed his research to be of a critical and strictly inductive kind: he was a chemist and physicist; he studied crystallography, improved the air-pump, experimented with colours, came near to the discovery of oxygen; he wrote about the eating of oysters and the advancement of spiritual greatness through Christianity. He came back

again and again to the great problem: what was the nature of matter? Starting from this point he came to reject the old teachings about the elements (*see* p. 37), and he tried to investigate matter in its gaseous state. Whilst doing so he discovered the law which was later more clearly defined by Mariotte. According to this law the pressure and volume of gases are inversely proportional to one another. He carried further the experiments of the 'ingenious gentleman Guericke', as far as Schott had described them in 1657, fifteen years before Guericke drew up the balance of his own discoveries. In the year 1659, working in partnership with Hooke, Boyle produced an improved type of air-pump; its glass receptacle can be seen on the left. The pump with its cylinder placed vertically operates from below; by fitting a winch and a rack he made the piston of the pump comparatively easy to move. An oiled brass plug has been fitted into a small hole at the top to serve as a valve, and above that there is a cock to regulate the entry of air. At the extreme top there is a disk with a raised rim fitted on to a ring which has been firmly cemented on to the outside of the glass sphere; in the middle of this disk a wedge-shaped bung has been fitted with a handle above. At this point objects could be inserted into the glass sphere for carrying out experiments. They revealed many unexpected things.

The right-hand picture on p. 90 shows a second receptacle designed by Boyle. One can see at the bottom the solid cement which prevents the air from entering, and in the inside a rotatable wooden rod in which holes have been bored at several points. A bell is hanging at the end of a curved length of strong wire. A steel spring with a clapper at the top end can be made to swing by a pin fixed horizontally into the wooden rod in such a way that the clapper strikes the bell. Boyle confirmed the amazing discovery of Guericke: the more air that was pumped out, the weaker became the sound of the bell. In a vacuum the bell maintained a ghostly silence. The ringing sound therefore required air for its transmission. And light? Things did not fade in the vacuum, but continued to look the same. Therefore light required no medium to carry it. Huygens tried to solve the problem when he advanced the hypothesis that light was carried by the ether.

When Schott published some of Guericke's experiments with the air-pump in 1657, he wrote: 'I think the sun has never shone on the like of this, certainly not on anything more wonderful, since the creation of the world. That is also the opinion of all the great princes and most learned men, to whom I have conveyed and explained these experiments.' The world looked on with astonishment as this young science of aerodynamics brought to light revelations such as that: the earth was weighed down by an air space of great weight, though it consisted of a substance which seemed to be weightless, and in this air space there were certain laws governing the variations in pressure; man could create a vacuum artificially and make sound inaudible within it, whilst the vacuum remained permeable by other forces such as light and magnetism; air was elastic like a spring; the height of mountains could be measured with a barometer.

Right: A well-known attempt by Boyle to establish how high a column of water can be maintained in balance by atmospheric pressure. A three-storeyed house of brick in London served as the solid support to which a monster water-pipe was fixed by wooden props. A plumber had to solder together straight lengths of one-inch tin pipe; between this part and the U-shaped piece at the top leading direct into the air-pump on the house roof, a glass pipe was cemented in with airtight joints so that the water level could be observed. The giant pipe was sunk into a deep water container which was filled to the top; an assistant stood nearby to pour in more water if this were necessary. As the pump began to operate, the water rose into the vacuum, just as the mercury had done in the Torricelli barometer. At a height of about 33 feet it stopped and remained stationary. The air pressure working on the water in the container had forced the water up the vacuum in the pipe to this height. Boyle made observations on the same day with a barometer and discovered by calculation that the mercury in it obeyed the same laws as the water in that apparatus of his, which for several historic hours became the talk of London. No pump in the world which works on the vacuum principle could raise the water higher than the pressure of the earth's atmosphere will permit.

LONGITUDINAL SECTION of a STEAM ENGINE 100 HORSES POWER, MATTHEW MURRAY ENGINEER, LEEDS.

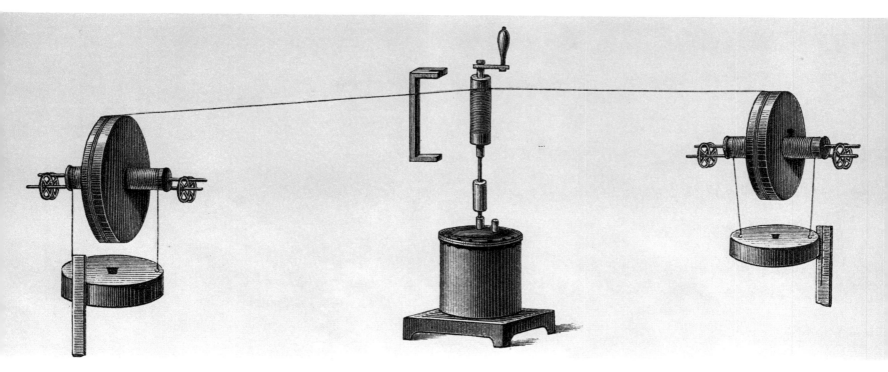

HOW JOULE DISCOVERED THE MECHANICAL HEAT EQUIVALENT

◀ Sadi Carnot, a young Parisian scholar, wrote his *Reflexions on the Motive Power of Fire* in 1824. He was the first man to get to the bottom of what mechanical action took place in the steam-engine of his time, that machine which was revolutionizing everything. He discovered that its effectiveness lay in the conversion of heat into mechanical work and that this only came about as long as there was a difference of temperatures inside the machine. His work remained unnoticed at the time, although he showed himself to be the most important forerunner of thermodynamics to launch out into the main problem of physics in 1850, namely the question of the conservation of energy.

One can recognize the decisive advances which were being made in the history of the steam-engine if one studies this fine monster of a machine (left), which keeps a water-pump in motion in the depths of a coal mine. The cylinder in the middle is the successor of the broad brass structure, which the French scholar, Denis Papin, had constructed in 1690 at the suggestion of Huygens. Hot steam, produced in this cylinder, forced the piston upwards; the steam was then cooled down by the removal of the heat, thereby greatly reducing the pressure in the cylinder, so that the piston was then forced down again into it by the atmospheric pressure from outside; so the cylinder was at the same time a pump. The English blacksmith, Newcomen, separated the boiler from the cylinder and the cylinder from the pump after 1700 and invented a large balancing lever with two arms which transmitted the rising and falling movement of the piston to the rod of the pump. This is illustrated on the left half of the picture. Finally, in the year 1768, the Scot James Watt separated the condenser which cooled the steam from the cylinder. This spherical apparatus can be seen below, near the condenser pump in the water tank. A delicate valve system to the right of the cylinder standing on a supporting wall ensures that first the steam (coming from a boiler which cannot be seen), and then the vacuum,

keeps the piston in fast and rhythmic alternating motion. The rising and falling motion of the piston is transmitted to the smaller balancing lever on the right which regulates the valve system and therefore the circulation of the steam as well: it is also transmitted to the large balancing lever on the left by way of a parallelogram of the kind designed by Watt which keeps the motion of the piston-rod exactly vertical.

Above: The steam-engine was an apparatus which was conceived by practical men; it continued to develop in all kinds of new forms, but as it conquered the world, it drew some meditative minds to consider certain basic questions of science still unresolved. What was the relationship between the forces of nature? Could the effort provided by a force be measured? Had the total sum of forces in the world remained the same or had it changed? What lessons were there to be learned from the steam-engine? Heat when applied to the boiler produced steam, the steam, by means of a process involving a substantial loss of heat, moved the rods, and this movement was converted into a different kind of movement in the pumps down the mine. Scholars began to notice with astonishment that there were many instances in the world of forces being transformed into other forces and this happened on a small and a large scale. But force, according to Newton's principles which were now being carried further, was the product of mass and acceleration: that, for instance, which was contained in the powerful swing of the sledge-hammer; energy on the other hand, the world's most mysterious quality, was the dormant or active faculty in things to provide work. Even heat was energy! The brewer and private scholar James Prescott Joule tried in 1843 to produce a definite measurement for units of energy. The apparatus (above) was supposed to ascertain how much work (and so also how much energy) was needed in order to produce a fixed quantity of heat by mechanical means. A paddle wheel with eight blades ploughed its way

THE PRINCIPLE OF THE CONSERVATION OF ENERGY AND THE END OF MANKIND

through the water inside a copper boiler which stood on a table; there was thus friction in the vessel and therefore heat; this heat was measured by a thermometer which was inserted through the lid by a small tube. How was the corresponding effort or work measured? Work, in physics, is the product of an operating force and the distance covered by the moving application point of the force; and the unit of work is the metre-kilogram—the effort necessary to raise one kilogram weight a height of one metre. In his apparatus Joule used for this purpose two lead rollers weighing fifteen kilograms and hanging horizontally; these sank to the ground alongside a measuring scale and as they did so they pulled on the string holding them which led over a wooden roller; this pulling action caused a vertical drum which had been fitted on to axle of the paddle-wheel to rotate, and with it the friction-generating paddle-wheel itself. (The rollers are turned 90° in the picture to show how they were hung.) Joule then quickly ascertained the temperature of the water: 450 metre-kilograms of effort raised the temperature of one kilogram of water by one degree of heat (in modern terms 427 mkg). He had thus discovered the mechanical heat equivalent—the figure which shows how many work (and therefore energy) units are equivalent to a heat unit.

Far away from these experiments, a few men conceived the idea, about 1840, of a cosmos of natural forces (and not only purely mechanical forces) which could be measured approximately by their heat equivalent. One of these men was the Dane, L. A. Colding (1843): another was the German, Julius Robert Mayer (1845). Did not all these forces operate together? Did not electric forces produce magnetic force, did not electric current produce heat and so on, like the coal burning in the steam-engine? And did not the coal have within it the solar energy which had passed by chemical assimilation into the trees in the forests of the carboniferous period? 'The truth is that there is only one force; in all the processes of nature there are only transformations of this force, there is no disappearance and no new creation of forces.' In these sentences written about 1845, Julius Robert Mayer was in fact already stating the law of the conservation of energy. Independently of him, about 1847, Hermann Helmholtz, a man of the widest knowledge, was to corroborate the law by thinking it out in a clear mathematical form.

Above: The idea of the conservation of energy led to depressing conclusions about the state of the world millions of years hence. People felt certain that when they looked up at the starry sky, it only seemed as if they were gazing into an infinitude of space; in reality the earth moved within an immeasurable yet finite universe. In such a system there must occur in some distant period of time an equilibrium of the temperature between the stars which continued to lose their heat, since the total energy of the world remained constant and was not renewed. One day all the processes of nature would come to a halt: all life on earth would die from heat or from cold.

The physicists of the second half of the century brought into the spiritual world their ghastly conception of the end of mankind. Pictures like the two reproduced above are typical of the period. The French astronomer Camille Flammarion conjured up in his novel *La fin du monde* all imaginable ways in which the world might be destroyed. The earth could cool down in the cold of the universe to the point where it simply drifts on, stiff and frozen, like a second moon (above right); proud cities are turned into deserts, the life of man, animals and plants is annihilated. The transformation of the earth by the ever-increasing heat of the universe into a landscape of death is the theme of the other picture. These questions, apparently solved, were again thrown open in the twentieth century, when atomic physics discovered in the nucleus of the atom an inexhaustible supplier of energy and when the astronomers no longer dared to state with such certainty that the universe was a closed system.

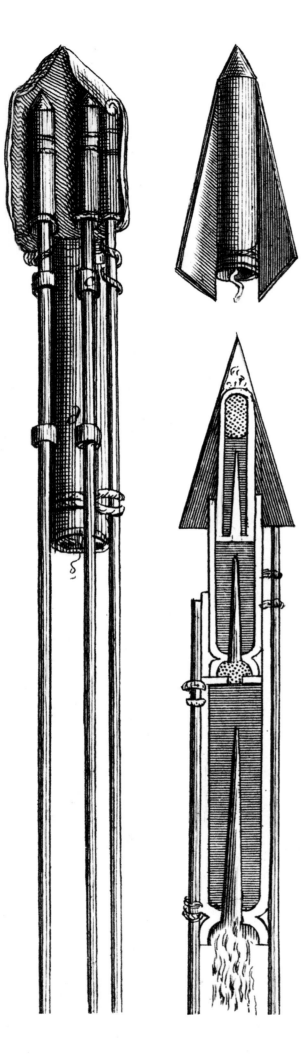

The picture on the previous page shows a fireworks display in Rome in the eighteenth century. In Italy and France in the seventeenth and eighteenth centuries perfection was reached in the art of harnessing fire and of sending it up high into the sky on festive nights so that it came down glittering in showers of sparks. Giambattista Piranesi records in his etching a magic display of these fireworks against the heroic silhouette of the Castello Sant' Angelo before astonished crowds. With their glowing sheaves of fire the fireworks rivalled those of China, where during the Middle Ages this art had been born. (It was in China too that the compass, the art of printing and many other things were first evolved.) Rockets played an important part in these orgies of fire. Who amongst the spectators at such pyrotechnic festivities would have thought that in the rocket there lay hidden the principle which man would one day use for his journey into space?

In 1741 there appeared in The Hague a *Treatise on Fireworks for Displays,* compiled by the French fireworks specialist, François Frézier. The book gives advice on how to entertain kings with fireworks displays and it is based on a very substantial knowledge not only of kings, but also of pyrotechnical mechanics. In the chapter on 'flying rockets' he shows amongst other things the rocket reproduced here on the extreme left. It carries in a long casing a quantity of coal, saltpetre and sulphur as a propellant; at the topmost point of the flight the fire passes to three small fireworks units which scatter glittering stars. As a counterweight to the heavily loaded nose there are three long wooden rods. The taller of the two models next to it shows that the idea of a multi-stage rocket did not originate in the twentieth century. In order to prolong the flight, three explosive charges are fitted one above the other. Each is placed in a rather narrow, cone-shaped cavity with an outlet through which the hot highly compressed powder gases escape; that is to say, the gases eject themselves from the rocket and thereby drive it upwards. When the first powder charge is used up, the second one ignites, and so on. In order to ensure a relatively even direction of flight three wings are provided; two of these can be seen in the top model.

One of the boldest questions asked by science and again repeated in later centuries was: what are the other planets like and is there any form of life there on the other side of that empty cosmic space which seemed impossible to cross? Gassendi and Leibniz, Dante and Swedenborg, Schiaparelli and many others discussed these problems with penetrating fervour.

A hundred years ago the French author, Jules Verne, in two strikingly effective novels, portrayed how man with the help of technology could reach the moon and return to earth. Verne put three intrepid contemporaries of his, two Americans and a Frenchman, into a well-padded projectile, and sent them off into space using the thrust of a gigantic explosive charge which had been fixed in a steel pipe deep in the earth; he left the rest to the gravitational forces of the earth and the moon. The sagacious Verne provided his three pioneers with twenty rockets which he inserted into the floor of the vehicle. These were not intended to propel the vehicle by backthrust as is the case with today's space rockets, but to provide a brake for the landing on the moon.

A few decades after Verne's astronauts had returned safely to earth, three technologists who were experts in thermodynamics began to work, quite independently of each other, on a serious realization of the old dream of a space flight. They had all recognized that only rockets which were propelled by backthrust and which consumed liquid fuel could master the space where there was no air. 'Mankind will not always remain on earth,' announced the Russian Konstantin Tsiolkovski in grand Utopian style, as he published his first precise technological suggestions in 1903. In 1923 new foundations were laid in the book *The Rocket in planetary Space* by Hermann Oberth. The two scientists were not helped in their research by anyone from their own countries. It was the American Robert H. Goddard who, in 1926 in Auburn, Massachusetts, put the first small model of a space rocket into the air.

Soon after 1650 there sprang up in Europe a number of important learned societies. In essence they were creations of the yearning for a great Utopia. The youthful spirit of an empirical, experimenting natural science which mistrusted uncorroborated speculations was spreading further and further in the seventeenth century. The wind of discovery was enveloping even those who were not setting off to find unknown continents, and the need for communications, both local and beyond national boundaries, was growing from year to year—scholars knew little about the work of others engaged on similar research. The pupils of Galileo, Torricelli, Borelli, Viviani and others, had gathered around the master and formed an experimental group; its name 'Academy of Experiment' disclosed its purpose. In London in 1662 meetings of scientists engaged in research led to the formation of the Royal Society. This was followed four years later by that of the *Académie des Sciences* in Paris under the patronage of Louis XIV; this was a real research centre supported by public funds, and foreigners of importance such as Christiaan Huygens were soon invited to join it. In Berlin the Prussian Academy of Sciences was created in 1700 in accordance with the far-sighted plans of the philosopher Leibniz. The journals of these academies soon began to appear—the *Philosophical Transactions* in London, the *Journal des Savants* in Paris, and so on, organs which carried out into the world the news about nearly all the most important new ideas in science. They remind us of the prophecies of Francis Bacon, the Lord Chancellor, who in his *Nova Atlantis* (*c*. 1620) had drawn up a plan of a scientific society which he called 'Solomon's House': this society sends out its 'twelve purchasers of light' all over the world to collect the new discoveries wherever they find them; the men employed in Solomon's House work enthusiastically on a form of research which aims at the extermination of illness and poverty and even the opening up of the realm of the air by flying machines, and the depths of the sea by submarines.

LeClerc has captured in his picture something of the idea of these learned societies. Everywhere in the courtyard of his academy 'communication' reigns supreme, and the individuals in the working groups are widening their experience. They are carrying on the heritage of antiquity, as their dress is supposed to show. The assembly of the sciences is complete, but anatomy, botany and zoology with a few skeletons and bundles of dry leaves have been edged to the side; so has chemistry with its distilling apparatus (below left) and the bookish science of theology (right). The triumphant sciences of the day are those which are exploring that part of nature which can be explained mechanically and mathematically, and are giving enthusiastic demonstrations of the laws of nature in their thrilling experiments. Supreme is mathematics with its world of figures and models; so is astronomy and above all physics. At the edge on the right the realm of physics begins with the so-called Archimedean screw, a small, water-lifting apparatus. Further to the left, behind the group which is studying the lever laws, an inclined groove has been set up, next to it a wooden frame for experiments in impact with hanging balls. At the edge of the group which is settling down to make drawings, there is a triangle for experiments with the pendulum. In the front of the picture on the left is a frame for experiments in perspective which calls the science of optics to mind; bottom right a magic lantern and, above the Archimedean screw, a round mirror for demonstrations with light-rays.

'THE ACADEMY OF SCIENCES AND FINE ARTS.' ENGRAVING BY SÉBASTIEN LECLERC, 1698

99

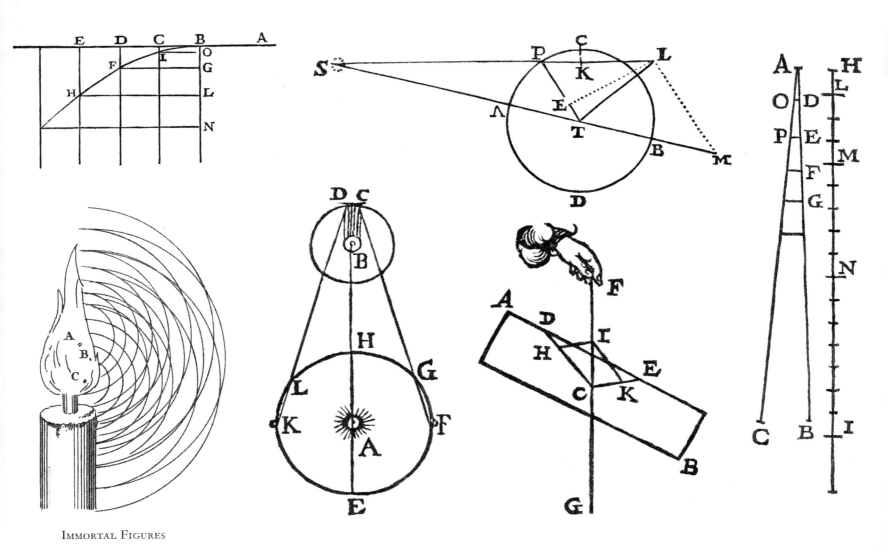

IMMORTAL FIGURES

For many centuries physics expressed in figures from the arsenal of geometry the laws of nature which it found. Many of these diagrams compress years of weary enquiry into a few strokes of the pen—a piece of reality to be recognized ever after as the truth. Six such figures, some drawn finely, others coarsely, have been assembled on this page. *Right:* The law of free fall (Galileo). The spaces traversed by a body falling with a constant acceleration are proportionate to the square of the time it requires to traverse these spaces. On the line A–B are indicated the regular time units AD, AE, and so on; HI represents the space through which the body falls with constant acceleration. HL is the distance traversed during the time AD, HM is the distance covered during the time AE. Then MH is to HL as the square of the time AE is to the square of the time AD. If one draws the line AC at any angle desired to the line AB, one can draw parallel lines at DO, EP etc.; in this way Galileo tried to demonstrate the relationship to each other of the highest speeds reached in each time unit.

Top left: The law of projectiles according to Galileo: from this it follows that the trajectory of a projectile fired horizontally is parabolic.

Top centre: Newton explained how the ebb and flow of the tide came about. The most puzzling thing about this movement of the sea was the fact that apart from the great tidal wave which seemed to follow the moon, a second wave went round the world every twenty-four hours. To the Italian Jesuit father, Cabeo (d. 1650), the puzzle seemed easy to solve because he assumed that the moon created on the sea-bed a spiritual substance which caused the flood. Stevin on the other hand explained it away by assuming the existence of a special point of attraction on the side of the earth hidden from the moon. It was Newton who first solved this problem with his theory of gravity. There is not room here to illustrate the very complicated play of powers of attraction and centrifugal forces between earth (T), moon (P) and sun (S). The moon attracts not only the water on the side of the earth facing it but also the centre of gravity of the earth, so that a great swell of water rises up on the opposite side too.

Below this, left: To measure the speed of a ray of light seems like the whim of a teller of fairy-stories. It was in fact a man from the land of the story-teller Andersen, the 'nordic Archimedes' Olaus Roemer, who in the year 1676 achieved the impossible, at a time when, just as in previous centuries, the whole world was convinced that the transmission of light took no time at all. For no one had observed a ray of light moving in the same way as the wind could be seen to travel through waving blades of grass. Light was simply all of a sudden there, like the fixed stars in the sky, when one opened one's

Optics

Amongst the forces investigated by physicists, none has attracted so many intellects of the first rank to study it as light, and there is none which penetrates so deeply into the everyday life of man. After each night, the rising sun gives back the outer world to his eyes. Light is an inexhaustible creator of communication between man and the world, between all living beings blessed with eyesight and their surroundings.

The retina and the optic nerve are highly refined mechanisms which serve to receive messages from the outer world in the form of vibrating light impulses and carry them to an area in which they are mysteriously transformed into experience of light, colour and form, and so into the images which live on in the mind of man. For thousands of years, scientists have not only attempted to explore light physically, in the form in which it manifests itself, they have also examined its nature from the theoretical point of view and its physiological effect upon the eye. They have examined it too as a life-giving force in those areas immediately above the earth's surface and immediately below that of the sea, into which more life is crowded than in any other place. It has been observed, amongst other things, that light and colours are capable in themselves of intensifying or restricting the inner life of man. The sixth part of Goethe's treatise on the study of colour is a classical work on the capacity of light to stimulate joy or suffering. The phenomenon of light is too rich for physics alone amongst the scientific disciplines to be able to do it justice. Anyone who wishes to grasp the full range of its effects upon man's inner life cannot afford to neglect even the religions of light, such as Zoroastrianism.

At the foundation of actual scientific optics, we find three achievements of the Greeks. From the school of Pythagoras comes the delightful suggestion that sight is to be explained by the light in the bright human eye. The eye, they reasoned, sends something out to the object which streams back, bringing with it information about the object's form and colour. Those thinkers who followed Democritus, however, claimed that objects exposed to light sent out small material particles of light substance towards the eye, or even perhaps merely their own image which, after all, was reflected in minute form upon the pupil. Such theories of emanation were the origin of scientific investigation into light. Further progress was made only when the human eye came to observe itself more precisely. At the turn of the first century, much influence, in this respect, was exerted by the work of the Arab mathematician Alhazen upon the basis of which the medieval neo-Platonist Witelo and later even Kepler continued to build.

The greatest impetus to the study of light was provided by Euclidean geometry. In it, the light ray, or light bundle, which flows in a straight line, was ingeniously separated from the indivisible realm of light. It was destined to provide scientists for all time with the essential information about light. Its behaviour seemed so regular that it could be expressed geometrically and numerically, as though

eyes. The Danish scientist who was working at the time in the Paris observatory, noticed that the innermost moon of Jupiter which circled the large planet (B) every 42½ hours was sometimes early and sometimes late in passing through the shadow of the planet. When the earth on its course round the sun (A) was moving away from the moon along the section LK of its orbit, the moon came late out of the shadow at D; but when the earth was passing along the section GF towards the moon, the moon seemed to enter the shadow early at C. It was unlikely that it altered its speed; but one could assume that the light on the way from the moon of Jupiter to the earth while it passed along the considerable cosmic distance LK, lagged to some extent behind the earth, and so lost a few seconds; whilst along the section GF the light was moving towards the speedily approaching earth and therefore brought the 'news' of the entry of the satellite into the shadow at C a little earlier. Roemer was able to establish by calculation how long a sunbeam took to pass along the vast cosmic distance LK or GF. He arrived at a speed of 140,000 miles per second. It was not until 1850 that Foucault produced in the laboratory a new figure, namely 187,000 miles per second, which corresponds almost exactly to today's figure.

To the right of this: A still rather clumsy attempt by Stevin to express geometrically the parallelogram of forces.

Far left: Huygens illustrates his theory of the wave-nature of light by means of three points of light, A, B and C, in the flame of a candle. The light points vibrate and create around them wave movements in the ether which spread outwards with the speed calculated by Roemer. Each vibrating particle of ether collides with all the others round about and creates around itself 'elementary waves' expanding outwards in a spherical pattern. It was not until the early nineteenth century that this wave theory carried the day in a more refined form. It could be applied to diffraction and interference. In Huygens' drawing something of such an application has been anticipated, although the designer could not have known it.

the light ray were a distant relative of the lever. Thus were formulated the laws governing the basic movements of light: reflection (Euclid), refraction (Descartes), and later the extremely subtle processes of diffraction, interference and analysis of white light in the colour spectrum (Newton).

Lastly, it was Greek thinkers, too, who first dared to inquire into the nature of light. The centuries-long history of investigation into this question shows how indescribably difficult it is to answer. An outstanding student of optics, the Italian Jesuit Francesco Maria Grimaldi, who discovered diffraction, was able to say, in a work which appeared in 1665: 'We do not know what the nature of light is.' Yet in the same century, the two conflicting theories were propounded which were to be reconciled belatedly in 1900. The Dutchman Christiaan Huygens explained the spreading of light as a wave-like movement which arose when the vibrating particles of an illuminating object made their impact upon an extremely elastic and very finely distributed substance: ether, the existence of which was assumed by Huygens (*see* p. 100).

'The great Newton claims that the sun's rays flow from the very body of the sun, and that very fine particles are projected with such inconceivable speed that they reach us in about eight minutes.' So the great mathematician Leonhard Euler of Basle, not without a suggestion of disbelief, summarized the opposing theory: the 'corpuscular' theory, which in fact Newton accepted only with some hesitation, and which in another form had been advocated much earlier by Descartes.

Since Planck and Einstein, scientists have reverted to a carefully circumscribed theory which ascribes certain optical phenomena—namely, the formation of the absorption spectrum and the fact that, according to Philipp Lenard, light is capable of releasing electrons from matter—to forces working in the manner of corpuscles, and they have attempted to amalgamate this with the old wave theory.

'Things which have been unknown since the creation of the world are beginning to unveil themselves', wrote the chronicler Petrus Martyr in the sixteenth century, sketching the discoveries of Columbus. The same may be said of what was brought about in science in the early seventeenth century by the unknown, possibly Dutch, glass cutters who first put together the lenses required for a small telescope and a microscope. Two or three pieces of cleverly fashioned glass which could be held in a clenched hand concealed the wonderful capacity to increase man's range of vision almost immeasurably, extending it both far out into the universe and down to forms of life so minute as never to have been seen before, which inhabit a drop of water in their thousands. On the tombstone of the optician Joseph Fraunhofer was written: 'He brought the stars closer to us.' It was no exaggeration.

TRANSCENDENT LIGHT

In the 28th canto of the third part of Dante's *Divine Comedy* the poet, led by Beatrice, ascends to the outermost edge of the world and the sphere of the fixed stars. There he sees a bright light mirrored in the eyes of his companion; he turns round and sees above him a place of radiance which sends out light of unimaginable intensity. Round this middle light nine choirs of angels surge forward, forming great circles and filling the whole sky; they are multitudes of shapes composed of light. A human being has been granted the supreme gift; he is allowed to see the empyrean, the transcendent. In the metaphysical Original Light is found the reality of God. That which seems to men to stream over the world as sunshine is like an earthly reflection, an analogue, of that holy metaphysical light and it derives from it. This is the teaching of Plato, of medieval Christianity and of many another traditional doctrines. A physical force is chosen to link the terrestrial with the divine. Its relationship to other forces is like that of gold to other substances in alchemy. The two figures as they stand before this supernatural sight attain the highest spiritual state: the tranquillity of eternal peace.

RAYS AND BEAMS OF LIGHT

Left: THE 'FEATS OF LIGHT'

They are illustrated in a woodcut which appeared in 1572 in the printed version of a work by the Silesian philosopher and scientist Witelo. These *Ten Books of Optics* are a well-arranged collection of the information the author had gathered during the thirteenth century from his own observations, but still more from Ptolemy, Euclid and Christian writers, and above all from a work of the Arabic mathematician Alhazen on the subject of light and vision. The author was probably a member of a religious order who had settled in Italy. In 1604 Kepler produced a critical commentary on Witelo's famous work. The woodcut gives an imaginative representation of the discoveries of the ancient world and of the Middle Ages in the puzzling field of optics—it was on this legacy that modern research into light was founded. Euclid's geometrical optics are demonstrated in an epic battle scene. The Roman fleet is besieging the city of Syracuse in Sicily in the year 212 BC. Archimedes mobilizes the sun for the defence of the town. Concave mirrors send forth its annihilating rays against the enemy. The straight path of the light, and its reflection—these betray clearly the spirit of Euclid. In a semicircle on the left are four optical phenomena which observers of nature have tried to explain since ancient times. At the front of this astonishing little panorama there is a male figure standing in the water, the purpose being to show how his legs are distorted by refraction when the eye sees them through water. To the left, the mystery of perspective: elephants, monsters, shrink to half their size, and the bridge is reduced to half its breadth, as they recede

from the observer. What has the man with the mirror to say? That light can quite simply make one into two by using the medium of a mirror. Witelo, with the mirror in mind, explained that he considered light as possessing the power of self-multiplication. Above, a rainbow is arched over the country. The rainbow has been placed in a position which is incorrect in relation to the sun; this has been done for artistic reasons and should not deceive us into supposing that the course of the light beams in the rainbow had not already been discovered. In fact, a Dominican neo-platonist, Dietrich von Freiberg, had explained this phenomenon; like Witelo he looked at light with the eye of one exploring nature and venerated it as being the reflection of light from the transcendent world.

Above: The isolation of a ray or a beam of light has been the main object of scientific optics ever since Euclid. He came to the conclusion that as the edge of the light ray was straight, light must be transmitted in a straight line. Having isolated the light ray he then 'isolated' a geometric symbol to represent it: the straight line, which we find in all works about optics from the Greeks to the present day. Our picture shows part of the private observatory which the well-to-do amateur astronomer from Danzig, Johannes Hevelius, set up about 1640 on the roof of his house. The lunar maps of this avid observer, engraved with his own experienced hand, were for a century the best. On the dark wall hang two of the well-known quadrants and sextants which he made himself. The sun's rays pass through a telescope and fall on a sheet of paper; it was on this that Hevelius, like Scheiner (*see* p. 334), used to make drawings of the sun-spots.

Left: Wherever in nature calm waters produce a smooth shining surface, an optical spectacle of a special kind begins to display its charm. A tiny fraction of the world is suddenly duplicated before our eyes. The slope of the river bank, trees, the sky, a human being are reflected with subdued colours; they seem to be as far below the reflecting surface as they are in fact above it, the only difference being that left becomes right and right left in the mirror of water. The beauty of the reflection, this simple movement of light discovered so long ago, has always fascinated painters. By introducing into their pictures the mythical figure of young Narcissus captivated by the sight of his own image, they have conjured up a visual experience which goes back to the earliest period of man: his encounter with his own image.

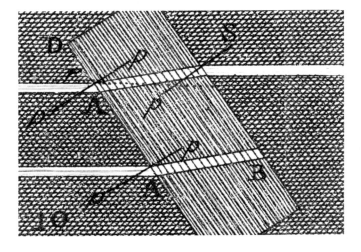

Right: We find that Euclid in his *Optics* about the year 300 BC described exactly in geometrical terms how a ray of light behaves when it strikes the surface of a flat mirror: the angle of reflection is exactly equal to the angle of incidence. The top picture demonstrates the law of reflection in the physical experiment book of Jacob s'Gravesande, which, with those of the French Abbé Jean Antoine Nollet and others, was read in the enlightened eighteenth century as eagerly as an exciting novel. More exact measurements were made possible by the disk illustrated here which had a scale dividing each quarter circle into 90 degrees (second picture from top); the disk was made by Nollet, the discoverer of osmosis. The angle of incidence can be read off where the ray enters through a screen mounted on the disk, the angle of reflection where it goes out through an oil-paper which has been similarly fixed on to a movable bracket. Displacements at the rim, but no change in the angle relationship, occurred if two parallel rays struck the mirror to left and right of the perpendicular line. Nollet established that the approximately pyramid-shaped beam of light from the hole in the window shutter also made the parallel rays diverge very slightly in front of the dial.

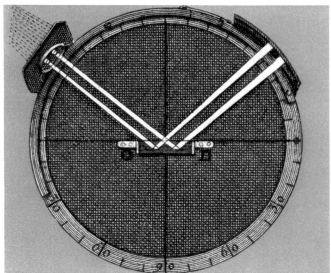

The ancient world had discovered that oars when used for rowing appeared to be broken, and that a man standing in the water appeared to have broken legs. Ptolemy of Alexandria and Alhazen were the first to do systematic research on this problem. In the bottom picture an illustrator of Witelo's *Optics* has gone to great trouble to show the experiments by which Alhazen measured the angle of refraction with a disk half-submerged in water. The Arabic scholar had confirmed the rule of Ptolemy according to which when a ray passed from a rarer into a denser medium (the second dark ring), for instance from air into water, the ray was refracted towards the normal. But the law behind these phenomena stubbornly evaded him, as the somewhat indeterminate lines indicate. Between this illustration and the one above it lie the discoveries of the philosopher Descartes: also similar discoveries by the Dutch physicist W. Snellius (about 1620), but these never became widely known. The Frenchman had made the ingenious calculation that the relationship of the sine of the angle of incidence to the sine of the angle of refraction is always the same for any two media. On this principle rests much of the science of technical optics. Nollet built a kind of aquarium for light and allowed two parallel beams to enter it. The upper beam is twice refracted and then continues its course in the direction of incidence; the lower beam, held up at B by a disk, shows conclusively that refraction takes place exactly at the surface of contact of the media.

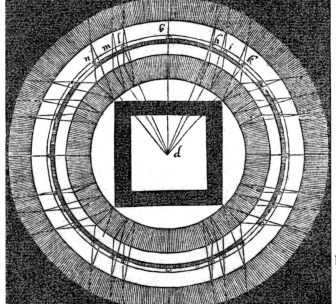

THE RAINBOW IN ART

Into a mountain landscape in the interior of Switzerland (one can recognize the pointed pyramidal shapes of the Grosse and Kleine Mythen near Schwyz), the painter Heinrich Keller has introduced a rainbow: a silent phenomenon of light which seems to originate from the beginning of the world, set in a mountain landscape equally primeval. The circular rim of the sun is reflected in seven colours on the rising wall of mist. According to popular legend the angels drop golden keys at the point where the rainbow meets the earth, or a treasure lies buried there. Some look with reverence at the rainbow, seeing in it the sign of peace set by God over his covenant with man.

To please those who look at his picture the painter built a second scene into this timeless one. The sun projects on to the driving mist the shadows of the group of people, gigantically enlarged. It is an idyllic variation of the 'Brocken spectre', which however in this case does not frighten the climber, but offers a welcome in the form of an optic echo to a family of the Biedermeier period.

Since scientific optics has come into existence, we have solved the puzzle of the rainbow. Aristotle assumed that the image of the sun appeared in the clouds because it was reflected by countless small drops; he recognized also that a second paler rainbow could build up with its colours in the opposite order to that of the main rainbow. Later the Arabs discovered that refraction played a part in the rainbow as well as reflection. It was not until 1300 that the phenomenon was explained more precisely by the German scholar Dietrich von Freiberg. He said that the sun's rays were refracted when they entered a drop of rain, were then reflected on the inner surface of the drop, and were again refracted as they left the drop. It was Newton, in his experiments with the prism, who first discovered how the colours of the rainbow originate.

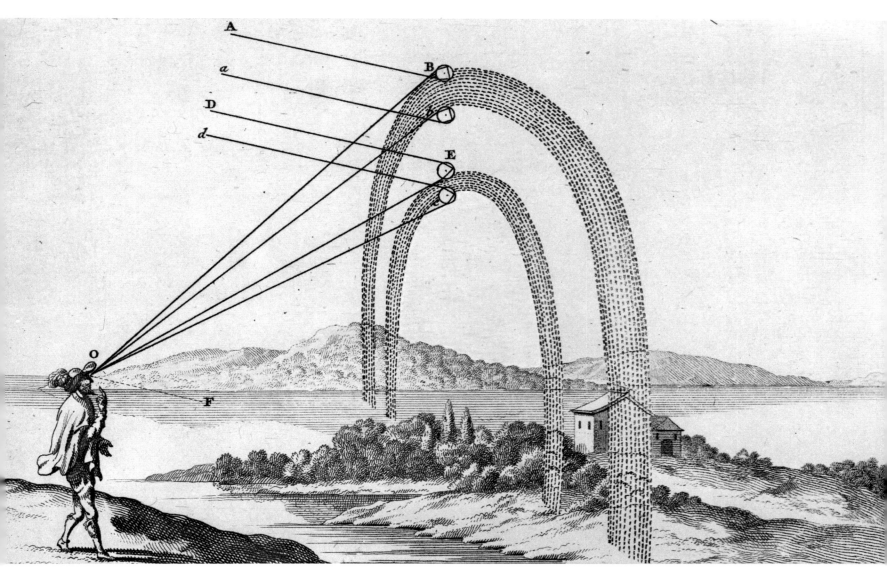

THE RAINBOW IN CARTESIAN PHYSICS

Descartes developed a basic mathematical theory of the rainbow with the help of a glass sphere filled with water which he used instead of the spherical raindrop. He found that the colours of the rainbow only appeared when the glass sphere was placed in certain positions: for instance when the sun sends out a ray from behind the observer which then travels along the axis F across his eye and from there at an angle of 42° to the middle point of the rainbow. Then he lifted the sphere higher; the colours disappeared, then reappeared a second time, but in the opposite order at an angle of about 51°. This evidently corresponded to the main and subsidiary rainbow which occurred in nature. Descartes, using the laws of reflection and refraction, then calculated the course of thousands of single rays into the drops of a curtain of rain, and arrived at the illustrative model which we have reproduced above. In the main rainbow the ray D is refracted as it enters the raindrop, is then reflected within the inner mirror-like wall of the drop, and finally, as it passes from the water medium into that of air it is refracted again and from there it reaches the eye of the observer. A ray A, which meets the raindrop at B in the subsidiary rainbow takes a different course within it: it goes upwards from below. In this case it is reflected twice inside the raindrop, which makes its light weaker. Finally it leaves the raindrop at an angle of 51°.

The discoveries of Descartes show the greatness of his logical and mathematical mind; and his way of thinking was elegant as well as sure. But it had its limits and these come to light in some of his theoretical explanations which are absurd whilst remaining logical. Another Frenchman, Pascal, who like Descartes was a supporter of the Catholic church, exposed the dangers of this speculative mode of thinking with some irony: 'All affirmations of this kind are as difficult to believe as they are easy to invent.'

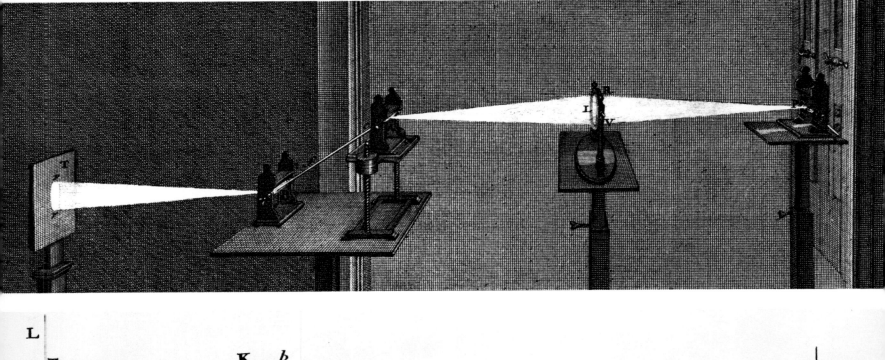

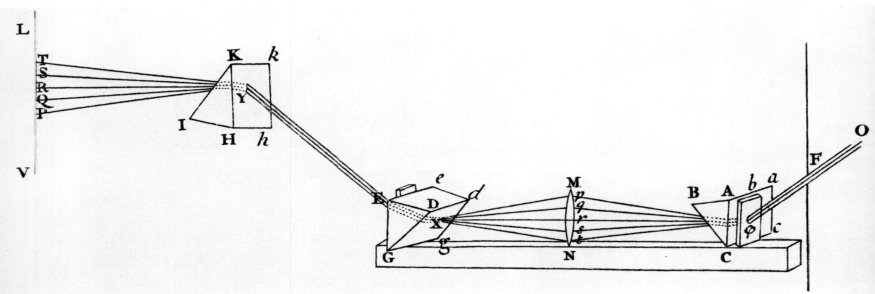

How Newton proved that White Light is not White

Natural light is colourless. This ancient finding of the human eye had been accepted by those who taught about light well into the seventeenth century. The bright colours in the world were qualities belonging to things and they became visible as soon as the colourless light lit them up. It carried the colour to the eyes. Grimaldi, the most punctilious observer of optics of modern times, having noticed about the year 1650 that a refracted beam in water had reddish and bluish edges, regarded the colour as belonging to the light, and in 1648 Marcus Marci made a prism experiment, which resembled that of Newton. But that penetrating genius Newton went ahead independently of Marci and neatly differentiated between the light-ray which the physicist examines and the experience of colour which these rays 'send right into our sensory organs'. This colourless physical light, as he proved in magnificent experiments, contains all the colours of the rainbow. He let a ray of light (F) which came through the window shutters pass through a small round hole on to a glass prism (ABC). This split it up into sets of coloured rays. He picked up the rays some distance

away on a piece of white paper: an oval composed of the most beautiful rainbow colours, the spectrum, was illuminated on it. If he then picked up this oval on a bi-convex glass lens (MN) which was large enough to contain the whole of it, then this lens, because of the force of refraction, collected the coloured rays again, and when a piece of white paper was held at this point, a white spot appeared. But if a second prism (EDG) was placed there, then a cluster of parallel rays of this white light went on to the third prism (IKH), which again split it up into the colours of the rainbow, but this time they were in the reverse order. Thus the artificially created white light at X was exactly the same as it had been originally. Newton's faultless diagram of his experiment illustrated a faultless process; this process looks equally faultless eighteen years later in the illustration in the experiment book of Jacob s'Gravesande (top). The individual homogeneous colours, of which the white light is composed, were not equally refractable; this is how the colour spectrum originated. The process can be expressed in mathematical laws and so, as Galileo had postulated, it can

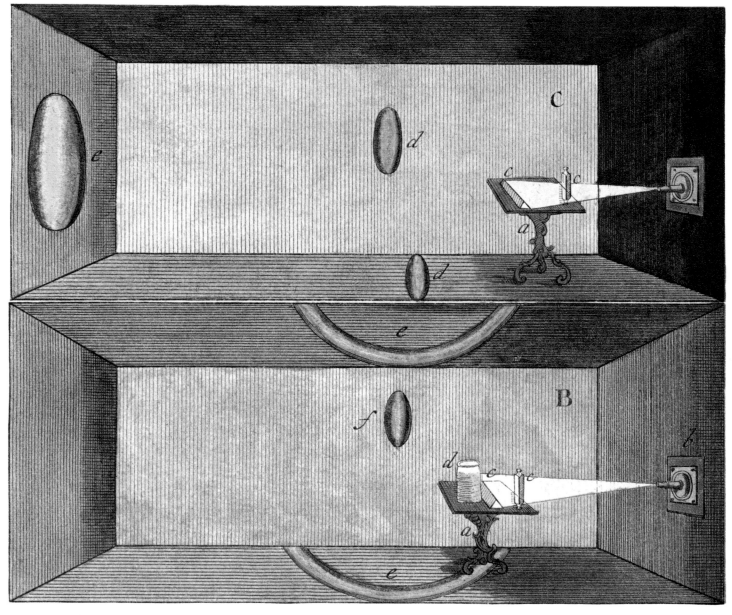

NEWTON'S TEACHING AND EXPERIMENTS BECOME FASHIONABLE

be proved by isolating it in an experiment. Together with Lavoisier's oxygen experiment and Herschel's research into infra-red light this is one of the immortal achievements in the art of experimenting. Newton already knew that the colour of a body was simply that one in the spectrum which it reflected, whilst absorbing all the others. The great physicist discovered also manifestations of interference.

Above: In the decades after 1700 physics was the most popular science in Europe. This is clear from the numerous books in our libraries, books once much read, in which a skilful author tried to acquaint his contemporaries with the impressions made on him by the revelations of the physicists. A masterpiece of this kind is Leonhard Euler's collection of *Letters to a German Princess on the Subject of Physics.* It goes without saying that the most illustrious name to appear in such books is that of Newton. *The Newtonian System for Everyone* was the title Voltaire gave to his book on the subject. In Italy there appeared a *Newtonismo per le donne,* and in England a similar work was published for young people. Books were also appearing at that time in German

with a wealth of tables on the subject of microscopy, which was becoming equally fashionable. An example of such a book is the *Pleasures of the Microscope for Mind and Eye* (1761–62 and 1778) by the Nuremberg lawyer Martin Frobenius Ledermüller. In it too appears a trace of Newton's optics. The above pictures are taken from this work. A sunbeam, picked up on a rectangular mirror in front of the window, shines into two darkened rooms. In the top picture the beam falls on the rim of a prism standing vertically on a small table. On both sides there appear oval figures (d) in the colours of the rainbow similar to the figure reproduced in enlarged form on the opposite wall. If a jam jar filled with water is placed behind the prism, a rainbow is made to appear on the floor and ceiling. In similar experiments the oval figure (f) was made to appear on a side wall. Newton would hardly have found convincing the course of the beams which the draughtsman illustrates in this picture. He would perhaps have felt more convinced by the views of the author, who was reverent enough to see in the infusoria the wisdom of God just as Newton did in the movements of the stars.

NEWTON'S ROOMS AT TRINITY COLLEGE, CAMBRIDGE

In the years of the Plague 1665–66, the student Newton had withdrawn to his home on a country estate in Lincolnshire and it was there that this deep thinker came to apply himself intuitively to the basic concepts of his future work: differential calculus, the science of light and colour, the law of gravity. The twenty-seven years of his professorship in mathematics at Cambridge (1669–96) made up one long determined endeavour to reap as many rich harvests as possible from these first seeds.

In the rooms supported by wooden pillars was born the manuscript of the *Philosophiae naturalis principia mathematica* in 1687; it was there that he set himself (and completed) such incredibly bold tasks as: 'Discover how the force of the sun enables it to disturb the movements of the moon or influence those of the sea', 'calculate the increase in gravity from the equator to the poles', and many other similar tasks. It was there that classic optical experiments were made, including one on the tower of the gateway where he tested the reflecting telescope he himself had built. Very seldom was this secluded man to be seen taking a walk in the garden. He became so deeply involved in the methodical development of his ideas into a comprehensive system that he forgot meals and sleep and, on occasion, waiting friends. He incorporated into his exhaustive system all that creative minds had discovered before him in physics. He clarified the connection between the force of inertia existing in all bodies, the motive powers working from outside, and gravity; and he recognized gravitation as being a force which uniformly determines the mechanics of earth and sky.

Newton's rooms had next to them on one side the college gate—the gateway into the world—and on the other the college chapel. That was a symbolic situation for one who, both as giver and receiver, was in close communion with the wide world and never doubted the divine origin of the universe. In 1696 he became controller of the Royal Mint and moved to London, where he was able to lead a life free of material worries until his death in 1727. The picture is from David Loggan's *Cantabrigia Illustrata*.

A SENSATION IN ENGLAND IN 1790: HERSCHEL'S GIANT TELESCOPE

Right: The idea of the reflecting telescope resulted from the dissatisfaction with the astronomical refracting telescope with its lack of sharpness and its rainbow colours appearing at the rim of the lens. The young Newton was convinced that the telescope of the future was the reflecting telescope designed by Niccolo Zucchi and James Gregory: the principle of this was that the image was projected by a concave mirror (AB) on to an oblique one (T) and was observed through a magnifying lens (F). This small instrument was built by his own hand. He proudly added to his picture the crown on the tower of a distant church as seen through his telescope (2) and through an ordinary one (3).

The reflecting telescope designed by Newton did not admit much light. William Herschel (*see* p. 118) gave the instrument a new life by increasing its dimensions. The largest of his countless constructions was a reflecting telescope with a focal distance of about 36 feet. The astronomer stood in the trellis-work box above and observed the image—this time brightly illuminated—through an eye-piece. The end of the tube containing the sensitive concave mirror was hidden in a wooden hut which also housed the measuring apparatus and so on. The king contributed £4,000 sterling to the cost. Herschel used the instrument mainly for observing Uranus and fixed stars. One day shortly before the instrument was mounted the royal patron led the Archbishop of Canterbury, crouching, through the tube which was still lying on the ground. 'Come along, Your Grace, I will show you the way to heaven,' he is supposed to have said.

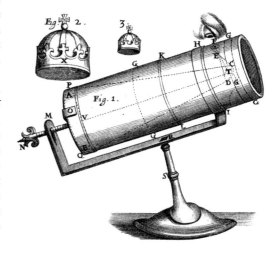

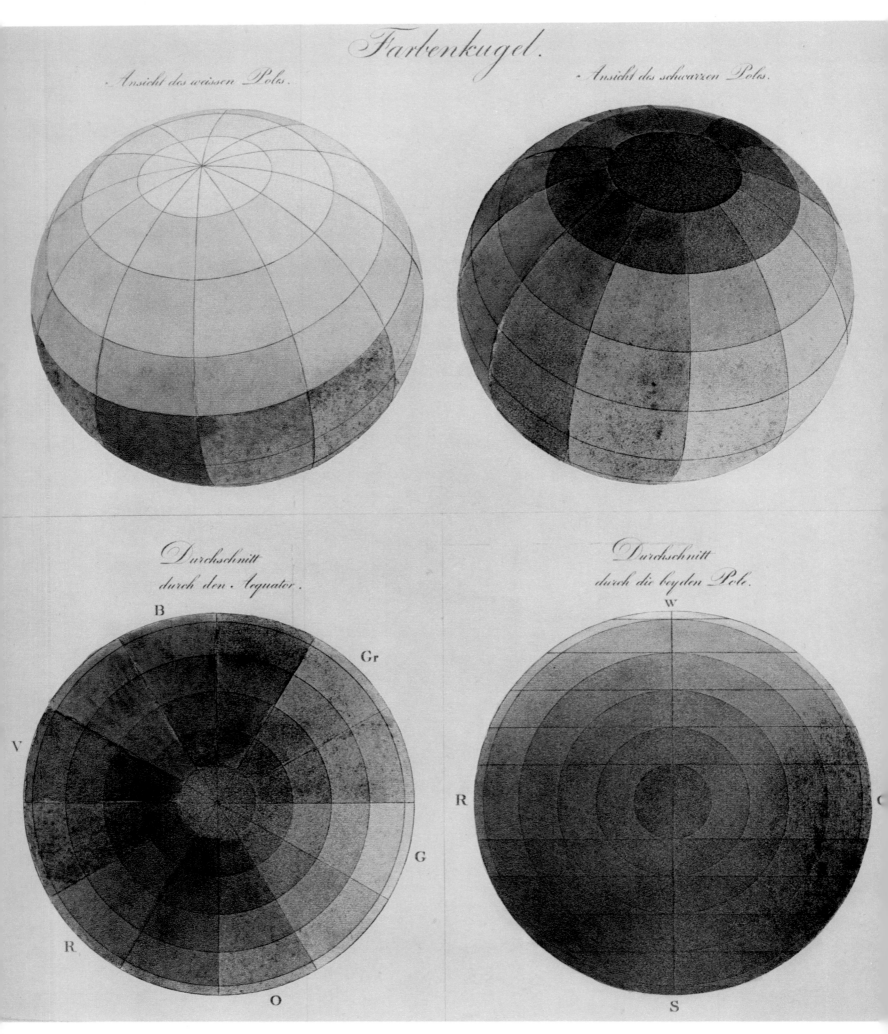

Farbenkugel.

Ansicht des weissen Poles.

Ansicht des schwarzen Poles.

Durchschnitt
durch den Aequator.

Durchschnitt
durch die beyden Pole.

114

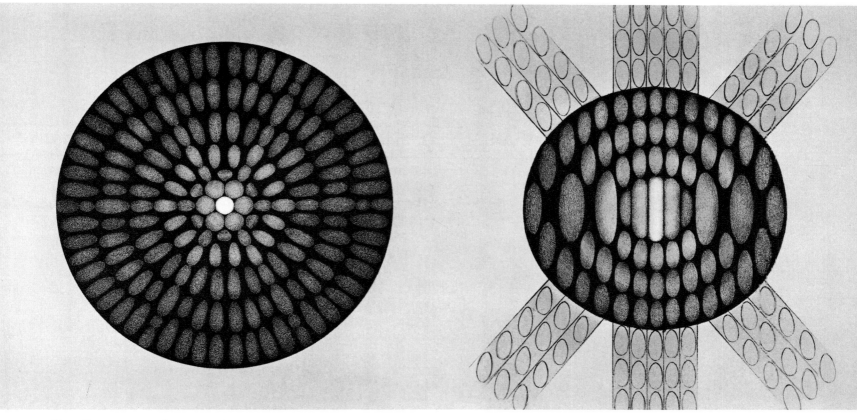

TWO DIFFRACTION SPECTRA FROM FRAUNHOFER'S EXPERIMENTS

Left: PHILIPP OTTO RUNGE'S COLOURED SPHERES (1810)

It was the artistic spirit which discovered that the apparently limitless realm of colour was permeated by relationships which obeyed important laws. The romantic painter Runge found in the coloured sphere (left) the possibility of presenting these relationships so that they could be seen at a glance— an idea which still seems to be bearing fruit today. He reduced the total number of colours to the three primary ones which cannot be further broken down: yellow, red and blue. He did this at the same time that Thomas Young, a doctor in London, discovered that by mixing the three primary colours one could produce all the others. Runge placed at the equator of his sphere between yellow (G), red (R) and blue (B) the three most important of their mixtures and indicated the close relationship between the near neighbours and their incompatibility with the colours on the diametrically opposite side: that is, yellow with violet (V), blue with orange (O), which when mixed gave a dingy grey. He placed them all in association with white (W) which lightens or black (S) which darkens; he did so by mixing in more and more white from the equator to the pole on one side, and more and more black on the other side until they reached their pure state. His coloured sphere was thus a cosmos of all relationships and contrasts of colour, mixture variations and brightness gradations: it provided the painter with a never-ending incentive to reflect on the mystery of unity in diversity.

Above: 'It is astonishing how many phenomena have up till now escaped the notice of the explorers of nature,' wrote the Bavarian optician Joseph Fraunhofer in 1821. He was thinking of optical phenomena which are difficult to explain, such as interference, polarisation and diffraction. It seemed as if a new class of young research workers were needed, endowed with completely fresh and at the same time more discerning eyes and minds, if the great new discoveries, for which everyone was waiting, were to be made. This new class of men seemed to be there all of a sudden and raised the first decades of the nineteenth century to a great epoch in optics. The first of these was Thomas Young, a manysided genius, who in 1803 made public a number of remarkable experiments. He had discovered that two minute points of light lying close side by side produced a system of dark and light bands on a screen placed some distance away where the light from these two points overlapped. They behaved just like the waves in a pool, when two stones have been thrown into it side by side: some waves flatten each other whilst others reinforce each other (*see* p. 141). Young named this phenomenon 'interference'.

The phenomena in the pictures above are akin to the aureole one sees forming when the sun or moon is behind a thin high veil of cloudy haze. In such cases the light passes through very small openings in a lattice of ice-crystals. These openings work like prisms on the white light: there appear coloured 'grating spectra'. Rays which pass through such infinitesimally small openings have built up the figures above: they are two out of countless varieties. The young Fraunhofer had tried to make minute fissures for the light to pass through by scratching with a diamond point on a glass sheet parallel grooves through which the light could not pass: he even made three hundred of these grooves in one single millimetre: a so-called diffraction grating. The

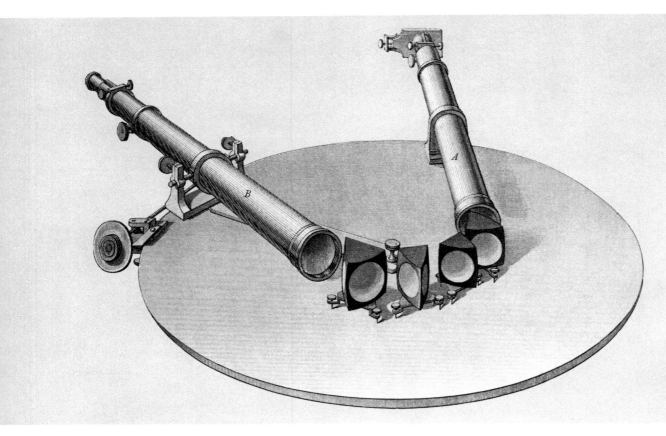

instruments used to investigate light were almost as immaterial as light itself! In the first instance the sunlight entered a dark room from two minute round openings bored side by side in a piece of thin brass plate. The light, diffracted into colour by passing through these narrow openings and separated up into a number of interfering waves, fell after a short distance on to the lens of a theodolite telescope. The right-hand picture shows what Fraunhofer saw through an eye-piece which enlarged it about forty times. The light pattern which forms after passing through the minute openings reflects their roundness. It shows separate patches of light with dark interference stripes between them. Each shines out in the colours of the spectrum. The spectra which are far from the centre are paler and appear arranged in six bands. The grouping in the left-hand picture came about when sunlight fell on the lens through three minute holes arranged in a triangle. These subtle experiments were used by Fraunhofer to study diffraction with and without grating spectra, and in the case of interfering rays to calculate from the distance between the light and dark bands the wavelengths of these rays—experiments in which accuracy down to ten-thousandths of a millimetre was required.

Whilst this was happening in Munich, a young civil engineer, Augustin Fresnel, was at work in France trying to establish once and for all the theory of light-waves Huygens initiated and to disprove the corpuscular theory then prevailing. He succeeded by experiment and with the help of differential calculus in showing clearly that interference and diffraction phenomena were due to the wave-nature of light. The polarization of light, discovered at that time by the French officer Etienne Malus, contradicted this theory. But Fresnel

then showed that everything could be explained provided one was bold enough to accept that light did not move in longitudinal waves like sound, but in transverse ones— like ripples in a shaken rope. Fresnel died in 1827, a victim of tuberculosis, Fraunhofer having succumbed to the same disease a year earlier.

'We do not know the nature of the sun,' Berzelius had written in the year 1833. About a century later, the Mount Wilson Observatory issued a table giving as many as fifty-seven chemical elements which were to be found in this 'unknown' sun. The fact that it had become possible to obtain this knowledge of a fixed star which was rotating in space ninety-three million miles away from the earth was due to a scientific achievement of the first order: the discovery of spectral analysis by Kirchhoff and Bunsen in 1860.

Fraunhofer had provided the initial basis for this—the solar spectrum reproduced on p. 117 (the original in the Deutsches Museum was engraved and coloured by his own hand). The man who achieved this great success was a self-taught practical man, who had begun as an apprentice in glass grinding. In his youth he worked in an optical firm in Munich where he improved the optical glass and the technique of the giant refractor to such an extent that this instrument began to rank equal with the reflecting telescope. Once he let the band of colour from a prism fall directly on to the lens of a theodolite telescope and examined the result through an eyepiece. He observed something which Newton's primitive prisms had not shown, but which the English physicist William Wollaston had described in 1802 in a statement now long forgotten: the solar spectrum was divided in an inexplicable manner at several points by dark

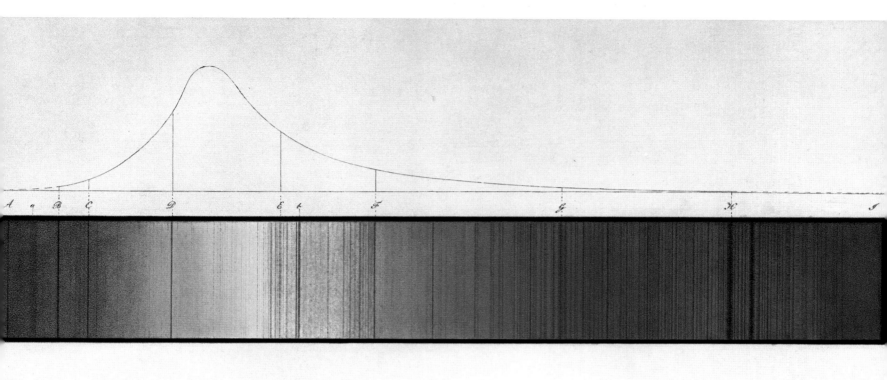

A Puzzling Message in the Solar Spectrum

vertical lines. Fraunhofer counted more than five hundred of them and gave the broadest the letters A to H; a curve indicated the relative luminosity in the colour-band. The double line D which it was very difficult to split up was one day to become historic; it opened the way for man to explore the substances in the universe. Fraunhofer had already noticed that a bright line which he had observed in the spectrum of an oil-flame lay in exactly the same position as the dark double line D in the solar spectrum. Wollaston had also established that certain elements when in an incandescent state possessed an individual line in the spectrum. But it was not until several decades later that the chemist Robert Bunsen and the physicist Gustav Kirchhoff carried these observations further. With the help of the Bunsen burner they were able to recognize numerous chemical elements from the colour of their incandescent gases. If the light from them was allowed to pass through a prism, coloured lines appeared at fixed points in the spectrum—a second infallible way of recognizing them. And so it was noticed that the yellow double line of sodium appeared exactly where Fraunhofer's D-lines lay. A large number of elements, including some unknown ones, identified themselves in this way. Some appeared as bright-coloured lines exactly where a puzzling dark line had shown in Fraunhofer's spectrum; for instance at C, F and G are hydrogen lines; at A and B oxygen lines (after the sun's rays have passed through the earth's atmosphere); at E one of the innumerable iron lines. In 1860 Kirchhoff succeeded finally in solving the whole problem: Fraunhofer's lines were without light, because gases which emit rays are able to absorb the same rays, when they pass from an outside source through the

gases. Under certain conditions dark lines form in the spectrum as a result of this absorbed light. A flame containing sodium through which the unobstructed light of the sun fell on its way to a prism, swallowed up out of this light the sodium ray and created a dark double line in the spectrum at the point where this flame on its own would have made a coloured double line. The same principle could be applied to the rays sent out by the huge incandescent bodies of the stars: the dark lines in the spectrum were their messengers. The messages could be deciphered, when the light signs—that is, the bright coloured lines—of substances found on the earth and appearing at the same places, were compared with the dark lines. So men went probing into the light of the stars—and they continue to do so today—and discovered that the substances in the visible universe even at the remotest distances are similar to those of the earth. All this began with the double line D of the Fraunhofer spectrum.

In order to be able to copy as comprehensively as possible the lines of the solar spectrum, Kirchhoff built a spectroscope with four flint glass prisms which broadened the spectrum considerably (p. 116). The telescope A carries instead of an eyepiece a metal fitting with a narrow vertical slit at the focal point of the lens. The sunlight passes through this opening which is adjustable and through the breadth of the lens and is then separated up into spectra by four prisms and directed on to the lens of telescope B. This telescope could enlarge the picture about forty times and be turned on to different axes with great ease by means of micrometer screws. With the first examinations of the Fraunhofer spectrum the science of astrophysics was born.

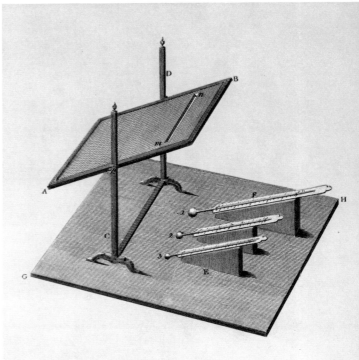

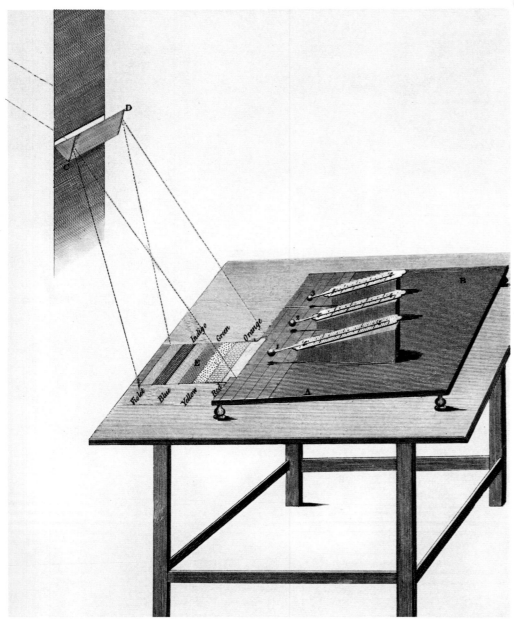

Frederick William Herschel, one of the greatest astronomers, began his career as a member of the military band in the Hanoverian footguards. He came with them to England at the age of nineteen and stayed on to work as a musician and music teacher. This man, who was to become a veritable Columbus of the fixed stars, taught himself astronomy with great enthusiasm. He is said to have watched the stars even in the intervals of concerts. In 1781 he discovered Uranus with a reflecting telescope which he had built himself. From 1782 onwards he received as astronomer an annual salary which enabled him to devote himself entirely to his studies. The pictures on this page show experiments in which, independently of others, he furnished proof of the sensational fact that part of the realm of light lay beyond the range of the human eye.

In his experiments with coloured glass he had noticed that red glass aroused a feeling of warmth round the eye, but blue did not. Not all the sun's rays seemed to possess the same powers of warmth, nor the same degree of light. How to make the colours of the spectrum fall one after the other on three thermometers (above), which, in order to guard against any technical failure, he had taken the precaution of buying from three different manufacturers? Herschel picked up the spectrum of a glass prism on a wooden board (AB) set obliquely on a stand; only a small section of this spectrum, that is only one homogeneous colour, could fall through the crack on to the stems of three thermometers. It turned out that in the case of red light the temperature rose higher than in the case of green or even violet.

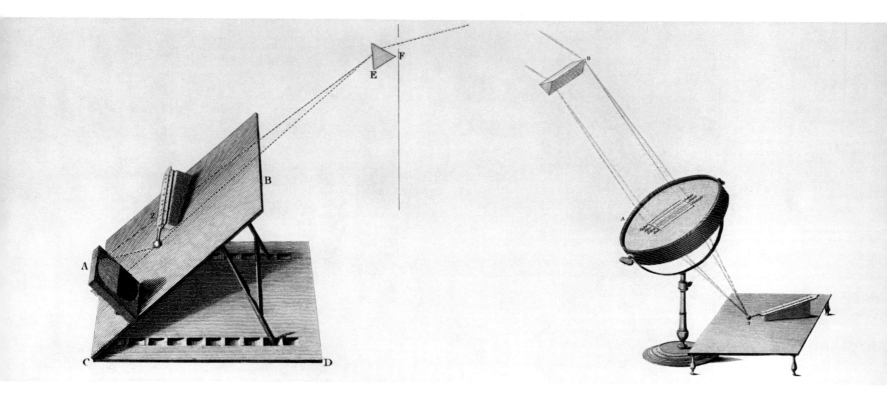

Herschel, in his researches into light which was not visible to the eye, applied all his skill to the question: Is there any light beyond the red end of the spectrum? If so, then a thermometer should register the presence of these invisible rays, that is to say the mercury when brought into contact with them would continue to rise beyond the temperature of the red colour. Herschel let the sunlight fall through a prism on to a table and where the spectrum reached its red end and ceased to be visible to the human eye, he placed a board (left). He fixed along one edge of this a scale which continued the colour-scale of the spectrum into the area where the colours were no longer visible. He pushed the edge of the board close up to the red band of the spectrum and arranged in a row not far away his three thermometers. The front one lay exactly in the invisible continuation of the spectral bands, the others further outside. And then something happened which revealed another of the world's mysteries. The temperature of the front thermometer rose, whilst the other two continued to register the temperature of the room. This meant that there were warmth-giving rays invisible to the eye beyond the red end of the spectrum, but not, it seemed, beyond the violet end. Herschel published his experiments in 1800, and exactly a year later Johann Wilhelm Ritter (*see* p. 55) discovered that there must also be invisible rays beyond the violet end of the spectrum. Their existence could be proven by chemical means; they left traces in silver nitrate. Shortly before 1900 it was discovered that healing forces were hidden in this part of the spectrum. In 1896 (a year after Röntgen's discovery of X-rays) the Dane N.R. Finsen brought the discovery to its final conclusion, as he came to realize that when cats lay in the sun, this was perhaps not solely on account of its pleasant warmth. He proved that ultra-violet rays had healing properties when applied to skin tuberculosis, and built quartz lamps for radiation treatment.

Herschel, in hundreds of imaginative experiments, probed deeper into the mysteries of infra-red rays (above, centre). On one occasion he placed a concave mirror (A) on a lectern (BC) and let a spectrum fall from the prism (E) in such a way that the red part appeared as a narrow strip just below the centre of the mirror. The upper half of the mirror, on which the infra-red rays had fallen, was covered with a semicircular sheet of board. The thermometer (2) was then pushed into the rays as they were reflected from the mirror; the mercury column remained, under the *visible* light of the red part of the spectrum, standing at 58°. Herschel then removed the board and covered the lower half of the mirror with it. Only the infra-red rays could then fall on the mirror. The thermometer when placed in the rays immediately rose to 93° but fell again to 58° as soon as the board was replaced on the upper half of the mirror. From this Herschel deduced that infra-red light like visible light obeyed the laws of reflection; otherwise it would never have reached the thermometer and warmed it. In another experiment a magnifying glass (A) was used (above right). It could be covered with a mask in such a way that as the rays fell on it from the prism (B), sometimes only the infra-red rays, sometimes only the visible red part of the spectrum, were refracted on to the thermometer. Again the difference in temperature showed itself; but this experiment proved above all that invisible infra-red light obeyed the law of refraction just as visible light did and also that it had its own angle of refraction.

With Herschel began the long intensive research into the spectrum which goes far beyond the two ends of the 'rainbow' portion into the field of other electro-magnetic forces (*see* p. 139 *f*.). Light is an unbelievably delicate form of energy which has been vibrating in the great mysterious cosmos of forces since the beginning of time in inter-relation with other forces such as warmth and electricity; it also affects the eye and brings it messages from the visible world.

Magnetism and Electricity

Left: THE GLORY OF LIGHT

Helmholtz, the physicist and inventor of the ophthalmoscope, said once that for the artist the essential was nature as a whole, not the multitude of laws governing it which the scientists examine with their mass of experiments. This wholeness of nature, revealed in the glory of light, is captured in this view of the small town of Laufenburg on the Rhine, which Hans Thoma painted in 1873. Reflection, refraction, diffraction, interference, colour—all the astonishing aspects of light, discovered over the centuries by optics; here they are all merging back again into the glorious unity of sunshine as it plays on gabled roofs, foaming torrents and wooded hills on a summer afternoon. The versatile Helmholtz saw the close relationships between the artist and the scholar. In lectures on 'the optical in painting' he showed how often direct and scientifically accurate experience of light is brought into landscapes painted in the realistic manner. He drew attention to the painters' understanding of aerial perspective. All through the atmosphere there are fine particles like water vapour, dust and so on which either reflect or refract the sunlight and thereby create that translucent mist known to artists as the cause of 'aerial perspective'. Helmholtz drew attention to the wide range in luminosity which gave such a sense of freedom to the landscape, a range which varies from the brightness of water spray lit up by the sun to the dark shadows behind the houses. The physicist could measure these, but the artist had to adapt them to the much narrower range of luminosity of the colours available to him for his picture. Irradiation phenomena appear at their clearest round a very bright light on a dark background. Thoma noticed one example in the opening in the wall directly above one of the figures: or to put it differently, his eye had reacted to the phenomenon in this way.

Helmholtz goes on to say that the painter feels how he can use colour and shape to influence the mood of the person looking at his picture. Perhaps when he said this he was thinking of the colour theory of Goethe's with which he was completely familiar. Parts of this theory can be put to the test in this picture by Thoma: 'Just as we feel we want to follow a pleasant subject which moves away before us, so we like to look at the blue not because it forces itself on us but because it draws us after it... Green: when the two colours forming it (blue and yellow) are mixed in exactly equal proportions, then the eye and the mind are set at rest by this mixed colour just as they are by a primary one. One does not want to go any further; indeed one cannot.'

The history of investigation into magnetism begins on a small scale with the observation of magnetite, an iron ore with natural magnetic force, but goes on to include forces which hold sway throughout the solar system. In the year AD 121, in China, the lodestone was already known as a stone capable of communicating its power to iron or steel. Soon, the compass was showing Chinese ships their way over the seas. In Europe, no trace is found of the magical needle before 1200, whereas the lodestone had its influence upon human minds in antiquity, and the explanations propounded for it were often as wonderful as the magnet tales of the east. Columbus noticed the fluctuating movements of the compass needle away from the north star, now known as its variation, and in 1581 the English seafarer Robert Norman made known the fact that the magnetic needle would continue to point to the north even if it had to move downwards, as though some force were drawing it towards the centre of the earth and not only, as had until then been thought, towards a fairy tale magnetic mountain in the far north, or a star.

In 1269, a Frenchman known as Petrus Peregrinus named the two poles of the magnet, and established by systematic investigation that like poles repelled and unlike poles attracted each other, even when the lodestone was broken down into splinters. He shaped it into a ball which he laid upon a sliver of wood floating in water and found evidence of cosmic concord in the fact that the little sphere obeyed its great counterpart in the heavens, and seemed to turn towards its north pole.

Over three centuries later, Galileo and Kepler were joyfully greeting the classical work on magnetism, built upon the foundations laid by its many predecessors, as the sign of a new, realistic age. The author of this book *De Magnete* was a doctor practising in Shakespearean London, William Gilbert (*see* p. 124).

The research field of the future was to be the magnetism of space. The man who possessed the intellectual power, the breadth of vision and the yearning for truth required for such a task was the astronomer Edmund Halley. In 1702, he set out his own quite new observations on a world map, showing degrees of variation. On this, it was to be seen clearly how changeable and elusive were the magnetic forces of the earth. On his journey to central and south America, Alexander von Humboldt, who was passionately interested in their mysteries, experienced them by means of his refined inclination-compasses. As the foundations of the work grew firmer, scholars became more critical and the range of their vision was enlarged. Soon, the work of a number of scientists brought to light the wonderful connections which exist between a tiny magnet which attracts iron filings and the earth, with the field of forces surrounding it, polar light and the cosmos itself.

In 1777, Leonhard Euler wrote: 'I am speaking now of electricity which has recently become so significant a part of the study of nature that no man can be allowed not to understand its workings.' This energy which, with magnetism, is explained by twentieth-century physics in terms of the forces at work within the atom, was first exposed to strictly scientific investigation in the eighteenth century. The striking power of the torpedo fish had already been observed by the ancient Egyptians, and the ancient Greeks knew how to draw sparks from amber (pieces of the fossilized resin of evergreen trees), yet thousands of years passed before it was known that these and the lightning in storm clouds were manifestations of the same force. Gilbert had hardly separated the ephemeral static electricity from the durable magnetic force, the influence of which was confined to iron and steel, and given it the name 'electric', when it began, like a will-o'-the-wisp, to put its bewildering magic into action. Gilbert, and Guericke after him, tried to discover where in nature its seat was. They rubbed the most widely different substances. When this was done to sulphur, glass or sealing wax, there was electricity, leaping out in tiny crackling sparks. If it was done to gold, marble or wood it made no appearance. So, bodies began to be divided into electric and non-electric. The carriers of this force behaved in a strange way. Guericke, the discoverer of the first electric machine, observed that if a ball of sulphur were rubbed with the hand it would pick up a feather from the floor at one moment, and at the next let it drop. In 1629, the Jesuit Cabeo too, bewildered, reported the power of electricity to attract and to repel. In London, Stephen Gray, old and poverty-stricken, who had been an assistant of the physician Desaguliers and was now pensioned, was occupied with the question how far the operation of electricity extended from its source. In 1730, a rich philanthropist Granville Wheler placed the whole large area of his house at the disposal of the poor pensioner, so that he could stretch out his long strings and wires and communicate static electricity to them at one end with a rubbed glass rod while Wheler watched at the other to see if a small ivory ball would attract some feathers. The electricity travelled at one movement immensely fast, and at another almost not at all, according to whether the long wire was hung on silk thread or on small wires (which conducted the electricity to earth). In this way, conductors were distinguished from non-conductors.

The truly great discoveries occurred between the years 1750 and 1870. In his famous experiment with the kite, Franklin proved the existence of atmospheric electricity; Volta discovered the electricity of chemical contact, Oersted the magnetic effect of electric currents, Faraday electromagnetic induction—to say nothing of experimenters who stopped half-way. And there came mathematical physicists to capture this mighty fluid, the least tangible of all natural forces, in firm mathematical laws. Coulomb formulated a law according to which unlike charges attract each other with a force which is inversely proportional to the square of the distance between them. In one week of the year 1820, Ampère set out all that had been discovered in several decades about the effect of electrical currents upon one another. Maxwell (see p. 142) provided mathematical support for what Faraday established visibly by experiment about the relationship of electricity, magnetism and light. And in the electrical currents which today provide the power for entire industries the will-o'-the-wisp which once flickered between the electrodes of the early electric machine makes its appearance as a mighty giant.

THE SAGA OF THE MAGNETIC MOUNTAIN

Goethe used to recount a fairy story about a magnetic mountain which he had learned from his grandmother. 'The ships which passed too near it suddenly lost all their metal; the nails flew to the mountain, and the wretched people on board sank to their deaths between the planks as they broke apart.' This is exactly what is happening in this woodcut (enlarged reproduction to the right) from an edition of the *Hortus sanitatis* of 1491. Even Ptolemy told stories of shipping wharves on the island of Borneo, where ships were built with wooden nails to protect them from the strange magnetic islands in the sea there. In *A Thousand and One Nights* this fanciful story becomes a grisly tale: the Arabs tell how the mountain bristles with the nails from the ships which were dashed to pieces against it. All the horrors which men suffered on a sinking ship were seen as connected with this mountain; so too was all the awesome and inexplicable attractive power which lay in the lodestone. Whilst the magnetic mountain of the oriental tales lay deep in the south, it was moved far to the north as soon as the compass needle became known to European navigators in the thirteenth century. We still see the mountain on a world map prepared by the well-known cartographer Mercator in 1569; it rises up as a lonely isle out of the cold waters of the Arctic Ocean to the north of the Bering Strait; he rightly placed it to the side of the North pole, for seamen had long before this noticed that the needle deflected from the geographical pole by a greater or lesser amount. Many people still thought at that time that the pole star, or a heavenly pole, or perhaps this magnetic rock in the sea pulled the point of the needle to the north. It was William Gilbert who for the first time in 1600 with his epoch-making experiments energetically refuted 'these ridiculous little tales' invented for readers 'who, being uneducated, revel in absurdities'.

MAGNETIC FORCES IN A SMITHY

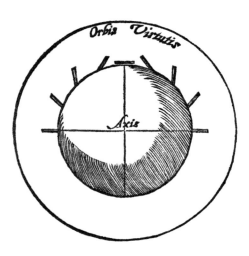

The secret of William Gilbert's research was to bring the smallest things into the widest relationships. On the anvil at the smithy he saw the forces of the whole earth at work. A piece of heated iron had only to be placed in an exact north–south position *(septentrio-auster)*, along which the forces of magnetic current flowed, and the iron was made magnetic solely by the strokes of the hammer, without ever coming into contact with a magnet. And as a result of the experiments he conducted with a lodestone ground to a spherical shape (below left), he drew the correct conclusion about 'the common mother', Earth. Such a 'miniature earth', or Terrella, could be proved to have its magnetic north pole and its south pole at the end of the axis connecting them. When the experimenter held a magnetized needle on a string over the equator of the sphere (the vertical line), it remained hanging in a horizontal position. But when he slowly turned the sphere, so that the north pole came to the top, the needle came into a field of invisible forces; its point sank lower and lower until, when the pole, instead

KARL FRIEDRICH GAUSS ON THE TERRACE OF THE GÖTTINGEN OBSERVATORY

of the equator, was at the top, it hung down in a vertical position. These magnetic forces were distributed throughout the sphere; they were weakest at the equator and strongest near the poles. They operated at a distance from the needle held above them—invisible 'effluvia' of an immaterial kind built up a sphere of activity *(orbis virtutis)* round the magnet. What Gilbert observed here was exactly what the mariners noticed in their compass needles: the inclination of the needle, the deviation downwards. The earth was simply a gigantic Terrella loaded throughout right to its centre with magnetic force. Gilbert was only able to explain the deviation of the needle to the side, the declination, as due to supposed attraction forces of mountains and so on; it was not until the first half of the nineteenth century that English navigators discovered at some distance from the south pole and the north pole those places where those fluctuating causes of deviation, the magnetic poles of the earth, are to be found; the one in the north was on the Canadian peninsula Boothia Felix.

Above: Alexander von Humboldt was shrewd enough to draw Karl Friedrich Gauss into the network of collaborators who were to observe the phenomena of magnetism throughout the world. It was in this way that the 'prince of mathematics', who in his childhood had been through the hard school of poverty, arrived at the centre of a world-wide organization. His contribution was certainly a princely one: close to the new observatory at Göttingen he built an observatory for terrestrial magnetism, a collecting place for observations from all parts of the world; he produced with Wilhelm Weber an atlas of deviation and inclination; he invented a refined form of magnetometer and created the absolute measuring system which made it possible for all physical phenomena and forces to be expressed in units of mass (milligram, today gram), length (millimetre, today centimeter) and time (second). In the picture, to the right of this great mathematician, who measured and calculated spaces on the earth and in the sky, is the heliotrope instrument which he invented as an aid to surveyors.

NORTHERN LIGHTS NEAR BOSSEKOP, FINNMARK, AT 6 O'CLOCK IN THE EVENING ON 21ST JANUARY 1839

Was this light the reflection of the golden shields, on which the Valkyries carried the souls of the fallen to Valhalla? This was the question asked in old myths about the origin of those shining arcs, those veils and ribbons of waving light, known as the 'Aurora Borealis', which sometimes fill the subpolar skies from west to east. The picture shows one of the many forms, which the French *Commission scientifique du nord* recorded in their atlas between 1838 and 1840. Some time before this, scientists had begun looking for a connection between this phenomenon and magnetism. Why did the magnetic needle point exactly to the summit of an aurora borealis thus aiming a little to the west of the geographical north pole? asked Edmund Halley, as northern lights stood over England in 1716. Why were the needles disturbed for hours in many distant lands just before Northern Lights appeared in the sky? asked Humboldt and Arago. Cook had seen something similar in the south polar regions. It seemed to be proven that the Northern Lights were a form of terrestrial magnetism which had become visible and stretched out into space. For some time it was assumed that they contained electric forces, but then in the period after 1850 scientists began to think that magnetic lines of force originating from the earth were meeting cosmic forces of the sun high up in the atmosphere. In 1852 the Swiss astronomer Rudolf Wolf discovered the fact that most disturbed movements of the magnetic needle took place in years in which the greatest number of sunspots occurred and the glory of the Northern Lights was at its best. Finally Carl Störmer, a professor in Oslo, and others who carried on their research in the light of atomic physics, came to the conclusion that the sun hurls out streams of particles; that these are deflected by the magnetic fields of force of the earth, which Gilbert had already discovered, towards the polar regions; and that there they shine out as they impinge on the highest air strata in those veils of light which German myths saw as the reflection of golden shields.

A FLASH OF LIGHTNING FROM DANTE'S 'DIVINE COMEDY'

The dazzling forked line of fire, which leaps to the earth during storms or jumps from cloud to cloud in a split second, is the most powerful electric phenomenon in nature. It is only in the last two hundred years that man has had the comfort of knowing what this means; yet he is still awestruck on seeing the lightning flash. The thinkers of ancient Greece had assumed that when lightning occurred inflammable vapours were exploding and bursting into flames or that a sulphurous fire was breaking out—the smell of ozone was taken for that of sulphur. Greek myths had seen in the lightning the flash of the flying spears of angry Zeus. In 1749, Benjamin Franklin for the first time insisted upon experiments being made to find out how it could be that during storms clouds became so strongly charged that they sent out flashes of light as long as a village or a small town. And so he came to discover atmospheric electricity and to invent the lightning conductor. (Picture out of an edition of Dante illustrated by Doré.)

Overleaf: ELECTRIC MACHINE AND LEYDEN JAR

The stately lecture-hall suggests an academic milieu, as does the physics lecturer, Professor van Swinden of Amsterdam. The motley assembly of brightly dressed people includes in addition to priests, merchants and scholars in the front rows, all kinds of people of the middle classes placed further back. The scene is a meeting of the society for adult education 'Felix Meritis' at Amsterdam: the subject of the lecture is electricity. In the laboratory the scientists had not yet progressed beyond frictional electricity, but here they have at their disposal an improved machine with glass plates, which can be rubbed at the top and the bottom with a leather cushion. The professor is pointing out the miniature lightning flash this was considered a miraculous invention of the human mind in those days. On the left behind the blackboard there are a few Leyden jars, the first electric accumulators discovered in both Holland and Russia.

Benjamin Franklin, an able printer and journalist, tried through the medium of the Press to educate his American fellow-countrymen to become enlightened citizens. For twenty years from 1738 he worked in Philadelphia, until politics robbed him of all his leisure, on research into the mysteries of electricity, remaining all the time in touch with scholarly circles in Europe. In 1749 he decided to establish beyond all doubt by experiment whether the lightning which passed across the sky and the little spark in the electric machine really were one and the same. The flash, its shape, the explosion, the capacity to be led along metals, the smell which was assumed to be that of sulphur—all these things were common to both, as had often been noticed. Franklin suggested that the best way of putting lightning to the decisive test was to place a sharply pointed metal rod on top of a high tower during a storm, since electricity seemed to have a tendency to collect on points of metal. But before he was able to carry out his experiment, the Frenchman Thomas François Dalibard proved in May 1752 that Franklin's theory was correct. In October of the same year Franklin went to work with a kite instead of a tower; on the top of the kite he fixed a pointed wire which was to be carried up with it as high as possible into a thunder-cloud. Franklin stood with his son under cover of a shed in an open field. The kite was made fast by a hempen string; a key fixed within reach of their hands was to deliver the spark and provide them with the proof that they sought. The only protection available to the unsuspecting and bold experimenters was a piece of non-conducting silk cord, which ran from the key to their hands. The 'electric fire' did in fact stream out of the charged air via the damp hempen string to the key. Franklin drew sparks out of it with his knuckles; a Leyden jar, which he held against them, was filled for the first time in history with electricity from the sky. The draughtsman, however, was as ignorant as Doré on one point about lightning—namely, that it never comes down in a zig-zag.

The important result of this experiment was the lightning conductor (lower picture). Franklin had boldly foreseen this in 1749: 'Cannot our knowledge about the force in these bare metal points be made useful to man for the protection of his houses, churches, ships and so on against being struck by lightning? That knowledge teaches us to set up on the highest point of such buildings upright needle-pointed iron rods gilded to prevent rust, and to connect the bottom of the rod with a wire passing down the outside of the building or ship into the earth or water.' Working on these principles he erected eleven years later the first lightning conductor on the house of the banker Benjamin West in Philadelphia. The installation stood up to its trial by fire—in the literal sense of the words—soon afterwards during a storm. Since then millions of lightning conductors have freed a part of mankind from the fear of this force. Only outside the areas where conductors are in use does Zeus with his incalculable fury continue to hurl his glittering spears.

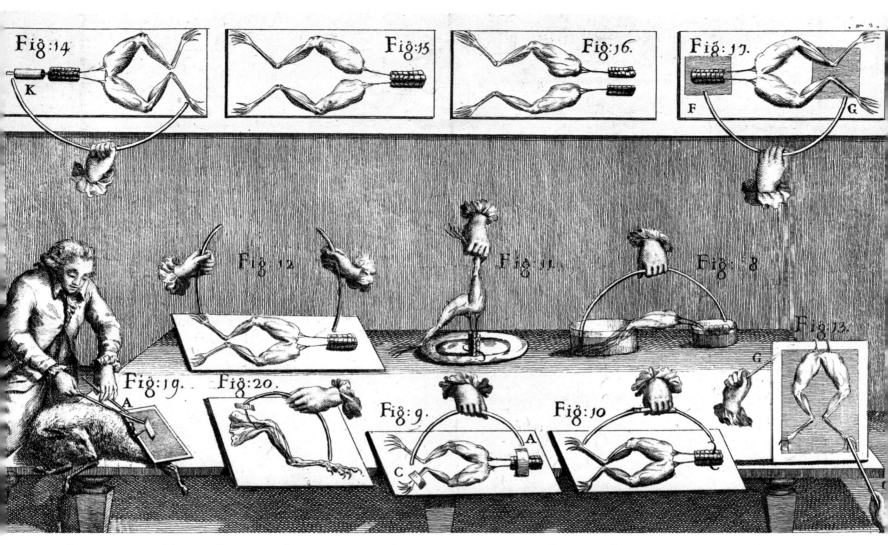

GALVANI STUDIES 'ANIMAL ELECTRICITY'—AND OVERLOOKS ELECTRICITY GENERATED BY CHEMICAL CONTACT

In the late eighteenth century an entirely new form of electricity was discovered in some frog's legs which had been carefully prepared for an experiment, but its true nature was not recognized. The doctor and lecturer in anatomy from Bologna, Luigi Galvani, was the man who made the discovery without realizing it. It had been known since the time of Swammerdam, Haller and others that muscles and nerves reacted violently to electric current. Galvani set himself the task of clarifying the whole question by allowing electric impulses to pass through the spinal marrow, thigh nerves and thigh muscles of the frog (Figures 15 and 16). In 1786 during these experiments something unexpected happened, as an animal which had been dissected in this way lay on the table close to an electric machine which was giving out sparks: 'As one of the people who was helping me nearby happened to touch the inner femoral nerve of the frog with the tip of a scalpel, all the muscles in the limb seemed to be drawn together as if in a violent spasm.'

Galvani knew nothing of electrical induction, so he sought the answer in countless experiments to this question: did the electricity, which seemed to have something to do with muscular contraction, originate from outside, or did it also exist in the animal's body itself? It was clearly important that there should be a circuit running through the frog's body closed by means of an electric conductor but without any source of current from outside. Galvani devised one contact experiment after another. Fig. 17 shows part of a spinal cord on a silver dish (F), with the legs resting on a copper dish (G); a connecting hoop of wire causes the thighs to quiver. In the case of a sheep (Fig. 19) and a hen (Fig. 20) the movement was less marked, but it worked with double the force when Galvani closed the circuit by coupling together conductors of different metals. So in Fig. 12 there is one copper wire and one silver one. They provide the connection between the nerves and the muscles. From dozens of variations of these patiently executed experiments Galvani concluded in his treatise, *De viribus electricitatis...* (1791) that a special kind of electricity existed in the animal body, a delicate fluid, which flowed from the brain through the nerves to the muscles.

The treatise caused a great sensation throughout Europe. The reaction which had the greatest consequences came from a man who turned from being a supporter of Galvani to being his most serious critic, although he never lost his respect for the great naturalist who had inspired him: Volta.

131

Alessandro Volta, grammar-school teacher at Como and later Professor at Pavia, inventor of various kinds of delicate measuring apparatus, was destined to reveal the undiscovered in Galvani's experiments. When he repeated them, he found that the source of the new electricity was not necessarily to be found in the nerves of the dissected animal, but rather in the different metals which Galvani had tied on to the animal's body. Volta began precisely at that point where Galvani's experiment in Fig. 12 had started leading in a new direction without his realizing it. By degrees Volta dispensed with the frog: he remembered rather the curious impression of alkaline flavour left on the human tongue when different metals such as silver or copper coins are placed on either side of it. Here in miniature was that triad which had been evident in his experiments for years; two different metals, which together with a liquid made a circuit through which electric current passed. When he placed small paired disks of zinc and copper, and then separated them with a sheet of board soaked in salt water, he could establish that there was a weak electric current, as soon as he closed the circuit with a wire or some other conductor. 'Here electricity was being generated in a manner quite unknown before that time,' he wrote later, after he had examined systematically the current-generating properties of all kinds of metal combinations. In order to obtain more electric power, he piled the tripartite elements on top of their neighbours into pillars, or he joined several pillars together, as in the picture below, where each pair of zinc disks (Z) and silver disks (A) is separated from each other by a layer of material soaked in salt water—this was to some extent the substitute for Galvani's frogs. The eight-layered pillars are linked by strips of metal to form a single battery; the lowest ones on the left and right lead into vessels of salt water; it was here that the circuit could be closed. This apparatus produced for the first time a continuous supply of current over a certain period. It was used for their research by all those scientists, from Davy to Faraday, from Berzelius to Oersted, who delved deeper and deeper into the wonders of electric power.

In Paris, on 7th November 1801, a year after Volta's comprehensive report about his research had appeared in the *Philosophical Transactions,* he was standing, as a prince of science, before the man who was to be the most powerful ruler in Europe: the First Consul, Napoleon Bonaparte. The scientist had been invited to present his discoveries to a group of illustrious scholars in the Institut de France. Volta produced out of a pile laid between four glass rods, as if out of some magic source of energy, the famous 'Voltaic current'. In front of the pile is a simpler form of equipment in a beaker. Napoleon promoted Volta, this admirer of Lavoisier, Voltaire and Laplace, to the high rank of count. Technical improvements were soon made to the Voltaic pile and its creator did not distinguish himself again. Meanwhile the quiet Galvani, little disturbed by the battle led by his supporters against those of Volta, had been dismissed from office by Napoleon's regime; he died in 1798.

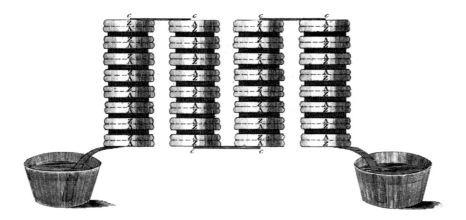

VOLTA DEMONSTRATES HIS CURRENT-GENERATING APPARATUS TO NAPOLEON

HANS CHRISTIAN OERSTED DISCOVERS ELECTRO-MAGNETISM

◀ *Left:* ELECTRICITY BECOMES FASHIONABLE

The well-known Abbé Jean Antoine Nollet used to guide his carefully selected Paris pupils through the whole fashionable science of physics in fifteen lectures. These were given in his chamber which was equipped with all kinds of apparatus. Excitement rose to its highest pitch when at the end of the course he began to instruct his pupils about electricity with the elegance of a conjuror. A young man was suspended in the air on a platform hanging from four silken ropes which served as insulation. When charged with electricity through a rubbed glass tube the man displayed the most curious properties: sparks could be emitted from his nose and his hand could attract or repel little paper balls. Thus it was proved that man, like iron, cotton and coal, was a conductor. *Above:* 'We must discover whether electricity acts in any way upon the magnet,' wrote Oersted in 1813. Oersted was a many-sided personality who traced with the eye of a romanticist the hidden relationships between the natural forces and their connection with the spirit ruling the universe. It had long ago been discovered that lightning and electric current magnetized iron; on the other hand it was also known that both forces possessed their own special properties. But in the year 1820 Oersted demonstrated to a small circle of scientific friends in Copenhagen experiments which showed a clear connection between them. He had discovered that a magnetic needle, as if subjected to some mysterious will, set itself at right angles to a wire held over it, as soon as current flowed through the wire. If the current altered direction, then the needle turned through an angle of 180°; it was as if the needle was compelled by the wire to gyrate within an invisible enchanted circle. The news that the two great forces magnetism and electricity had been decisively shown for the first time to be inter-related swept through the world of science like wildfire. Oersted's reputation rose when in France in the same year the mathematician André Marie Ampère discovered that currents acted upon each other; there was attraction when they flowed in the same direction, and repulsion when they flowed in opposite directions. Ampère also discovered that electric and magnetic forces probably originate from the molecule—which was a very prophetic line of thought.

FARADAY DELIVERING A LECTURE AT THE ROYAL INSTITUTION ON 27TH DECEMBER 1855

The history of the natural sciences abounds in personalities who obeyed a call from within and were prepared for any sacrifice. Without these men, science would come to nothing. Faraday's research fell into this class; and it was perhaps the finest and most distinctive of all. From the poverty of an apprenticeship in bookbinding, he advanced to the position of laboratory director of the Royal Institution, in whose building his own accommodation and laboratory were also situated (*see* p. 54); there he spent many hours, days and months, until he was completely exhausted, probing ever deeper into the unknown realms of electrolysis and electro-magnetism. Even when the exorbitant demands on his strength at the beginning of his sixties forced him to take long periods of rest, he continued to broaden his range of ideas, always by observing reality, never restricting himself simply to quantitative work with mathematical systems. Thus he saw that the phenomena of magnetism, electricity and light were closely inter-related; they were energies working their way round in space in lines and fields of force with finite speed, unlike gravitation by 'tele-

kinesis' without the time factor, which was the prevailing view of the time. He eventually abandoned his work without bitterness, as in the last years of his life his memory became so over-taxed that he forgot how to spell many words. In his letters of this time there appear as if out of a dialogue with another world the words: 'just waiting'—a sign of his unquestioning accord with the great laws of existence.

In the picture above Albert, the Prince Consort, sits on the left in the front row and listens as one of a carefully selected audience. On his right sits his eldest son, the future King Edward VII. Faraday never wanted to bring his students together into a 'school'. He liked to have educated laymen as his audience and, most of all, the young people of London who were ready, like himself, to pursue the sciences with enthusiasm and imagination. It was for young people that he gave that famous Christmas lecture about the natural history of a candle. Sanderson (standing on the right behind Faraday) worked as his assistant. He was a former soldier, who according to London gossip is supposed to have said: 'I make the experiments, he does the talking.'

Between 1820 and 1862 Faraday recorded many thousands of experiments immediately after completing them: he wrote them down in his laboratory journal, numbering them all in an orderly manner, and he added hundreds of sketches. It seems as if his inner voice had on one occasion told him: 'Convert magnetism into electricity.' Oersted, Arago and others had converted electricity into magnetic force; why should it not be possible in this boundless realm to do the opposite? The above sketches record some stages on the way. The middle one at the bottom and the one to the right and above it suggest attempts, which have miscarried, to bring about induction and electro-magnetic rotation. But on 29th August 1831, for the first time, through the agency of a magnet, an induction current was created in a metal object. Round a ring of soft iron (top, centre) two well-insulated separate copper wires were evenly wound. The pieces of wire jutting out on side B were connected with a galvanometer. When the ends of the wire (here shown too short) on side A were connected to a battery, in order to make a closed circuit of current, the iron ring became magnetic; in the wires at B a current was induced through this magnetism. The needle of the galvanometer was then deflected. Every making or breaking the current in A produced an instantaneous electric current in the wire B. A month and a half later there appeared for the first time an apparatus which pointed to the dynamo of the future (centre, right): a cylinder-shaped magnet is quickly moved to and fro through a coil of wire: each time, a current impulse occurs in the wires—the mechanical movement of the magnet has been converted into electricity. Above this are two sketches drawn in the same month—a third triumph. Following the pattern of Arago's rotation magnetism, Faraday succeeded for the first time in generating a continuous current by making a round copper disk rotate between the two poles of a horseshoe magnet. Copper brushes led the electric power to the magnet needle or the galvanometer (side-view without the magnetic poles). In the sketches on the extreme left Faraday tried to show the course taken by currents. What was achieved here with enormous effort laid the basis for the whole of high-voltage current technology.

ELECTRIC WIRE LINKS THE OLD AND NEW WORLDS

From 1840 onwards a network of telegraph wires began to spread over Europe and America, the first practical use to which electric current was put on a large scale. The American pioneer of telegraphy, Samuel F.B. Morse, had already called for a direct link between the two continents. The difficulties were enormous. Did cables exist which could be protected against breaking and were resistant to salt water? Would a message sent over this long distance ever arrive at all? Were there dangerous currents at the bottom of the sea? Was there a ship in existence which could be used to lay a gigantic cable of this kind? Four times between 1857 and 1865 the most powerful cable-laying ships sailed across the Atlantic in the service of America and Britain, and each time the cable broke at some point. In the summer of 1866 the New York business man and financier Cyrus W. Field made a fifth attempt. The telegraph station of Valentia in Ireland was to be connected direct with that of Heart's Content in Newfoundland. The giant steamer *Great Eastern* took on board 2,400 miles of insulated cable weighing 4,000 tons and unrolled it slowly in twenty days between the two continents. On the return journey a still

bolder attempt was made. A piece of cable was laid as far as the spot on the sea bed where the break had occurred in 1865 in the cable connected with Ireland. After thirty fruitless attempts the broken end of the cable was raised. Before it could be spliced with the end which led towards America, a test had to be made to establish whether it was still connected with Ireland. On 1st September this exciting test was made in the electrician's room of the *Great Eastern*. The end of the broken cable led from the floor to the very sensitive steel magnet of the reflecting galvanometer invented by the physicist to the expedition, William Thomson; this served as receiving apparatus. Would the distant Irish telegraph station answer the signal which had just been sent? Everyone gazed enthralled at the code-scale of the apparatus by the light of a lamp. At the table with slightly bent head is the haggard figure of Cyrus Field. Two minutes later cannon shots, rockets and the cheers of the crew were celebrating the receipt of an answer from Valentia. The two halves of the cable were spliced and submerged—two cable links had been created at one stroke between the Old and the New World. (Painting by Robert Dudley, 1866.)

Waves, Rays and Atoms I

The physicists have described in a series of classic investigations the basic laws of the infinitely complex motions of the solid, liquid and gaseous matter filling the world around us, from free fall to the course of the stars and the vertically or horizontally oscillating material waves. Similarly Newton, Laplace, Euler and others sought to express them in mathematical terms. Soon after Augustin Jean Fresnel had demonstrated the undulating character of light, an immaterial, phenomenon, there appeared in Leipzig in 1825 a *Wellenlehre auf Experimenten gegründet* by the brothers Ernst Heinrich and Wilhelm Weber. It considered the properties common to mechanical, acoustic and optic waves and demonstrated close connections between the main departments of physics.

The wave concept seemed more and more destined to become one of the most important coordinating and classifying concepts in the whole of physics. If a wave were, generally speaking, conceived of as a periodic change of state spreading outwards in space with finite speed, then the heading 'wave motion' could be made to cover almost all the varieties of energy which the physicists of the last hundred years were so proud to have discovered, from electro-magnetic waves to the gamma rays of the disintegrating atomic nucleus.

That mysterious power called electricity is undulating in character. In 1887 when Heinrich Hertz's bold experiments first proved that electric waves could be artificially produced, a thrill of excitement went round the scientific world as it did when the idea of the conservation of energy was announced. His work was taken up by technical experts who from the top of tall masts emitted electric waves into the air with the speed of light and had them picked up by distant receivers, for example Guglielmo Marconi who broke new ground in 1897 when from off the Welsh coast near Cardiff he sent wireless Morse signals over to the mainland. Today these waves carry words, music and pictures all round the globe.

The invisible rays discovered in 1895 by the Würzburg physicist Wilhelm Konrad Röntgen were also of an undulating nature. They were connected with the cathode rays previously investigated by Crookes and Hittorf (*see* p. 143). In 1912 Max von Laue showed that Röntgen's 'X-rays' also travelled in waves (*see* p. 144).

Moving water, the traditional domain of waves, had from earliest times familiarized man with their typical motion. In the last hundred years he encountered this motion again in the spheres of reality lying far beyond the visible world, this time in phenomena which appear completely non-material in comparison with the waves in air, water and earth. And yet they all obeyed the laws of reflection, refraction and diffraction. Herschel and Ritter had gone beyond the oscillating red and violet rays and boldly invaded the invisible world, but in the twentieth century the newly discovered undulating electro-magnetic motions covered a span ten thousand times broader. The labours of generations of scientists have created a broad range, an electro-magnetic spectrum in which all physical phenomena possessing the characteristics of electro-magnetic waves can be classified according to their wavelength. These lengths range from a high figure in miles in the case of electric alternating currents right down to the ten-millionth part of a millimetre in the case of radiation from atomic nuclei. Even in this department of physics which has so far dominated the twentieth century we encounter yet again that primary shape, the wave.

In 1924 the French scientist Louis de Broglie advanced the theory that the electron whirling round the nucleus of the atom, which had always been assumed to be a minute particle of matter, was at the same time an electro-magnetic wave which vibrated as it revolved round the nucleus of the atom. Three years later the Americans Clinton J. Davisson and Lester H. Germer succeeded in demonstrating the accuracy of the theory. Erwin Schrödinger expanded it into a highly complex general system of wave mechanics and applied this dual nature of light (see p. 102) to the whole of matter. 'Its corpuscular nature was later shown both theoretically and experimentally to be paralleled by its undulating nature on equal terms,' as Arnold Sommerfeld put it.

About 1900 scientists were—or were not—still working with Dalton's and Avogadro's atomic and molecular theories. Many important nineteenth century chemists and physicists, such as Liebig or Faraday, averse to the quantitative approach, had regarded atomic explanations as no more than inadequate hypothetical auxiliary constructions. When the Austrian physicist and philosopher Ernst Mach was asked his opinion of the atom he would say brusquely 'Have you ever seen one?' The three decades since 1896 witnessed the paradox that at the same time as this very atom, with the help of the most refined circumstantial evidence known in the history of science, was raised to the rank of a real entity, the new atomic physics was ruthlessly destroying the 1900 conception of the atom and replacing it by completely new views of the mysterious innermost heart of matter.

This innermost heart had already given a hint of its existence in Faraday's electrolysis experiments. But not until the end of the nineteenth century did two natural phenomena set research on a fresh course. Johann Wilhelm Hittorf and after him William Crookes and others had noticed that when electric energy passed through a vacuum tube the cathode emitted 'radiant matter' as Crookes called it. In 1897 J. J. Thomson in Cambridge recognized it as negatively charged particles and they were given the name coined by the Irish physicist G. J. Stoney, 'electrons'. The previous year Henri Becquerel had discovered in his laboratory in the Jardin des Plantes that uranium ore emitted remarkable rays which acted on unexposed photographic plates even through thick padding. A Polish woman chemist living in Paris, Marie Curie, suspected the actual source of the radiation was not in the uranium ore but in a material concealed within the ore and still unknown. She did not rest until, with her husband, she had refined a whole ton of pitchblende with exemplary attention to detail. In 1898 she obtained from it a few milligrams of the new elements radium and polonium, the first of which gave infinitely stronger radiations than pure uranium.

Continued on p. 145

WAVES OVERLAP EACH OTHER

The *Wellenlehre* (theory of waves) by the brothers Ernst Heinrich and Wilhelm Weber (1825) contains a summary of everything which had been discovered from Isaac Newton to Augustin Cauchy about the laws of water, sound and light waves, laws which, curiously enough, coincide closely, though this is only partially true of light waves. This work by the Weber brothers is also full of new observations. What happens inside a wave? How is the rippling effect on the surface of a stream maintained as it is borne down the valley? What reduces the height of a wave as it progresses and what is the law behind this phenomenon? Working as they did in this spirit the two brothers saw in an experiment they made with a round wooden vessel (right) a second of time fused into eternity. The vessel was filled with mercury. In the middle of the radius on the left drops of mercury were allowed to fall in quick succession out of a paper funnel which had been pierced at the bottom. The liquid swirled back in a circle and rose around the small hole made in the surface by the sinking drops of mercury; its particles had been moved out of their stationary position by the earlier drops and tried to find their way back to that position as they oscillated up and down. As the half-waves on the left after eight transverse oscillations touched the edge of the vessel, they ran back again from each point in such a way that the angle of deflection—as with the reflection of light—was the same as the angle of impact. And as with light and sound, the rebounding waves, now with a straight front, moved through the newly created ones and built up with them the most wonderful shapes in accordance with the law of interference. After twenty-four oscillations the front of the half-waves on the right had reached the edge of the vessel; even as they increased, their ends were thrown back from the edge. There arose from the quick interplay of the overlappings curious heart-shaped formations with small pointed triangles, and as the eleventh and twelfth waves rebounded (counting from the right edge of the vessel) there appeared finally an image shaped like a loop. The two scientists drew the conclusion that if the vessel had been a curved mirror, this would be the point where the reflected rays of a light standing where the drops fell would pass each other; and that in a circular concert hall where the orchestra's position was the same as that of the light, the unfortunate person who was sitting where the loop formed would be subjected to a deafening cacophony of sound.

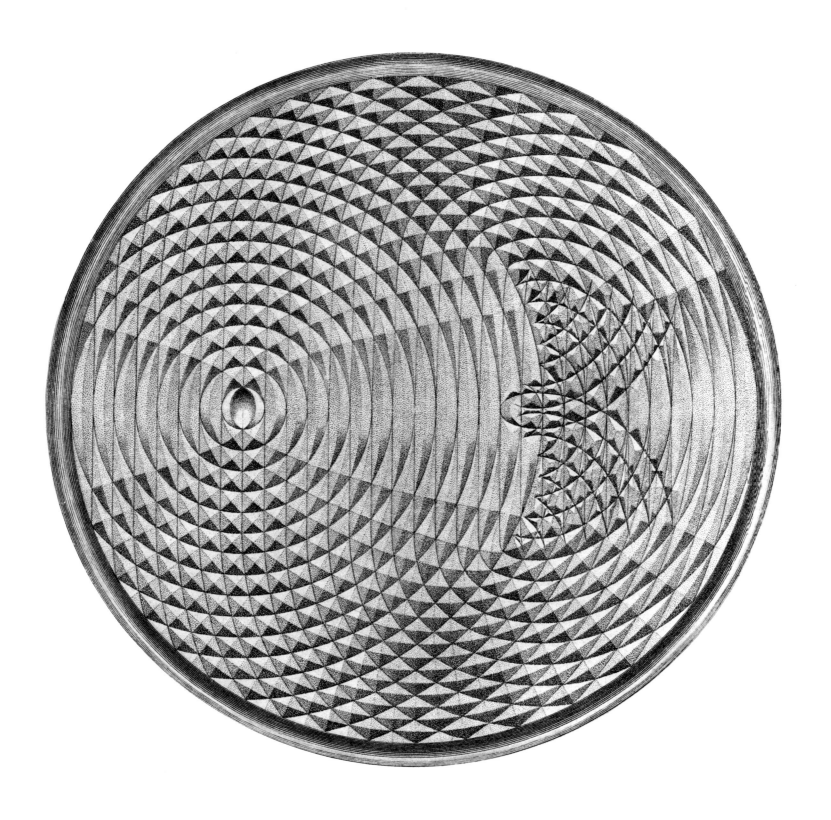

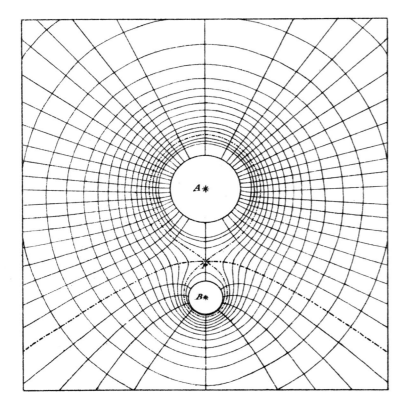

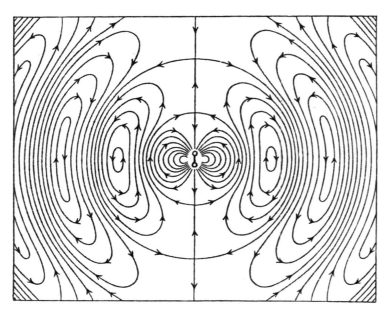

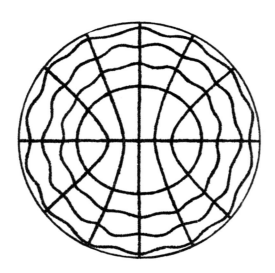

Wave figures with their countless variations appear as a familiar feature in the pioneering works about the physics of rhythmically oscillating liquids and of sound. Moreover since the year 1785 the wide range of figures used in physics has also included the most curious of all illustrations of acoustic waves: the sound figures which the German physicist Ernst Chladni published in hundreds in his *Discoveries about the Theory of Sound* (bottom, left). They showed lateral oscillations in thin circular metal plates, whose vibrations passed through the air as longitudinal pressure waves until they reached the ear, thereby plunging it into a welter of tones and sounds. Chladni scattered sand on these plates and then drew the bow of a violin vertically along them. They began to vibrate and the sand slid from the oscillating to the quiescent part of the plates and collected there in regular line formations.

In the years 1865–71, between a professorship in London and another one in Cambridge, James Clerk Maxwell produced in the seclusion of his Scottish estate a work which Planck reckoned to be one of the 'greatest and most wonderful achievements of the human mind': these researches under the title *Treatise on Electricity and Magnetism,* were imbued with the spirit of Faraday, and they forged the strongest links between the phenomena of magnetism, electricity and light. Maxwell summed up what was common to them in elegant mathematical formulae: starting from the fact that the speed of transmission of electro-magnetic waves as reckoned by him was the same as that of light, he went on to conclude that these waves had a basic relationship with the 'speediest of all messengers', that is, light as Helmholtz had described it. 'Was it a god who wrote these lines?' asked the astonished Ludwig Boltzmann when he saw Maxwell's equations. Mathematical methods were not always adequate—so Maxwell drew in addition almost playfully 'experimental lines on paper', using his pencil to bring his thoughts to bear more closely on partially completed researches, as for instance in the diagram at the top on the left. Two bodies of unequal size, A and B, both charged with positive electric energy, build up around them in the ether, which was assumed to fill space, lines of force and equipotential surfaces forming two distinct systems. In the fine web of electric radiations, wave formations are already evident; in fact Maxwell proved, in theory, that electricity is propagated in wave formations. The proof of this by practical experiment was provided fifteen years later by the young German physicist, Heinrich Hertz.

In Heinrich Hertz's hands a theoretical structure, the electric wave, became something which actually existed and could be produced—an achievement of the greatest practical importance. In order to prove the existence of electric waves, he had to find ways and means of producing oscillations of very high frequency. In his *Investigations into the Propagation of Electric Force* (1887) he gave copious descriptions of the ingenious apparatus by means of which he was able to generate electric waves with an oscillator, demonstrating them in the form of a shower of weak sparks induced in a resonator at the other end of the laboratory, and measuring the substantial wave-lengths. But he went further than this; he was able to provide proof that they were similar to the (shorter) light waves, that they followed the same laws of reflection and were refracted in the prism, that their oscillation was transverse, and that they too, could be polarized. Since then these waves without wires have revolutionised technology. 'In the evening worked hard on electrodynamics, following Maxwell,' wrote Hertz in the middle of May 1884 in his diary. A bare five years later this impassioned believer in direct methods of research had proved by experiment the correctness of Maxwell's fundamental theses. The diagram in the centre shows an oscillator made from two spherical conductors. With each discharge a system of lines of force, each one in the opposite direction to the last, is sent out into space with the speed of light. Intimately connected with these waves are magnetic fields, and together they build up an electro-magnetic field which travels away at a speed of 186,000 miles per second.

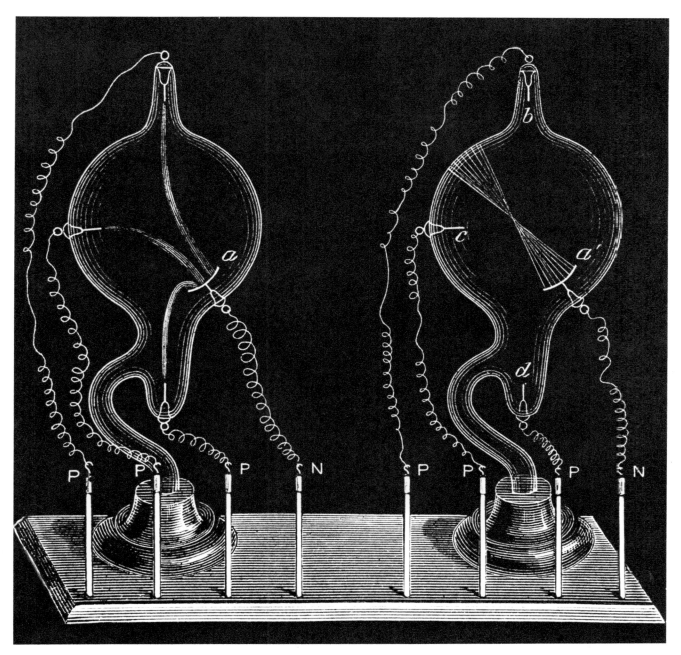

THE PUZZLE OF CATHODE RAYS

About the year 1860 improved glass tubes for electrical experiments in a vacuum appeared on the market; they were produced by the inventive glass-blower (and later honorary doctor of Bonn university) Heinrich Geissler. From then onwards men began to study with renewed interest that violet blue or green glowing light which makes its ghostly appearance when high-voltage current is led through a highly rarefied gas. The most zealous of these experimenters was William Crookes of London, an independent scholar of many talents; a man who was always in the forefront when promising fields of experiment beckoned. In the two tubes shown above there are three platinum wires fused into small glass heads. These three supply positive electricity (P); a fourth, negative, wire carries a cathode in the form of a concave mirror (a). When the voltage is low and the gas in the tube is only slightly rarefied, then the ray from the cathode is attracted to the three anodes, one after the other (left). But when

the voltage is high and the gas is highly rarefied, the cathode rays begin to show their real nature: they are projected in a straight line right through the focal point to the wall of the tube on the opposite side, where they develop a green fluorescence (right). They can be deflected by a magnet held outside against the tube; a little paddle wheel when put in their way begins to turn, as if struck by invisible particles. When a piece of platinum foil is placed at their focal point, this begins to glow, as Hittorf had shown. Were these unknown invisible rays, was this a new kind of electricity? Crookes came to the conclusion that molecules ('radiant matter', later called electrons) were torn away from the cathode by the negative current, carried through the vacuum, causing the most curious manifestations. 'We have reached the frontier region, where matter and force seem to pass into each other. Here, it seems to me, lies ultimate reality.' Crookes's words struck the right note.

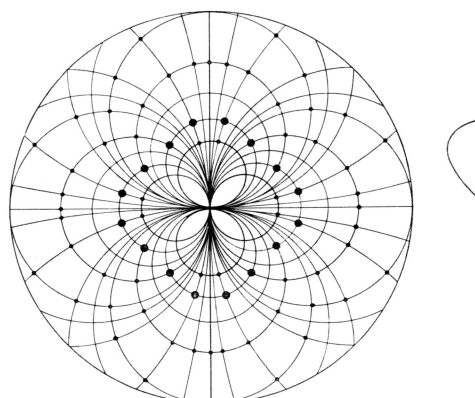

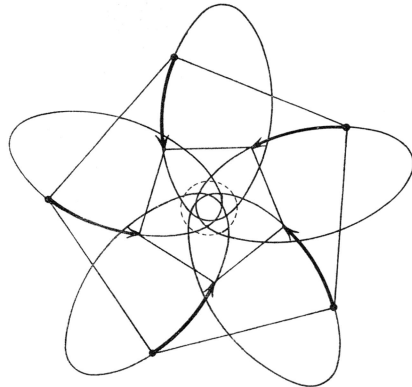

CRYSTAL PHYSICS   THE PATH OF THE ELECTRON

When the rays in a cathode tube leave it through glass or a metal plate, it becomes apparent that in the space beyond it they pass invisibly through some bodies, but are held up by others, and the silhouette of these obstacles (for instance bones in the human body) can be recorded on a screen; these were the X-rays discovered by Röntgen in 1895, the indispensable aids to medicine. Their wave-lengths were so short that they could neither be deflected nor reflected nor diffracted through any kind of grating.

In 1912 the German physicist Max von Laue hit upon an idea which promised to lead to the solution: nature itself was to provide a grating. The atoms in crystals, as Haüy had shown, were arranged in lattice-like configurations. Narrower passages than those between crystal atoms were barely conceivable. So the experimenter passed X-rays, twice collimated, through a crystal on to a photographic plate. Dark points appeared arranged in perfectly symmetrical and often distinctly beautiful patterns. The rays were diffracted behind the narrower passages, and where they were added together by interference, a black spot appeared on the photographic plate. Laue and his assistants succeeded in taking one of the first photographs, as they passed X-rays along one of the fourfold axes of the spherical crystal. A few decades later he had the photograph copied and he joined the points together with zonal curves (above, left). All this could only be explained by the wave-properties of X-rays. Max von Laue had made two sciences the richer: crystallography obtained a new insight into very fine structures which could not be observed by direct means, and physics received data about the nature of short-wave rays. The Englishmen William Henry and William Lawrence Bragg, father and son, improved on this system. They succeeded in showing the wonderful regular patterns in which the atoms or molecules that make up crystals are arranged.

In the entrance halls of every research institute of nuclear physics curious objects hang from the ceiling nowadays: for instance a central sphere made up of small red and white spheres, and round this at a distance of a few feet there is a network of aluminium wires in concentric circles and ellipses; on each wire there is a yellow, green or blue celluloid ball, or several such. They are models of atoms, the symbols of the physics of our time, made to help us conceive the inconceivable. In the early years of the twentieth century the physicists Ernest Rutherford, Niels Bohr and Arnold Sommerfeld contributed the most important calculations to this image of the atom.

Here are some of the lessons to be learned from the model of the atom, converted into words: the atom consists mainly of empty space (in the model [above, right] the space has had to be shown as much too constricted). Strong attractive and centrifugal forces make the electron swirl round the nucleus of the atom so that its own movements cause hard shells to form around it. Sommerfeld's drawing picks out five such movements in the hydrogen atom which can be regarded as so regular that 'pulsating polygons' can be sketched in. In this, the lightest of the atoms, one single negatively charged electron balances the positively charged nucleus. When atoms join together into molecules in chemical experiments, they interchange or share electrons in their outermost shells and so bind each other firmly together. This is the lesson which chemistry learnt from the very theoretical science of atomic physics. Sommerfeld discarded his own atom models and those of others, which oversimplified the problem. How could definite paths be imagined for the electrons if, as Werner Heisenberg had shown in 1927, it was at best only possible to give estimates of the position *and* speed of electrons?

Waves, Rays and Atoms II

Enrico Fermi, an Italian physicist in American service, discovered in 1942 that graphite had both a damping effect on the velocity of neutrons, and also the property to bind electrons together (later cadmium and boron were to be used). The terrible consequences of an uncontrolled release of neutrons from fissioned nuclei of uranium were thus prevented. The inexhaustible energies in the atomic nucleus, when mastered by man, was one day to overshadow all the technological visions cherished by classical physics. The atomic physicists found that in their field of research the strictly deterministic laws of physics as formulated up till then were no longer adequate. The most exact of exact sciences failed to help them in their investigation into that most mysterious object, the atom. Had not de Broglie suggested that in the atomic field matter was to be regarded sometimes as immaterial wave phenomena, sometimes as material particles in space? And the antithetic nature of light? And the minute quanta of energy, which according to Max Planck were released and absorbed intermittently and not in a continuous flow, in this infinitesimal order of things? In contrast to classical physics, with its incontrovertible laws, atomic physicists began to find the truth in contradiction. Was perhaps traditional physics invalid with its insistence on a predictable sequence of events? Its substantial achievements in the macrophysical field have remained valid, even if one has to see in some of its discoveries only approximations; only the ignorant spoke of the collapse of classical physics.

The physics of the atomic nucleus and the forces working within it melt away so easily into abstract mathematics, and it is and remains a rather unprofitable task to reduce quantitatively to protons, neutrons and electrons the colourful and inexhaustible abundance of chemical substances or the functions of the human, animal or plant bodies; or to reduce them to electron configurations which form imaginary shells encircling the atomic nucleus and representing equal energy levels. On the other hand the atomic physicists had developed new conceptions of a physical entity which had never been seen but whose existence had been proved—the 'atom'; they had opened up the most powerful source of energy on earth; they had given a new weapon to medicine in the form of the artificial radioactive isotopes of elements not normally radioactive; and a whole era has been given the name of 'their' atom—an era which is both full of hope and at the same time haunted by the fear of annihilation.

The nature of this 'radioactivity' of the radiant elements was discovered by the British scientists Frederick Soddy and Ernest Rutherford. They saw it as the entirely spontaneous disintegration of the atomic nuclei of certain heavy elements which split into positively charged alpha rays, and negative beta and gamma rays (a powerful type of X-rays), obviously energies from the interior of the atom. After this change, lead remained behind. What the alchemists had never succeeded in doing, namely transforming one element into another, was achieved spontaneously by nature in the radioactive elements. The alpha rays were subsequently shown to be atomic nuclei of the element helium and the beta rays were found to be electrons. And the no longer radiant lead remaining after the fission was complete had now, depending on the type of radioactive element from which it had originated, a different atomic weight!

In 1919 Rutherford succeeded in changing one element into another by artificial means. Through a container filled with nitrogen he sent a stream of alpha-particles from radioactive polonium. Brief flashes on a fluorescent screen at the end of the container signalled the periodical arrival of protons, and analysis of the gas after the experiment showed that some of the nitrogen had been changed to oxygen. What had happened was this. Every so often an alpha-particle (two protons and two neutrons) hit a nitrogen nucleus (seven protons and seven neutrons) fair and square. The result was an unstable nucleus containing nine protons and nine neutrons; one proton shot out, leaving an isotope of oxygen, O_{17}, with eight protons and nine neutrons. This process, taking only a minute fraction of a second, is the forerunner of the giant 'atom-smashers' of today. The already outdated picture of the entirely indivisible and unchanging atom was superseded by a complex structure held together by forces partly electric, partly still more mysterious. It was composed of a heavy nucleus with electrically positive protons and electrically neutral neutrons (discovered in 1932 by James Chadwick), a whirling envelope of almost non-spatial, electrically negative electrons and a series of other, mostly shortlived and variously interacting 'elementary particles'.

In 1938 the German scientists Otto Hahn and Fritz Strassmann succeeded in their experiments in splitting the uranium nucleus by bombarding it with neutrons so as to yield two fragments: crypton and barium nuclei. Great heat was released and in addition two or three equally explosive neutrons were projected, capable of releasing further atomic fission in a chain reaction. It was calculated that the fission of one kilogramme of uranium with negligible loss of mass released energy equivalent to the combustible energy of 2600 tons of coal. A theory advanced in 1906 by Albert Einstein was now borne out in fact: the mass of any given body represented a type of highly concentrated energy. Mass was convertible into energy and vice versa. The origin of the sun's energy was now explained: every second the sun converts millions of tons of its mass into pure energy, which escapes into space as radiation.

BOTANY

Since primeval times anyone familiar with medicinal herbs and poisonous plants has been able to find in the woods the means to cure or to kill. For incalculable ages plants were valued for extrinsic reasons. They were bound up with human life because of their utility and their medicinal properties; they were worshipped as a gift from the gods and are to this very day closely connected with wicked princesses in our children's fairy tales.

In ancient Greece one of Aristotle's pupils, Theophrastus, went beyond the sphere of medicinal and practical questions, undertook the comparison of plants and already distinguished between monocotyledons and dicotyledons, finally establishing an extremely shaky anatomy. Not until the earliest explorers set sail for America and Asia did a few botanists—Valerius Cordus, Leonhard Fuchs and others—also break fresh ground and learn, when confronted with a plant, the method of careful observation and representation. In the centuries immediately succeeding the Middle Ages, voyages of discovery revealed to the naturalists an almost unmanageable abundance of plants and animals hitherto unknown. Now their task was not merely to describe them, but also to classify this abundance systematically according to definite principles. Linnaeus' world inventory was the most famous of these attempts at classification, attempts which are still not concluded. About 1855 the cytologist M. J. Schleiden scoffed at those botanists 'whose entire wisdom is spent in determining and classifying this artificially collected hay'. This ill-natured comment came at a time when the botanists had long since trodden the road of deeper understanding of plant life. By the end of the eighteenth century they had gradually, in a series of permanent achievements, come to discover why the blossom emits colour, the purpose of the leaf and the structure of the fruit. Then there arose for the second time a botany of the unexplored when in the nineteenth century researchers with improved microscopes penetrated the invisible world of cellular structures, thus obliging it to become visible. One hundred and fifty years earlier Malpighi had been thrashed by his university colleagues because they found his microscopic discoveries too unusual for them. From now on the microscope led hosts of naturalists deeper and deeper into a secret world, from plants without blossoms right down to unicellular bacteria, into the marvels of the tissues, the growth of new substance and the operation of heredity.

TWO EGYPTIAN GARDENERS

Long before botany became a science man was making close studies of plants as farmer, gardener and collector of medicinal herbs. Amongst the ancient civilized peoples the Egyptians had a strong liking for flowers and shrubs, although they had to grow their plants under a perpetually cloudless sky on artificially watered lands. Many centuries before the Greeks they produced their stylized flower-pictures; one and a half millennia before Christ the names of herbs with healing properties were recorded for posterity on a long papyrus. A bas-relief from Beni-Hasan (right), is one of the valuable prizes which French archaeologists and draughtsmen brought home from Napoleon's unsuccessful Egyptian campaign of 1798–99, and published in their magnificent series of books, *Description de l'Egypte*.

'I made a canal for this city when Upper Egypt was in distress and saw no water; I had an abundance of the corn that grows in Lower Egypt, when the land was afflicted.' Thus boasted a prince of Middle Egypt about the year 2000 BC; and this is how great building projects came to be carried out—such as irrigation works and granaries—in order to preserve the main source of food, wheat and barley. In the life of ancient Egypt we find again and again traces of this ideal close relationship between man and plant. Whereas nowadays in the land of the Nile cotton provides a favourite material for clothes, in those days it was flax. Men enjoyed the fruits of the date-palm, the vine and the fig-tree; when land was sold in the areas which were short of water trees in carefully tended gardens, so the story goes, were considered to be as valuable as springs of water. Lettuces and pumpkins were planted, so were onions and leeks; and the vegetable oils were in demand as much for the care of the skin as in

the kitchen. The Egyptians believed that the plant would flower even in the gardens and fields of the other world.

In our century an exact study has been made of ancient Egyptian prescriptions; and this has led to the most astonishing disclosures about the skill of those early doctors in the use of drugs from plants. They discovered the soothing soporific effect of the poppy and the henbane; the chemist of today knows that the operative agent in both plants is scopolamine and that this has the power to incapacitate certain parts of the central nervous system. Herodotus recounts that radishes, onions and garlic were distributed in large quantities to the masses of workmen who came to work on the building of the pyramids and were obliged to live in closely packed houses nearby. Today it is known why this was done. The operative agents in these vegetables (the radish seed has raphanin, garlic and onions allicin and alistatin) militate against bacteria which cause epidemics.

The Spanish doctor Nicolas Monardes, who was the first to describe the American tobacco-plant (in 1570), said of Dioscorides that he had won more fame from his book on medicinal plants than if he had been a general who had captured many cities. The man who was thus so enthusiastically described was a Sicilian of Greek origin and as a medical officer in the armies of the Roman emperor Nero he travelled far and wide in the world. The original of his work is lost, but it was copied many times and was also illustrated; until the Renaissance it was regarded as the standard work on the subject of medicinal herbs. There are two points in this picture of a thistle which show that his influence was felt in many lands and over a long period: on the right at the top an Arab user of the book has written an inscription on the parchment in his own characters; a Syrian has done the same at the bottom. This work has evidently come down to us by the same route as so much of the civilization of the ancient world; first it reached the area of Arab culture (where as early as 854 a translation of Dioscorides was available to Arab doctors) then it came to Europe at the time of the medieval scholastics or of the early Renaissance— in 1478 we find it already in print for the first time. The illustrator, probably an Alexandrian of the ninth century, followed the original realistic plant pictures of the Hellenic doctor Crateuas, a contemporary of Dioscorides, and reproduced the entire plant from the blossoms to the roots.

The passing of nearly fifteen hundred years has left its trace on the Byzantine picture (right), which dates back to about 512 and illuminates a Dioscorides manuscript. The learned doctor is entering one of his botanical descriptions into a parchment codex. On the left a painter works at his easel faithfully reproducing a mandragora plant. In front of him stand the colour-shells. The plant is being held out towards him by Epinoia, who symbolizes meditation. The plant shown here, the mandragora, which resembles a human being in shape, has been the subject of popular superstition since time immemorial. It brought into the house of its owner power, luck and good health.

ιστωρφ . . δϊοσκουρι . .

149

Once in the time of Charlemagne, who is shown below, the plague was raging and engulfing mankind. The emperor was weighed down with deep sorrow. One night an angel appeared to him in a dream. He told the monarch to shoot an arrow into the air; the herb on which it fell would provide deliverance for the people. On the next day the emperor's arrow pierced a thistle-like plant; it was the carline thistle (*Carlina acaulis*). It was given to the sick and the disease began to decline. This was the story still being told by the herbalists around Modena in the sixteenth century, and it was at this time that the herb was given the name Carline in memory of the emperor. The story inspired a German artist living in Italy to record it in an illuminated botanical manuscript which is now in Munich. We see here the spirit of medieval botany: an emperor kneels before a healing plant which is being brought down to him from heaven. The picture of the plant is completely true to nature, like those hedge roses which the stonemasons carved in the arched doorways of Gothic cathedrals. But it is at the same time a creation of God, as the dog roses were, even a means of Grace, as the story of the miraculous thistle shows.

Right: There was one writer of the ancient world whose tales of wonder enriched medieval science as no others did; he said of himself that he regretted ever having to take a walk because it kept him away from writing or copying from countless works of knowledge; this was Pliny the Elder (*see* p. 64), the most well-read though not the most discriminating of all Romans. From his *Natural History* a picture of nature more peaceful than any painted by the imagination of man before the Christian era found its way into the medieval tradition: the Isles of the Blest, somewhere in the warm seas of the south where man, animals and plants live in harmony, as if in paradise. Blossoming trees pour forth sweet scents, the earth proffers its fruits, the sky sends down cooling breezes. But sailors who had once landed on the islands and later looked for them again could never find them. (Enlarged copy of a miniature by the so-called Maître de Charles d'Angoulême.)

Carlina

Since ancient times and throughout the Middle Ages to the modern era we find conceptions about the life of the plant which have grown in man's imagination rather than in the flower beds of botanical gardens. It was in the Middle Ages that they flourished most profusely, often enhanced by genuine observations of nature. The extent to which the seventeenth century also, with its passionate quest after curiosities, took pleasure in such things is shown in a book by Claude Duret published in Paris in 1605: *The astounding history of the wonderful... plants and herbs in nature.* In this book there is amongst other things a story about trees which give birth to animals; this was told particularly of those trees on the distant Orkney Isles which Aeneas Sylvius, the alchemist Michael Maier and others described. As we can see (above, left) such a tree has large buds like tulips or mussels. When these open, a gosling slips out, falls plump into the water (for the Creator in his wisdom caused the tree to grow on the seashore) and swims happily away.

This same Duret tells of a tree on the island of Cimbubon near Borneo which he read about in Pigafetta's description of Magellan's circumnavigation of the world. The leaves of this tree have four short legs sprouting from them, two on the right and two on the left. The leaves fall to the ground and when anyone touches them with a stick, they scuttle off—perhaps because a beetle is crawling beneath them (above, right).

From a different source comes this pumpkin floating securely like a giant cork on a stormy sea (above, centre). It belongs to that large group of flowers, fruit and trees which men regarded as having some special significance for their own lives, and so accorded the rank of emblems or symbols. This is why the clumsy pumpkin is given a place beside the pure lily, the humble daisy and other flowers in the voluminous book *Mundus symbolicus* (1687) by the Italian Jesuit father Filippo Picinelli. The pumpkin represents a figure of courage, which is washed and purified by storm and rain but is not destroyed.

This is certainly not botany in the scientific sense; it is rather that imaginative popular plant lore which until the end of the Middle Ages and often far beyond that date was closely linked with the more practical botany of the medicinal herbs. Just as physics kept for a long time its magnetic mountain and zoology its mythical bird, the phoenix, so also botany had its goose-breeding trees. It is quite clear why man developed such concepts: in their way they brought his mind into closer touch with the world of nature.

Before botany could become an exact science, the ancient bridges which had brought all this romantic fantasy into the plant world had to be broken down. A new start had to be made at the point where the observations of nature as found in the classical herb-books had ceased and where the only Greek botanist of importance, Aristotle's pupil Theophrastus, had begun: with systematic, comparative descriptions of the structure of all plants. The titles of some German herbals of the sixteenth century and particularly the illustrations in them emphasize this new trend.

It was no accident that the men who created this much more realistic kind of botany were usually doctors of various nationalities. Otto Brunfels called his herb-book which appeared in 1530, *Herbarum vivae icones;* what was new in this was the 'living images,' the woodcuts by Dürer's pupil, Hans Weiditz. Whilst the text is taken over from Greek and Arab authors and from folklore, the plants come immediately to life in the pictures which reproduce them faithfully, showing them exactly as they are. This is the case, for instance, with the freshly drawn white hellebore (bottom) with its strong rootstock and subsidiary roots containing the medicinal agents; this plant has large flowers which bloom in winter and have thus given it the name of Christmas rose, and it has leaves with sharp saw-like edges towards the point.

The fuchsia we have in our gardens bears the name of another medical botanist of that time, the Tübingen professor of medicine, Leonhart Fuchs. His *Historia stirpium* (1542) contains illustrations of 400 native and 100 foreign plants and it soon became available to the layman in a much sought-after German edition known as the *Neues Kräuterbuch* (new herb-book). The aim of this book, says the publisher in the foreword, is 'that the ordinary man will take the trouble from time to time to plant and cultivate herbs in his garden and so the knowledge of herbs will grow daily throughout Germany and never be forgotten'. Fuchs went much further than Brunfels. The picture of the cuckoo-pint *(Arum maculatum;* top, right), taken from the *Neues Kräuterbuch,* is intended to help the doctor or chemist to recognize with certainty an important poison-bearing plant. It is still botany seen with the eye of an experienced doctor, who concerns himself above all with the pharmacological value of the plant. But he also goes beyond the consideration of its utility and studies the structure of the plant independently and with all his powers of observation. Compared with the Christmas rose below it, this plant seems to have been deliberately stylized. He goes further still, and gives us a 'biography of the plant'. He shows in his picture the many changes which a plant undergoes at its blossoming time and in autumn, when the fruits look 'like beautiful corals' (left). Just as the anatomists of that time dissected the human body, so here the plant is opened up (right). At the bottom of the bud are the female pistils, above them the male stamens and at the top the rim of hairs which cuts off the retreat of insects. There is no mention in the text of the function of these parts; similarly Fuchs never succeeds in defining clearly in his register of botanical terms what, say, a pappus or a stamen is. But the picture is more advanced than the text. Later generations were to measure with a thermometer the temperature in the interior of the involucre; they were to discover that this is a kind of warm room which entices the insects in for shelter overnight; that the insects unload the pollen they bring with them on to the stigmata there; and that later, when the way out upwards is again opened up for them, they take with them new pollen from the anthers which break open after pollination only.

The miraculous botany of fantasy gradually receded as the new science disclosed the marvels of each plant as it really was.

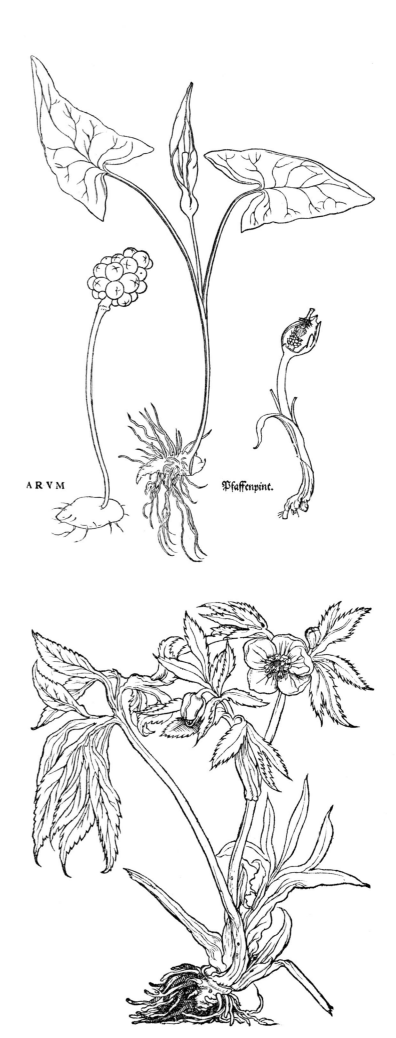

ARVM   Pfaffenpint.

The English country parson Stephen Hales was the first great experimenter amongst the botanists. 'He made the plants themselves talk,' said Julius Sachs. With a very modest equipment of espaliers, glass tubes and pigs' bladders, he sought in particular to investigate the nutrition mechanism in the plant. By his sunflower experiment (left) he made considerable advances into new fields. He covered a flowerpot with a round plate of sheet lead; even the opening *l* at the bottom was shut off. Through the little tube *d* the soil received air, and it obtained water from the tube *g* which could be closed when necessary with a plug. For five weeks every morning and evening he weighed exactly the amount of water taken in by the roots, and also the amount evaporated by the leaves, which he had wrapped in pigs' bladders. He established that there had been a considerable transpiration through the plant. Since Böhm's experiments (1893) we know that the suction effect of the evaporation process is the main reason why the water rises from the root to the bud. Hales then cut the stalk close above the lead plate and allowed the plant to dry. Even in its dried-up state the plant weighed much more than when it was first planted in the pot, on the other hand the weight of the earth in the pot had not decreased—therefore the sunflower could not have drawn its increase in substance out of the soil or at least not solely from the soil. At that time nothing was known about the chemical composition of the air. So the bold experimenter came to a full stop when just on the threshold of discovering the secret of how plants breathe.

Hales wanted to find out more about the puzzling movements of the saps which carried the nutrition. He put a branch of an apple-tree which he had severed both at the top and at the bottom upside down in a jar of water (above, right); the other end was cemented and bound with a pig's bladder. The water was immediately sucked from *b* to *x* and distributed into the branches. Even when he cut a root off from its nutrition in the earth and exposed it, a branch sprouted (left); this proved that even in the root the saps could flow in the opposite direction to the natural one.

In the very dry August of 1723, Stephen Hales dug a hole close to the foot of a plum-tree (right). He had decided to measure the suction force of the roots. For this purpose he cut one of the bared roots through at *i* and put the end of the root into a glass cylinder. When he had filled this with water, he closed it with an airtight seal round the root at the top with strips of sheepskin and wet pigs' bladders, then he painted these over with a coat of beeswax and turpentine and bound them with string. Into the lower end he inserted a glass tube *dz* which also had an airtight seal. He turned the lower end of this upwards whilst he filled it with water, then held his thumb over it and plunged it quickly into a vessel of mercury which stood on the floor of the hole. To his astonishment the roots sucked the water from the tube and the glass cylinder with such force that the mercury went up after it to point *z* in six minutes. Further experiments showed him that the capillary operation of the narrow ducts in the plant overcame the laws of gravity. With the same ingenious apparatus Hales measured the suction force which operated in the opposite direction at the end of a branch (above, centre). A long time passed before botanists carried further what the industrious parson had discovered in those summer days in his garden.

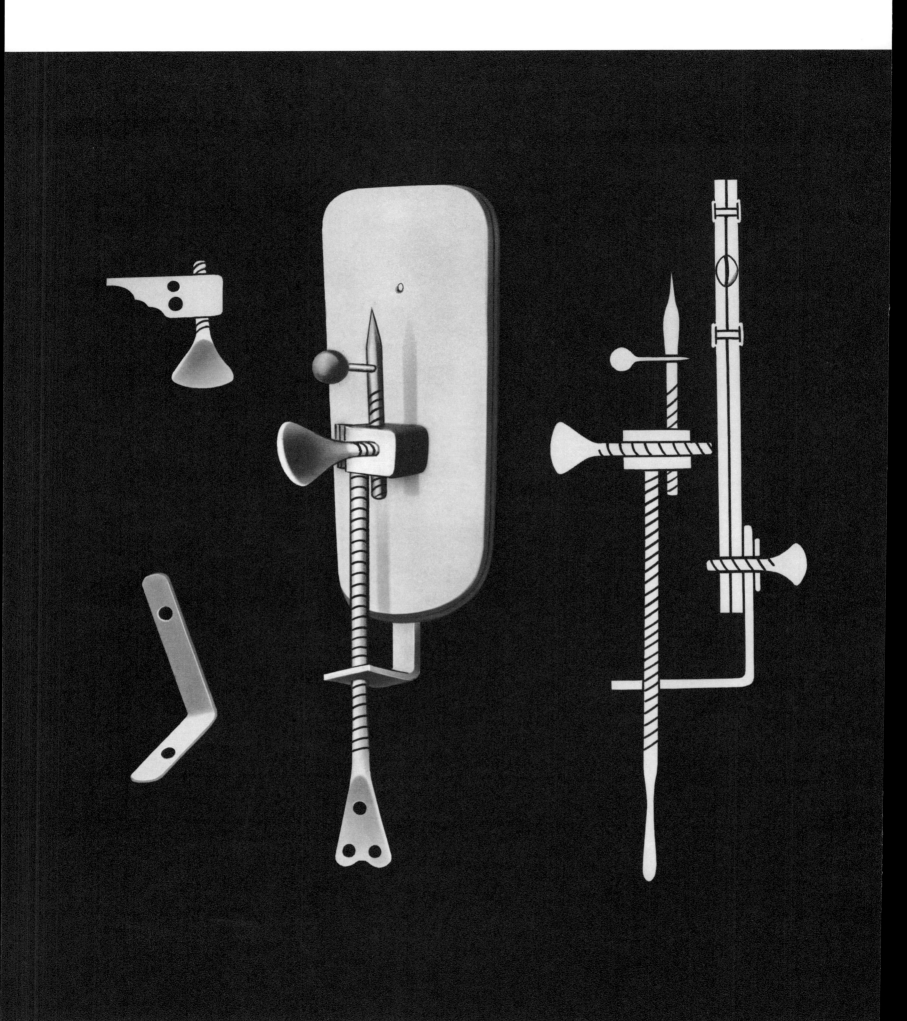

At the beginning of the seventeenth century the first micro-scopes composed of an object lens and an eyepiece appeared in Holland and almost at exactly the same time in Italy. Before that there had been the magnifying glass, which was known in Italy about the year 1300. Three men of the same generation, Marcello Malpighi, Robert Hooke and Nehemiah Grew, using simple lenses, discovered very small structures in plants and animals—this was a kind of anatomy which had never been seen before; the magnify-ing lens has been continually providing new surprises and decisively altering the image of creation in men's minds. A fourth, the Dutchman van Leeuwenhoek, as he looked through his minute one-lens microscopes, was the very first man to see forms of life of which nobody had ever thought even in a dream: bacteria and protozoa of the most varied kinds. They entered history with the not very scientific name of 'little animals', since the discoverer was no scholar, but a simple draper at Delft. In every free hour he examined with his in-satiable curiosity everything which his many home-made, almost spherical, lenses enabled him to see. They were the most powerful lenses of his time; the best magnified 160 times (according to other estimates 250 times) in the narrow-est field of view. He even wanted to examine a quantity of exploding gunpowder through the microscope he had built himself. Encouraged by the doctor, Regnier de Graaf, he described some of his observations in 1673 in a letter to the Royal Society. It was only at his death in the year 1723 that this correspondence ceased; several of the letters, published in the *Philosophical Transactions,* became topics of the day in the scientific world. In this way protozoa were described for the first time in 1664, bacteria in 1676, spermatozoa in 1677, together with countless other structures from the microscopic realm of botany, crystallography, entomology and so on. Leeuwenhoek's strong point was his power of observation, not the scientific treatment of his subject. As time went on he himself became a subject for scrutiny by sightseers. Even the Czar, Peter the Great, climbed the stairs to his workroom in 1698 and looked through one of those finger-length instruments into a world of unexplained forms of life. The picture opposite gives a head-on view of the edge of the two brass or silver plates (right), between which, at the top, the single bi-convex lens was inserted. The object to be examined was placed on a metal point and pushed into the focal point of the lens.

The pictures on the right show enlarged reproductions of some of Leeuwenhoek's discoveries. Top, a find in human blood, which did not by any means consist only of liquid; disk-shaped blood corpuscles 'one hundred of which arranged close together would have about the width of a grain of sand'. Below this are bacteria (today called *Leptothrix bucca-lis),* little sticks of different lengths, taken with a pin from cracks in the teeth of 'two females who to my certain know-ledge clean their teeth every day'. Also a freshwater polyp *(Hydra)* about 5 millimetres long with the tentacles on the left which draw in food. On its underside a much smaller animal of the same type seems to be sitting, whilst at the top a structure with a small 'horn' is slowly growing out of it. After studying this for several hours the astonished Leeuwen-hoek saw the lower animal free itself whilst the upper structure had already grown four 'horns', that is tentacles, which it was moving. The draper of Delft was thus the first witness of a sexless form of reproduction: gemmiparity. At the bottom are camphor crystals.

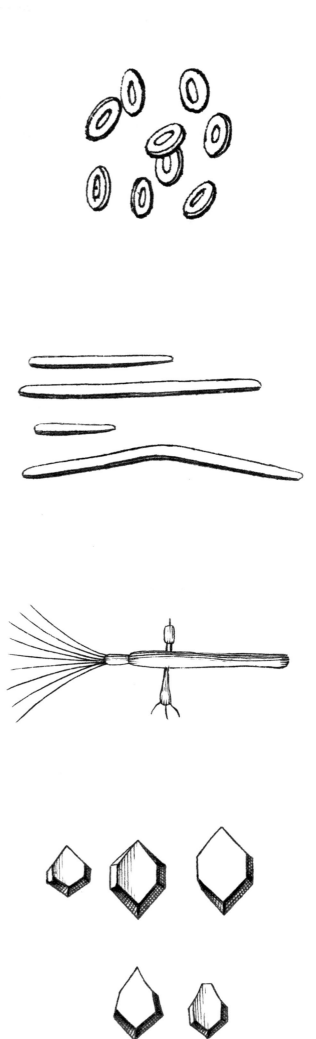

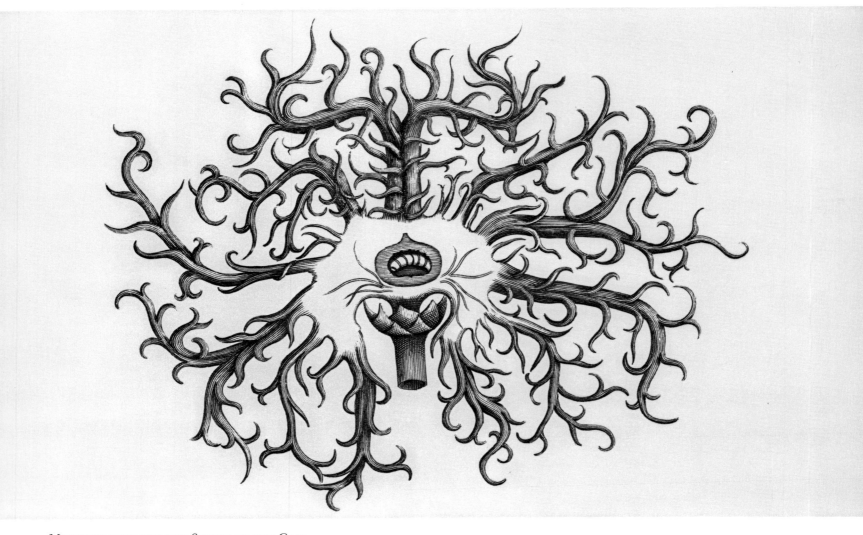

MALPIGHI DISCLOSES THE SECRET OF THE GALL

'Nature has so arranged things that not only the higher animals should provide food for each other... but that also insects inherit in the plants a fertile breeding place, and nature has endowed them with such ingenuity that they force the plants to provide the uterus and, so to speak, the nourishing breasts for the eggs they lay on them. This service provided by the plants results in their own disfigurement in that they often develop a disease in the form of a swelling to which we like to give the name 'galls'. In these words Marcello Malpighi in his *Anatomy of plants* (1675 to 1679) dealt a death-blow to a widely held superstition, according to which galls appeared as a result of witchcraft on the leaves of oaks and other trees; or they were thought to be structures which a plant produced like buds or fruits. His drawing (above) shows that the gall (in this case the fruit-gall *Cynips caput-medusae* on the acorn of a Mediterranean oak: *Quercus pubescens*) is the well protected feeding chamber of a parasitical insect larva; the long ovipositor of the gall wasp has sunk the egg, into the tissue of the host plant.

When Malpighi published this finding, he had the full benefit of the experience he had gained as one of the earliest microscopists. In his view wars and political convulsions did less damage to science than the false methods used by his contemporaries as they followed word for word the tenets of Galenic and Arabic medicine. *His* method was different: it was to go deeply into nature, and discover the smallest organs and structures, which had never been seen by the human eye, of beings which were well known. He did this on a broad basis with the help of the one-lens microscope. As doctor and lecturer in medicine at Pisa and Bologna he turned his attention first to what had never been seen before in the bodies of men and animals and discovered amongst other things the capillary plexus of the lungs, traced the beginnings of life in the animal embryo and demonstrated the inner structure of insects; finally he set forth in his comprehensive plant anatomy what his 'reason, situated as it was in a sick body, had discovered as consolation for the soul'. He examined roots, bark, branches, buds

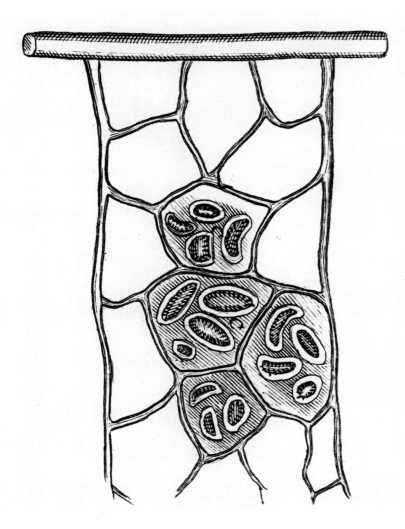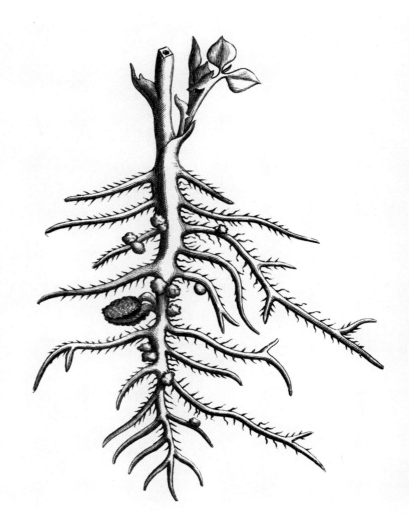

MALPIGHI DISCOVERS BREATHING OPENINGS (STOMATA) AND ROOT-NODULES

and leaves with the microscope; even if his conclusions were sometimes not quite correct in this entirely new realm, his eye never erred. From time to time he made records of his ingenious experiments in bold drawings; two of these are reproduced here (above).

It was not until the nineteenth century that the minute openings which are shown in the left-hand picture were recognized as stomata. Malpighi was the first naturalist to see them on the underside of an oleander leaf, and he incorporated them into his sketch of the network of very fine veins which run through it. (*See* p. 177 for later discoveries on the respiratory organs of plants.)

He drew whole sheets of pictures to record the first days in the life of a plant. The other picture (above, right) shows roots (enlarged) of a thirty-day-old bean-plant. Side roots with fine hairs on them have developed; at one point he saw a pair of curled gold-yellow leaves growing out of the root. But what was the meaning of the nodules which he found on the roots of leguminous plants? He was inclined

to take them for galls. Late in the nineteenth century the chemist Marcellin Berthelot showed that Malpighi, without knowing it, had detected a most astonishing instance of symbiosis. There are earth bacteria which have the capacity to fix the nitrogen from the air in the loose soil. They establish themselves in the cells of the root-bark of leguminous plants. The root-nodules are a kind of cell community developing from host cells which have been induced to propagate. If the bacteria inside die, the nitrogen is acquired by the host; it is in this way that the cultivation of leguminous plants enriches the soil with nitrogen.

Malpighi and other microscopists of his time opened up new and highly fruitful avenues of research. Some of Malpighi's university colleagues lampooned as ridiculous and useless the microscopic observations made by this impassioned experimenter and one day forced their way into his house in masks with a few accomplices and set about him; evidently they did not possess quite the right degree of historical instinct.

LINNAEUS' PUPIL SOLANDER EXPLORES THE SOUTH-SEA ISLAND HUAHEINA

In the centuries since the discovery of America the number of unknown plants requiring description and classification increased like an avalanche. Amongst the botanists who sailed forth about 1750 on explorations, there were many pupils from the school of the Swedish natural scientist Carl von Linné (Linnaeus) in Uppsala. These men were such enthusiasts that they seemed ready to brave all dangers in the interests of their science. Solander accompanied Cook on his first circumnavigation of the world, during which the botanists were able to study tropical country like that pictured above: this is the Pacific island Huaheina with the enormous screw-pine which stands on the left in front of a 'House of God'. On the stand are sacrificial gifts. Thunberg explored South Africa and Japan, Osbeck China; Hasselquist perished in Asia Minor, Löffling in Venezuela—their master published their reports after they had died.

Linnaeus, an inspiring lecturer, passionately devoted to his science, also travelled himself, though only through parts of his native Sweden which had not yet been opened up to the botanist. His richest prize was the one he brought back in 1732 from the infertile north of Lapland at the age of twenty-five. He had a picture of himself incorporated in a report on his travels (opposite); he is dressed as a Laplander, with the midnight sun forming its circle over the rocky mountains whilst nearby his favourite plant, the twinflower, is blossoming; he gave it the name *Linnaea borealis*.

As early as 1736 this young enthusiast was classifying his discoveries in his *Flora lapponica* according to his own ingenious system which was soon to be accepted throughout the world (*see* p. 162). 'I thought everything out by my twenty-eighth year,' he exclaimed on one occasion. He early decided what his life's task was to be: he wanted to take stock of all the plants, animals and minerals in the world and classify them by a system which would remain valid for all time. Everything served this one purpose—his own expeditions, his studies in botanical gardens in Holland, France and England, his library, his pupils' tours throughout the world, his botanical garden in Uppsala and his herbarium: a world-wide collection which by his death had run to 15,000 specimens. This is how he described his life as he looked back on it: 'God allowed him to peep into his secret council chamber. God granted him the favour of seeing more of the works he created than any mortal before him, no one before him classified all the creations of nature with such exactitude, no one before him sent out his pupils into so many parts of the world...' His approach seems to have changed since the days when he went in search of the simple *Linnaea borealis*.

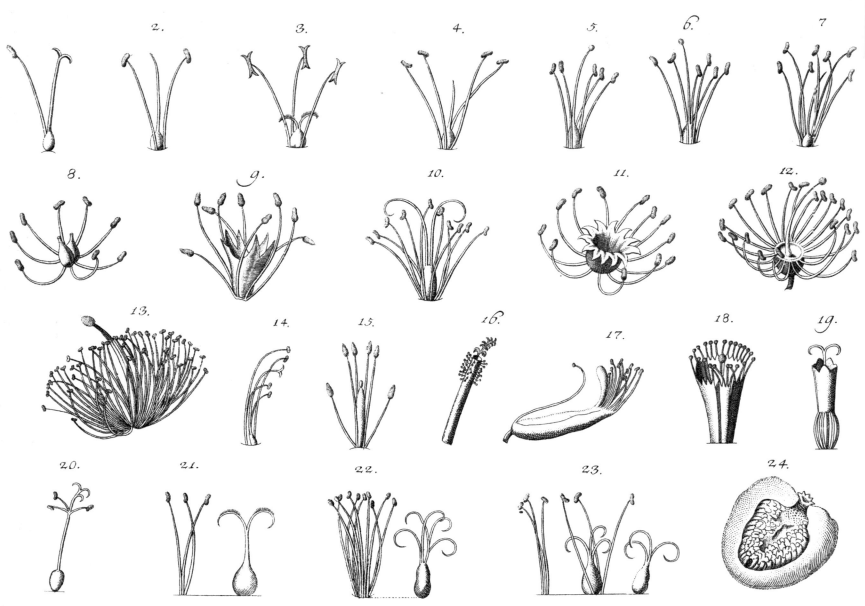

THE TWENTY-FOUR CLASSES OF LINNAEUS' SYSTEM

Linnaeus' *Systema naturae,* which appeared in its first edition in 1735, begins with the stars, proceeds to the earth, taking in the four elements on the way, and builds up the realms of minerals, animals and plants arranged in classes, orders, genera and species. In the last edition he described 8,500 plants and 4,236 animals. He was imbued with certainty that God had from the beginning created all species constant and invariable and that the greatest human task was to recognize everywhere the clearly ordered plan of creation.

Classification means sub-division and designation. Linnaeus inspired by Tournefort's pupil, Sébastien Vaillant, classified the flowering plants according to the number and structural detail of the stamens and pistils. In one class—the 24th—he listed the plants with hidden reproductive organs. The other twenty-three were divided into three (21–23) which had separate male and female flowers, and twenty with hybrid flowers; these twenty classes were subdivided into those with isolated stamens (1–15), and the others (16–20) in which the stamens and pistils grew together. Linnaeus then further subdivided the classes with isolated stamens accord-

ing to whether these were of equal (1–13) or unequal (14, 15) length; finally, the first thirteen groups were subdivided according to the number and position of the stamens. This system took no account of the natural affinities of plants, but it provided a sure method—which is today still workable—of classifying a plant. He regarded the creation of a natural system as his final goal, but he was able only to provide sketches for this.

Linnaeus also introduced a clear binominal nomenclature for all living things and for this he went back to the attempts made by Caspar Bauhin and others: a Latin double-name gave the genus and the species. 'I regard it as a religious duty to honour the memory of a botanist with the name of a genus.' This is how the exquisite plant (opposite) which was brought over from North America, received the name *Rudbeckia laciniata,* in honour of Linnaeus' master, Olof Rudbeck the younger. The picture, painted by Nicolas Robert (the inscription indicates that it originates from before Linnaeus' time) comes from the collections of the Jardin des Plantes in Paris (*see* p. 167).

Corona Solis, foliis amplioribus laciniatis. Inst. rei Herb. 490

N. Rob. p.

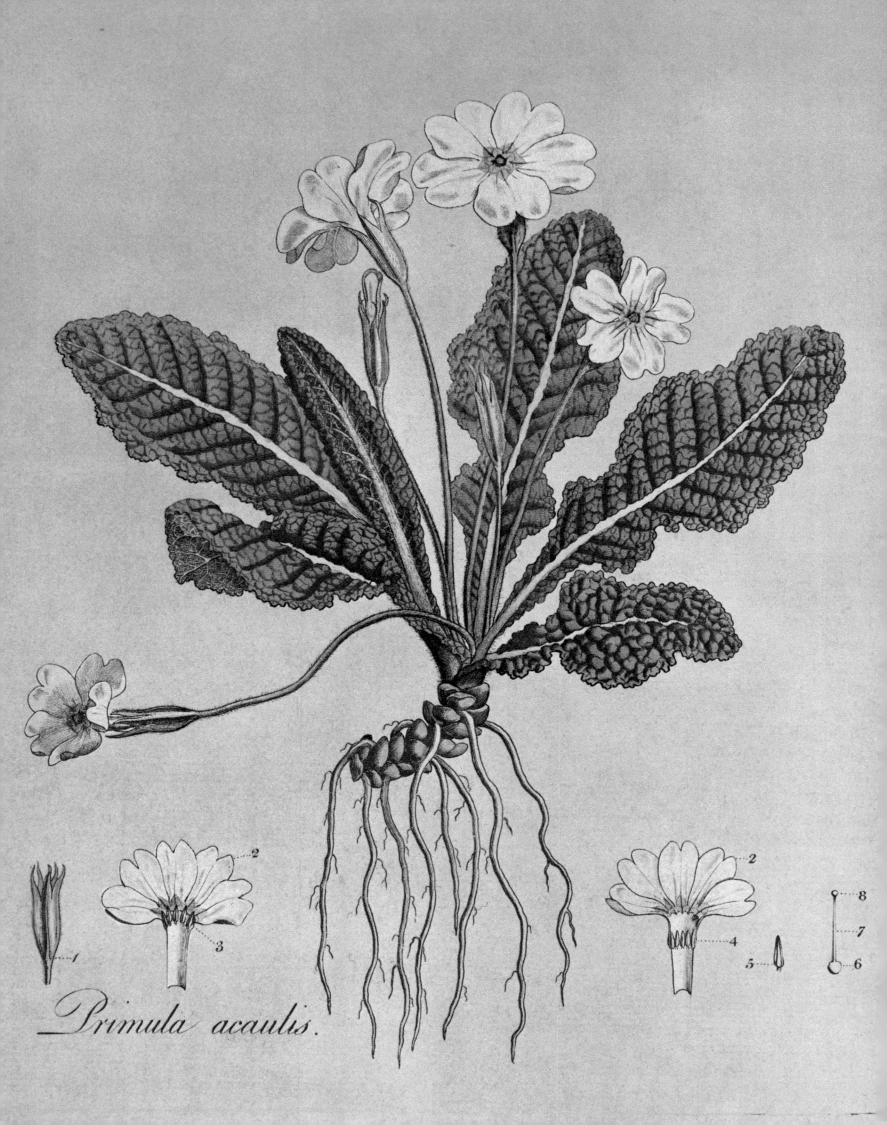

Primula acaulis.

THE APOTHECARIES' GARDEN IN CHELSEA

On preceding pages: The creation of botanical gardens was inspired by that scientific curiosity which wishes to see and touch the plants and not merely to meet them in books. Originally they served the medical profession. Later their aspect changed as naturalists strove after an ideal of universality: they were to provide the classifier with a small-scale reproduction of the vast universal plant realm. One example was the Jardin du Roi in Paris, later called the Jardin des Plantes. The painter Jean-Baptiste Hilair has caught something of the magic of these gardens in the partial view of them he painted in 1794. The exotic plants are accommodated in two tall greenhouses—on one can be seen the twin furnace that supplies the warmth needed to shield them from the Paris winter. In the beds, which are filled mainly with herbaceous plants, there stands a gay little cluster of name tabs, witnesses of those famous methodical botanists who established here their artificial or natural systems of classification. The plant families of today correspond broadly to the arrangements which Antoine Laurent de Jussieu conceived in 1789. Two botanists are deep in a learned discussion. It is no coincidence that Hilair shows one of his colleagues from the famous School of Illustrators at the Jardin des Plantes sketching in the garden (*see* p. 217).

Above: The Apothecaries' Garden (Chelsea Physic Garden) was founded in London in 1673. In the eighteenth century it was much enlarged under various energetic benefactors (later a statue of one of them, Sir Hans Sloane, was erected in it). The patrons, who are seen here bending over their charges, are humorously portrayed by an artist of a later age. A lasting memorial to their activity, which was made possible by the generosity of the one-time apothecary William Curtis, was the work, magnificently illustrated with 435 plates by various artists, *Flora Londinensis* (1777–87).
The picture of a primrose (opposite) shows how faithfully plants were depicted in the spirit of Linnaeus with views from every angle right down to the roots. It was not overlooked that in some flowers the stamens were situated above (3) the stigma (8), in others below (4). Charles Darwin was the first to find an explanation for this, when about the year 1860 he studied in his experimental garden how hybrid flowering plants avoided self-pollination, a process which would clearly have been unfavourable to the continuation of the species. This ingenious arrangement which occurs in the so-called dimorphous plants enables them to hinder bees and other insects from dusting the stigma with pollen from the same plant.

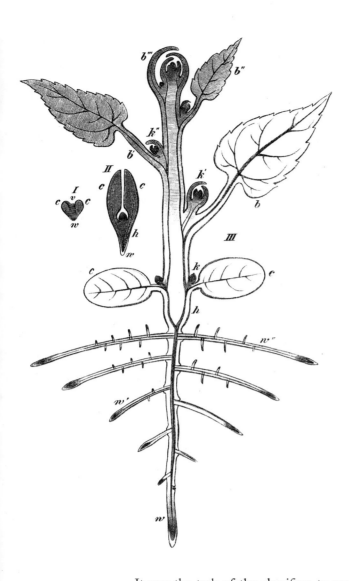

It was the task of the classifiers to make a clear differentiation between species and genera according to outward characteristics. Some natural scientists of the late eighteenth century (among their predecessors are Grew and C.F. Wolff) were deeply conscious of the inadequacy of this process. They felt that it had quite lost sight of the cardinal aim of research—of laws applicable to plants of every species and genus. The structural plan for plants drawn up by Linnaeus was not the only one in nature; there were other concepts, for instance that of great ideal archetypes which became manifest, in many metamorphoses, in the shapes of individual living things. The idea of the prototype plant, as Goethe portrayed it in 1790 *(Attempt to Explain the Metamorphosis of Plants)*, shows the value of this conception. What was the fundamental form of the plant, hidden away amongst the confusing miscellany of individual types, the fundamental form to which everything could be traced back as if it were a 'secret law or a sacred mystery'? Goethe summed it up in the concept 'leaf': 'The same organ which opens itself out as a leaf on the stem and transforms itself into all kinds of shapes, contracts in the calyx, expands again as the leaf of the flower, contracts in the reproductive organs in order to expand again for the last time in the form of fruit.' Goethe never recorded in pictorial form this concept of the prototype plant in which 'everything was leaf' but some botanists of a later age who favoured it did so in the interests of morphology, the science of the form of living creatures. Amongst the sketches inspired by Goethe is the one reproduced above (from Julius Sachs'

Lectures on Plant Physiology, 1882). It is the structural plan of the dicotyledonous plants with roots, axis of shoots and leaves. It is leaf, always leaf, which forms the appendicular organs of the axis; it is leaf which again appears, 'metamorphosed' according to its function, above the roots as a two-part cotyledon (*cc*), as bud in the axil (*k*), as foliage expanded to become the breathing organ, and above, serving the fruit as it forms, as calyx, corolla, stamen and carpophyll. The science of the structure of living things was represented in France by Etienne Geoffroy Saint-Hilaire; Geneva had Augustin-Pyramus de Candolle, and in England Richard Owen (*see* p. 215) applied this science ingeniously to the variety of forms in the animal realm, as Goethe had already done. Today it has become available in a new form to young people through the pictures of biological structures in schoolbooks and is thus adding to their store of knowledge.

Right: WILLIAM WITHERING STUDYING A FOXGLOVE PLANT

Five years before the *Metamorphosis of Plants* a man of the same generation as Goethe, the English doctor Withering, published a *Report on the Foxglove.* His medical botany too was informed by the spirit of idealism of the day. Withering's line was not that of the enlightened rationalists; he did serious research into the experiences of the poorer people with medicinal woodland plants. He thus became the first scientific discoverer of the healing properties of the digitalis plant. In the year 1775 he heard that an old woman herbalist in Shropshire had with the help of a medicine of mixed herbs cured dropsy in cases which had long been given up as hopeless by the doctors. The effective, that is to say purging, diuretic and emetic ingredient in these mixtures was the poison of the foxglove plant. Withering set up a daily surgery for the poor. 'These surgery hours gave me the opportunity to put into practice many ideas, for the number of poor people who came to see me for advice reached two to three thousand a year.' Many of them had all the symptoms of dropsy—they were gasping for breath, their faces were sunken, and their bodies were badly swollen. Withering tested with these patients the efficacy of popular medicine. Were roots, leaves, flowers or fruit an effective cure? He achieved cures with leaves which he collected at blossoming time and dried out after removing the midribs. Quacks sometimes made disgraceful mistakes in dosage. Withering prescribed very small doses, which he dissolved in warm water. He cured countless people not only of dropsy, but also at the same time of the heart condition which caused it. In his footsteps came chemistry which in the nineteenth century isolated just those substances in the plant which were efficacious; they were very difficult to extract. Our picture is a twentieth-century document in memory of this great physician.

Research into Cells

JOSEPH DALTON HOOKER EXPLORES THE PLANT
LIFE OF THE HIMALAYA

The English botanist Hooker travelled halfway
across the earth searching out the plants in their
home countries. At twenty-five years of age he
went to the Antarctic, that is, to the borders of
the area beyond which no life exists, to study the
plants there; in 1847–51 he crossed tropical
India, discovering countless new species on the
way, and went on through the mountainous region
of the Himalaya—perhaps it was not quite such
a romantic journey as the artist saw it in this
picture, drawn in the style of his time. Hooker
investigated how plants lived in the Rocky Mountains, in the Atlas Mountains and in the Le-
banon. Like his expeditions, which made him the
most travelled botanist of the century, his
writings too tend to be all-embracing; 1865
to 1885 he was director of Kew Gardens, where
the plants from the greatest empire in the world
were gathered together, and during this period
he issued the *Index Kewensis,* a list of 375,000
plant-names known at that time (the list has been
issued frequently since then in one new edition
after another), and with George Bentham he
undertook the task of showing in the *Genera
plantarum* all known genera. This was the spirit
of a classifier and geographer of plants, who no
longer believed like Linnaeus in the immutability
of the species, but rather like Darwin in their
slow continuous evolution. The whole world had
become for the expansionist Europe of that time
not only a battle-ground for power politics, but
also a field for the new unlimited study of plants
and animals.

Matthias Jacob Schleiden, a solicitor who gave up his career and
devoted himself passionately to the study of medicine and botany,
once said that for botany the period from Malpighi to the beginning
of the nineteenth century had been 'the most sterile desert'. He
overlooked the achievements of the systematists and above all the
fact that between 1750 and 1800 a more refined physiological
approach had revealed the ingenious functions of blossom, leaf and
fruit (*see* pp. 174–79). The reason for such vehemence is the fanati-
cism of a man who from 1830 onwards collaborated in a swiftly
emerging new science, cell research. It perceived in the cells of
plants and animals the basic structure of organic nature in which
lay concealed the ultimate secret of life. It was a science which,
according to Schleiden, 'will be the sole and richest source of new
discoveries and will remain so for many years'. Even now cell research does in fact bring to light almost daily fresh discoveries about
the working structure of living things.

This was a field of research in which feverish activity prevailed at
Schleiden's period, powerfully aided by G.B. Amici's improved
achromatic microscopes. Scientists took over the legacy of observations made by the seventeenth-century microscopists, the greater
part of which were unexplained. They had been the first to see plant
cells with their simple instruments. Cork cells had reminded the
physicist Robert Hooke of the tiny divisions of the honeycomb and
he had called them 'cells' in 1664. As early as 1682 Grew made
engravings of them clearly inserted in the cell ligatures of the tissues—
discoveries arrived at visually, but not yet grasped by the rational
intellect, for this very term 'tissue' coined by Grew embodies
misconceptions.

More scholars could vie with each other for the honour of having
been the first to give a really valid definition of the concept of the
cell than Greek cities sought the fame of having been Homer's
birthplace. The German Romantic naturalist Lorenz Oken propounded the idea in 1805 that all forms of life, whether animals or
plants, were composed of tiny units which lived according to their
own law and simultaneously the law governing the total organism.
He called them 'infusorial mucilage utricles'. During the first
decades of the century the French scholars Mirbel, Dutrochet and
Turpin and the Germans Treviranus and Meyen evolved more
accurate conceptions. One of a number of extremely precise pieces
of research carried out by the Scot Robert Brown designated for
the first time the cell nucleus of orchids (1831), thus providing what
is still an inexhaustible and important subject for cell research. In
1844 K.W. Nägeli observed that cells increase by division and in
1846 after these decades of feverish research Hugo von Mohl
completed the groundwork of cellular theory when he coined the
term 'protoplasm' for the 'cloudy, viscous, granular, whitish liquid
which, apart from membrane and nucleus, occupies the cell'.

In these researches the botanists were generally one step ahead of
the zoologists. Plants were, after all, easier to observe under the

microscope because their cells, in contrast to animal cells, possess a clearly visible cell wall. But the findings of botanical research were immediately drawn upon by the zoologists. Bound by their common research into cellular structure both botany and zoology developed as genuinely parallel sciences, as exemplified at the very outset by those two scientists who were quick to sense the significance of the cell conception, Schleiden and Theodor Schwann. In 1839 the latter continued Schleiden's researches into plant cells and also envisaged the body of an animal as a combination of cells. *Microscopic Investigations into the Similarity of Structure and Growth in Animals and Plants* was the descriptive title of his book. For both men the cell held the same significance as the atom for the chemists: the ultimate, elementary vital units in the animal and the plant with a similar structure in both, as though indicating a very remote common origin. The tiny structure under the microscope measured from $1/10$ to $1/1000$ of a millimetre, whether it was part of the body of an elephant or of the leaf it consumed. Slowly the concept of the (somewhat inappropriately named) 'cell state' began to form part of man's picture of the universe, the organism composed of countless cells with many specialized functions, known now as man, now as plant, now as animal. 'What infinitely varied results nature achieves by means of these simple resources,' exclaimed Schleiden.

Not until the late nineteenth century did it become clear that the supposedly simple cell was in fact a most complicated arrangement. Its mysteries increased in direct ratio to the magnifying power of the microscope and the jungle of theories on membrane, nucleus and protoplasm. The cell was suspected of being the ultimate seat of life and death. Great things were at stake in the investigation of the extremely small, particularly since it had been discovered in the late nineteenth century that the principle of heredity, which had been worked out by a Augustine monk, Gregor Mendel, was most intimately connected with the functioning of the cell nucleus.

Nineteenth-century botany did not, however, consist entirely of cell research. It was carried a step further by the new science of ecology (*see* p. 197) which studied the plant as a whole in its complete setting, thus removing it from the laboratories and placing it in its total living conditions. Light was also shed on the hitherto dark, strangely primitive realms of mosses, ferns and seaweeds (*see* pp. 182ff.). They were included and fitted into a botanical universe ranging from the tree as tall as a cathedral down to the invisible spores of the bacterium—until here too the electron microscope, developed in 1933, revealed a new underworld, that of the viruses, remarkable hybrids midway between dead matter and creatures, which live as parasites within foreign cells.

The London doctor Nehemiah Grew published in 1682 his *Anatomy of Plants;* it was a picture-book of roots, branches, leaves, flowers, fruits and seeds, just as his perfect eye had seen them through his imperfect compound microscope (right, top). The strangest cell and tissue formations revealed themselves to him, as is shown in this fan-shaped cross-section of a young elm (the actual size is shown on the right). Grew called the cells 'vesicles', a union of cells 'parenchyma'. He introduced the term 'tissue' into biology and combined with it the incorrect notion that the cells were held together like a piece of woven cloth by a network of very fine fibres. He also sought to prove how wood-forming plants thicken. Each year, so he assumed, the rind itself divided into two, part of it becoming bark, and the other, the inside part, becoming the annual ring; and in the parenchyma of this the medullary ray was formed and the vertical channels for air and saps. Today we would regard A as the periderm; under this is the rind and bast layer H and then the cambium S, that layer of cells which propagate fast and so cause the thickening process—as François Brisseau de Mirbel discovered in 1828 and Franz Unger in 1840. The four light curves within the segment are the divisions between the annual rings, and right in the inside is the pith.

The left-hand drawing shows one of the most interesting discoveries from the early research into cells. It was made by Schleiden in 1838; at the same time it turned out to be his greatest error. It shows three cells out of the hair of a potato plant. Within each nucleus a second smaller nucleus can be seen—today we would call this a nucleolus; Schleiden, however, regarded this as the germ of a new cell, born out of the old nucleus. Schwann and many others fell into the same error over the propagation of cells. The arrows in the middle cell indicate directions of flow in the plasm. Bonaventura Corti pointed this out for the first time in 1774—his was an astonishing discovery. The cell had life hidden within it! Corti was forgotten as more and more experimenters described the process; Robert Brown did so with the greatest accuracy in 1831. Even today it has not been fully explained.

The other pictures come from a selection of illustrations of structures of all shapes which the zoologist Schwann produced in 1839. Inspired as he was by the discoveries of the botanists, he sought to prove what a vast number of functions, and therefore also shapes, the cell took on in animal tissue. He found in each organism a sort of pre-stabilized harmony between the independent life of each cell and the will to live shown by the whole body. Bottom, right, a fat-cell from the cranial cavity of a young roach; the nucleus has been forced to the edge by the contents. The other four structures are pigment cells from the tail of a frog larva.

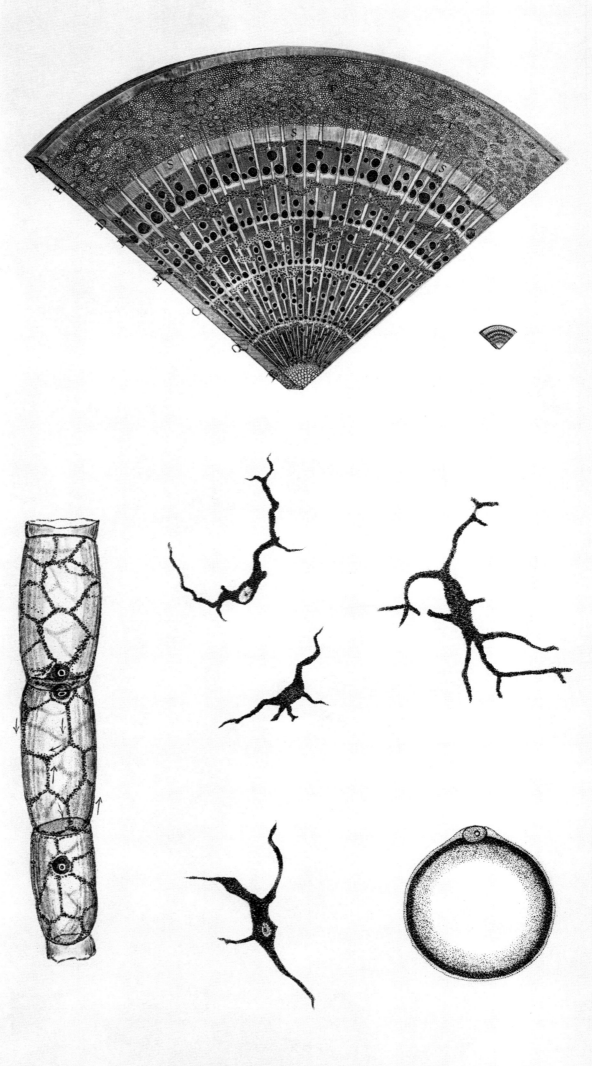

'THE SECRET OF THE FLOWERS DISCOVERED'

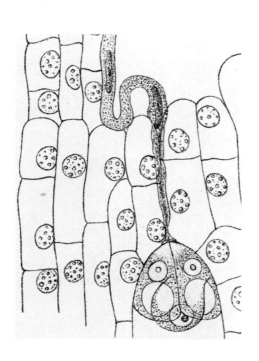

Civilized peoples of all periods have been accustomed to make their festivals more festive with flowers—with that part of the higher plants in which an intensified form of life bursts out from the uniform green of the leaves: blossoms, curiously shaped, sending out a scent, attracting the attention with their striking colours, like the flower groups on a rhododendron branch from Sikkim drawn for J.D. Hooker in 1849 by the well-known English flower painter W.H. Fitch (opposite). The secret of this profusion in nature was not revealed until late in the eighteenth century. Grew had declared in 1682 that the stamens must be the carriers of the male fertilizing substance, and the Tübingen professor of medicine, Rudolph Jacob Camerarius, in the face of countless sceptics, had dared to express the opinion in the year 1694, following upon fertilizing experiments, that the plants also had a sexual system. Yet in 1819 the Berlin Academy was still setting as the question for a prize competition: Are plants fertilized? Joseph Gottlieb Koelreuter had drawn attention in 1761 to the most important aids (apart from the wind) to pollination, the insects, but it was Christian Konrad Sprengel who first opened the eyes of the world to the truly wonderful way in which the blooms of nectar-bearing plants are adapted to their visitors and the visitors to the blooms. It was the bees which led Sprengel to his conclusions; he became a devoted observer of nature in the open air, year after year, neglected his post as rector of the Spandau college, was dismissed, continued his research, and finally died a poor lonely man in Berlin, embittered by the failure of his work *Secrets of Nature Revealed in the Structure and Fertilization of Flowers* (1793). One of the classic examples he used was the *Nigella arvensis* (Love-in-a-mist). The blossom (above, left) is two days old. Most of its stamens stand upright like spears. The sweet-smelling nectar is stored for the bees at the base of bright-striped tubular organs; the fine petals arranged horizontally like a wheel offer a landing-place. Some of the stamens have opened their pollen chambers as they bend over, and are lightly brushing the back of the insect with the grains of the fertilizing pollen. The five female pistils in the meantime tower above the stamens, inaccessible to the pollen of their own plant. The situation is quite different with the plant next to it which is six days old (above, right). The stamens, now emptied, are lying on the petals, but the pistils have rolled themselves into spirals and are lower down. As soon as the bee brings pollen on its back from a neighbouring plant, the sticky stigmata will take it in. Eduard Strasburger, a master of microscopy, had in 1884 been the first to see with his own eyes what happened inside the pistil; the plant he examined was the *Orchis latifolia* (bottom, left). Two nuclei wander through the pollen utricle, which the grain of pollen has driven from the stigma to the germ-sac. One of them will merge itself with the egg-cell, having first discarded the membrane covering it.

THE LEAF'S HUNGER FOR LIGHT

In the year 1754, Charles Bonnet, a naturalist from Geneva, expressed the bold view: 'Plants are planted in the air much in the same way as they are planted in the earth.' His words echoed the past and pointed to the future. Hales had established that the substance of the body of a plant came not only from below, from water and earth; something must be added to this, out of the air. But further progress was barred at this point. Bonnet brought the sun into his researches. Evidently light had an important part to play in the processes taking place in the leaf. He thought out ingenious experiments in order to prove the powerful thrust of the plant towards the light. He bent a young vineshoot down towards the earth with string—but it immediately turned upwards again (above). The direction originally given to the plant by nature was one which forced it towards the light. The experimenter was unable to explain why this happened. He noticed further that, under water, small air bubbles appeared from the leaves, but he ascribed this to the effect of warmth not of light. Towards the end of the eighteenth century the key to the solution of the problem was finally provided by the new chemistry of gases. Priestley had noticed that plants thrive in 'vitiated' air in which animals and candle flames die out and they convert air of this kind into 'vital air'. They seemed to remove from the atmosphere something which was fatal to animal life, but to put back into it something which was life-giving. These observations aroused the passionate interest of the Dutchman, Jan Ingen-housz. In the three summer months of the year 1779 he carried out five hundred experiments on plant-breathing. He found that the driving force for the purifying action of the plant was the sunlight and discovered that only their green parts developed gases—life-giving gases in the daylight, but dangerous ones at night. The same thing happened with plants in water—under the influence of a transforming force in the plant, as the scientist assumed. Three years after the appearance of his investigations, a Genevan botanist, Jean Senebier, published his *Mémoires physico-chimiques*: he was a man who devoted his life to trying to answer the great question: how does every living thing on earth breathe? In this and later books, revised under the influence of Lavoisier's works, further fundamental insight was gained into the nature of plant-breathing. Senebier repeated, with more accurate measurements, all the experiments of the Dutchman and added new ones. He placed his plants in a vessel which was partly filled with water, but the rest of the space was a vacuum (opposite page, top, right); a notched measuring scale enabled him to measure the quantities of gases which developed. The dish, which was filled with water, shut off the outer air. Then Senebier pumped various quantities of carbon dioxide (this was the

'vitiated air') into the water and established that as the light had a greater and greater effect, the amount of oxygen given off by the leaves (this was the 'vital air') increased proportionately. At night this little gas laboratory was almost completely still. Senebier was unable to confirm the nightly observations made by Ingen-housz. The base of the left-hand vessel was raised up high into the bottle. The plants he placed in this air-filled hollow space to be tested could have water poured round them between the glass walls, and the water could be dyed different colours. With the help of leaves cut into very small pieces, he proved also that only the fleshy green parts effected the conversion. Later the term 'chlorophyll' was to be used to describe the active substance which decomposes the gases. By the year 1792 Senebier had progressed as far as he could: it was established that the green parts of the leaves take carbon dioxide out of the air and then, operating according to the amount of light energy available, they decompose it into oxygen which they return to the air, and into carbon; this last they develop into special plant substances. The water rising from the roots assists the process, since the plant evaporates less water than it takes in through the roots. Finally in 1804 another Genevan, Théodore de Saussure, provided decisive information about all these things. The plant takes its carbon from the air, nitrogen and mineral salts from the earth, and stores starch, sugar and fat in the fruits and leaves. 'Breathing' is thus an act of nutrition, made possible by light-energies—hence the plant's hunger for light. Thus step by step over six decades, Bonnet's remark that all plants were planted in the air as they were in the earth came to have its full meaning.

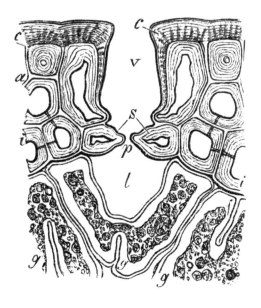

The botanist Julius Sachs had already seen through his microscope the stomata of a leaf which he took from the cluster-pine (right). At the entrance are cells (s) which open and close it; these had already been seen by Malpighi. The front area (v) is surrounded by hard-edged epidermis cells (c) (the tree being a conifer); below this is a tissue containing a great deal of chlorophyll: it has a loose structure and this facilitates the passage of air.

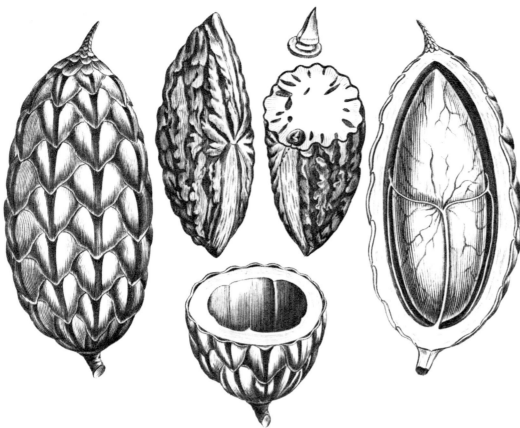

The Fruit of the Sago-palm

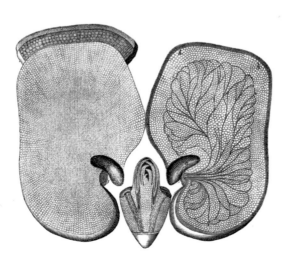

Joseph Gärtner, a pupil of Albrecht von Haller, was the first to devote years of systematic study to the fruit of plants. Quantities of fruit were sent to him from all over the world. So by the time he finally published his life's work *De fructibus et seminibus plantarum* (1788–91), he had become the Linnaeus of beans, dates and corn-grains. His picture of the sago fruit reveals the analytical mind of a classifier and morphologist. Top, left, the fruit with its covering of smooth scales. Above, next to it, the part of the fruit which conceals the seeds—conical pointed structures. On the extreme right, the fruit cut lengthwise. Most of the seeds of the sago-palm are barren, because it propagates itself mainly through suckers from the roots.

'There is no special Providence keeping watch over plant seeds,' Konrad Sprengel wrote, and he had an exact knowledge not only of flowers, but also of all the multiform seeds with the egrets, fins, little hooks and so on, with which they are provided before being scattered out into the world. There was nothing absurd about such a statement coming from a pious man; the men who carried on research into plant seeds knew better than anyone else what an incredibly large number of them fail to survive.

Aristotle had already noticed that the new plant is formed from only one part of the fruit. Grew was the first to examine with great reverence and in more detail the first delicate formative process of the plant at its birth. By making an extra-ordinarily accurate cross-section of a bean he already provided the essential information: the hard protective peel of the fruit (shown in section above), the nutritious tissue, which later provides a part of its substance to the cotyledons as a food reserve for the young plant. Within the cotyledon on the right one can just see one of the tender new leaves; isolated in the middle, is the germ-bud itself, which, as was established in a later period, obeys the slightest stimulus from the light above and sends out the shoot from the bud, whilst the root begins in the darkness of the earth to play its part—also under the influence of so-called growth-substances.

The beauty of healthy, well cared-for fruit is shown in the picture (opposite) of cherries of a well-rounded, juicy species. The plate comes from a work by Henri Duhamel du Monceau, a well-known French agricultural reformer who lived in the mid-eighteenth century.

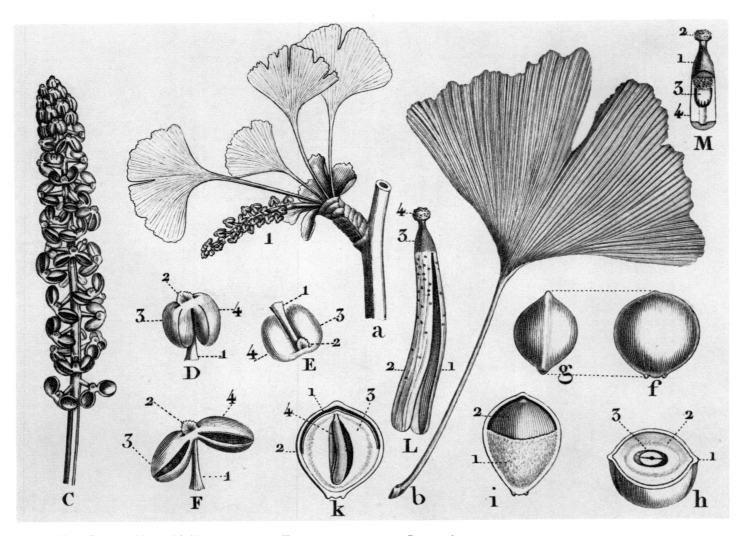

THE GINKGO TREE: 'A TREE FROM THE EAST ASSIGNED TO MY GARDEN'

Above: Parts of the curious ginkgo tree, as L.C. Richard, a French classifier, drew it about 1800: the catkin-like male inflorescence (C) is formed out of a large number of stamens each with two pollen sacs; the female buds (L) consist of a long stalk-like fruit leaf and two seed structures sticking out obliquely. The seeds look like stone-fruit. The ginkgo originates from before the carboniferous period; its unusual leaves, with their veins standing apart from each other like the stretcher of a fan, have been found in fossil form in three continents. In modern times it has been native only to eastern Asia, but it was introduced into Europe in 1754. Many of its characteristics suggest it should be classed as a conifer; but in 1896 the Japanese Hurasé discovered that in this case, as in the earliest times, fertilization took place through free-moving spermatozoa. So the new class of *Ginkgoales* was created; it is closely related to the conifers. But for Goethe the two-in-one leaf became the love symbol: 'Is it one living thing which divides itself in two; or are there two which select each other, so that they can be seen as one?'

Right: A NORTH AMERICAN CONIFER

In the Grand Ducal library at Weimar there were two books about the genus of pines and firs, which Goethe used to consult again and again: *A Description of the Genus Pinus,* produced in 1803 and the following years by Aylmer B. Lambert. It was, said Goethe, a joy to look at these plates, for nature could be seen in them but the art was concealed. This is how the greatest of German poets praised one of the greatest botanical illustrators, Ferdinand Lukas Bauer from Feldsberg near Vienna. His *Pinus* pictures, giving with their delicacy and precision an almost three-dimensional effect, record everything that was known about firs and pines at the time when Napoleon had himself appointed Emperor of France. There is one characteristic pointing to the gymnospermous group with its many species, the group to which these trees belong: the fruit-scale (D) carries both seeds uncovered, not enclosed in an ovary as is the case with other flowering plants, but the syncarpy of cones which are gradually turning into wood protects the growing seeds. Male and female buds are crowded on to the points of the young shoots. B shows two male single buds, enlarged; the wind has already removed from their pollen sacs the fertilizing pollen; f is a fruit scale with a protuberance, g shows the pair of wing-shaped seeds, I is an enlargement of a leaf-tip. Strasburger, Hofmeister and others threw light on cell activity in flowers. *Pinus inops,* native to North America, has trunk and branches which secrete great quantities of resin.

Ferd. Bauer delin.

Pinus inops.

Mackenzie sculp.

THE SECRET OF SEAWEED (ALGAE)

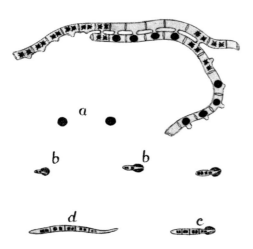

The ancient seafaring peoples, from the Chinese to the Greeks, had found uses for the seaweeds and seawrack. They were used as manure for the fields, sometimes they served as food. But it was a long time before botany was able to answer the questions posed by these strange forms of life which were to be found both in fresh and salt water. Where were the roots of the plants and where were the flowers? In the bush-shaped types it was difficult to know whether the branches were leaves or the leaves branches. How did they propagate, on what did they feed? Countless attempts in the eighteenth century to classify them systematically came to nothing because of the confusion caused by the continual appearance of new kinds, some giant varieties, some mere dwarfs. The English botanist, L.W. Dillwyn, said in despair in about 1802 that the classification of the algae should be begun anew, 'as if nothing had ever been done before'. The foundations for a valid classification were laid in the following decades by two Swedish scientists, Agardh father and son, working together; in 1813 Lamouroux suggested dividing them up according to the colours green, blue-green, red and brown, and this sys-

SEAWEED ON THE COAST OF ALASKA

tem has survived. The picture on p. 182 (top) shows the brown alga *Macrocystis angustifolia*. Jean-Pierre Vaucher, parson and lecturer in botany at Geneva, applied an exemplary microscopic method and a still more exemplary patience to the algae of the Lake of Geneva. About 1800 he carried on his experiments with the thread-like *conjugales* where the Dane, Otto Friedrich Müller, had left off, and established more clearly than his predecessor that with these minute plants propagation took place both sexually by copulation and also without sexual mechanism by spores. From the threads of two algae (far left) a number of narrow short arms were found to branch, by means of which the threads joined themselves together. Through these channels pass the contents of the cells, consisting evidently of either male or female sexual substances, into the neighbouring cells, and here as a result of the union a small grain-shaped structure is formed, the zygote. The alga disintegrates but from the zygote there forms cell by cell a new thread of algae (a–d).

Above: In the years 1826–28 several Russian exploration ships sailed round the world under the command of Count Fedor Petrovich Lütke. Their main task was to survey exactly those coasts of Siberia and Alaska which belonged to Russia. The German naturalists Von Kittlitz and Mertens were members of the scientific staff. The picture records an episode from the long history of botany—by then a worldwide science. Mertens is accompanied by a marine who is carrying the algae they have collected; they have just discovered a small bay. The tide is ebbing and the seaweed is clinging to the banks, waiting to be caught up by the water when it rises again. A last ripple of current plays on the long, gently drifting algae plants. The water is so clear that one can see almost to the bottom. Mertens is pulling out the yard-long narrow ribbon of a *Laminaria saccharina;* at its end can be seen the cup-shaped clinging organ (in the *Macrocystis,* opposite, a discovery of the same expedition, it has the shape of a small disk). Many of the large kinds of algae are assembled in these 'gardens of Poseidon' (this was the name usually given to the tangles of floating plants in the Mediterranean). Beneath the water (centre) are the long, narrow ribbons of the *Alaria esculenta,* resembling the *Laminaria;* on the right next to it, with onion-shaped floats, the *Nereocystis luetkeana,* which bears the name of the commander.

PTERIGYNANDRUM *gracile*

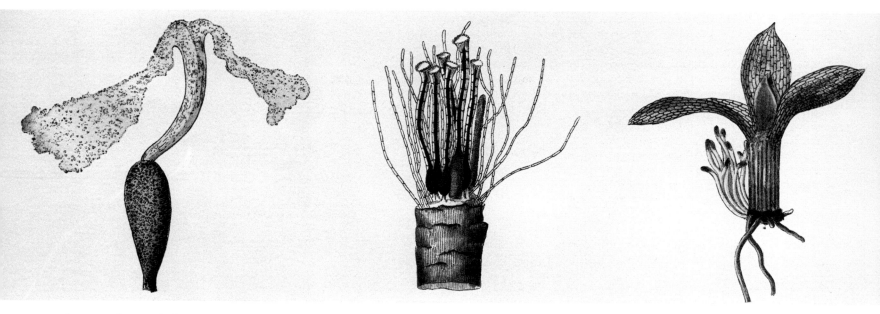

JOHANN HEDWIG'S DISCOVERIES CONCERNING MOSSES

The insignificant moss plant was first really discovered in the scientific sense when the German, Johann Hedwig, came to study this minute living thing; he had the eyes, the microscope and the sensitive physician's hands needed for the preparation of specimens, and he devoted forty years of patience to the work. Tabernaemontanus had made this disdainful note on mosses in his herbal in 1591: 'Some of them grow on the trees, some on the earth, some on stones, some even on the sea-shores, and they are nothing but hairy filth and excess matter from the trees, earth, stones and water.'

Hedwig's name has been and always will be connected with mosses, not only because of his research on them but also on account of the drawings he made. He himself illustrated his own works (on the page opposite is an example, a frondiferous moss from his *Descriptio... muscorum frondosorum,* 1787–97).

Above: The method of propagation, as Hedwig saw it. He did not allow himself to be misled by the capsules which rise on tall stalks from the moss-branches, like others who have so often taken them for buds. Malpighi diagnosed a capsule of this kind which he had drawn (lower picture, left) thus: 'Capsule, which can be closed by a pointed cover, filled with green pollen, that is with seeds.' Hedwig found the sexual organs hidden on the ends of the stalks and distinguished the beetroot-shaped male antheridia (above, left) from the narrower tube-like structures of the female archegonia (centre). On the left an antheridium is bursting open and releasing 'a host of living monads', as C. G. Nees von Esenbeck described them three decades after Hedwig; how these male fertilizing cells found their way to the archegonia, Hedwig did not know. But he did make an astonishing discovery: a capsule grew on a long stalk out of the archegonia; it opened and released a cloud of dust-like particles, from which there grew not a new plant but its youthful stage, a little tuft of thread-like protonema (right). He thought they were cotyledons, because a new plant grew from the bud at their base. More than half a century later as a result of very accurate observations these highly paradoxical processes were explained in a coherent manner. The botanist Wilhelm Hofmeister recognized in 1851 that Hedwig had witnessed the so-called metagenesis: the mosses propagate like the ferns asexually by the spores built up in the capsules, but this alternates with a sexual propagating process in which the male cells from the antheridia are united with the female egg-cells on the base of the archegonia. He succeeded also in seeing the male cells: they were corkscrew-shaped spiral structures which moved towards the archegonia (bottom, right). The medium was not the wind or an insect, but rain-water. This metagenesis went on, mysteriously concealed, as Hofmeister discovered, in the realm of flowering plants as well. Later it was discovered that this activity survived from a primeval period, when the ancestors of the mosses lived in areas bordering on sea and land. The archaic features of the flowerless plants had been revealed to botany.

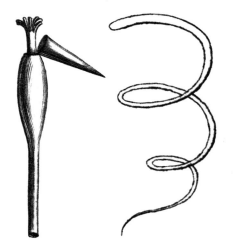

In every natural history museum pictures such as this one look down from the walls on the visitors: landscapes from primeval periods of the earth, long before the appearance of man, built up stage by stage by scientific imagination on the basis of fossilized plants. These plants slumbered for many millions of years in the earth's crust until one day an explorer dug them out and reconstructed from them the story of the great periods of the earth. Before us we see a primeval forest growing luxuriantly on swampy ground, raised only a little above the shallow waters of the sea's edge; the climate is that of the moist and sultry tropics. Vapours rise from the marsh. On the left a tree-fern stretches out its protective fan; below this a fern plant winds its way up a broken tree-trunk towards the light. Hollow tree-trunks lie on top of each other on the ground and will later slowly sink into the morass; the uppermost one exposes its widely splayed roots which it once used to hold fast in the soaked soil. In the bark there are vertical rows of indentations like seals—perhaps marks left by leaves which had been there; the trunks lying below this have a rough scaly surface. Thus it is possible to distinguish between sigillate trees *(Sigillaria)* and squamous trees *(Lepidodendron),* one of which is spreading out its framework of branches in a twin fork in the background to the right of the centre. The bright green, slim, pagoda-like plants with their whorls of stiff, thin branches standing round their stems are giant horsetails, whilst on the right are two of the first ancestors of the later deciduous trees and conifers. Through the brooding stillness of the primeval forest there flutters a flying insect, the oldest to be discovered amongst the fossils: the giant prehistoric dragonfly *(Meganeura);* the *Sphenophyllum* plant has spread over the fallen tree trunks. It is a world of flowerless 'vascular cryptogamia'; they propagate by means of spores. The moss, the horsetail, the fan of ferns or the clubmoss plant of today are botanical prehistory in miniature, dwarf descendants of those living things which about 300 million years ago stood as trees in the moorland forests or covered the swampy ground as tangled creepers.

The carboniferous period lasted many million years, time enough for the trees and plants to sink by degrees into the marshy ground, generation after generation, and, as we see in the moorland of today, to turn into peat and later into coal. The cells of prehistoric plants have again become visible as a result of microscopic examinations of mined coal; the combustibility of the 'black stone' reveals its origin as plant matter: where factories stand now, the sunken forests of the carboniferous period often lie below in the ground. Their fern leaves, their scaly bark (bottom left), their root stems and sometimes a tree-trunk have been preserved for us in fossils. Similar fossilized structures can be seen in the geological picture on page 12. The nineteenth-century palaeobotanists, the Frenchman A.T. Brongniart, the German K.M. von Sternberg and others, after overcoming extreme difficulties, collected and prepared the fossilized plant remains. (Painting by Zdenek Burian, 1950.)

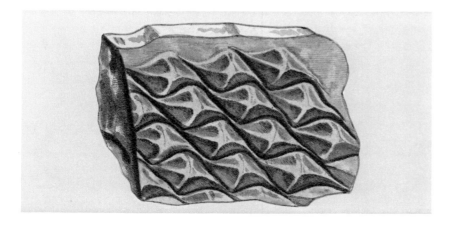

THE SWAMPY FORESTS OF THE CARBONIFEROUS PERIOD

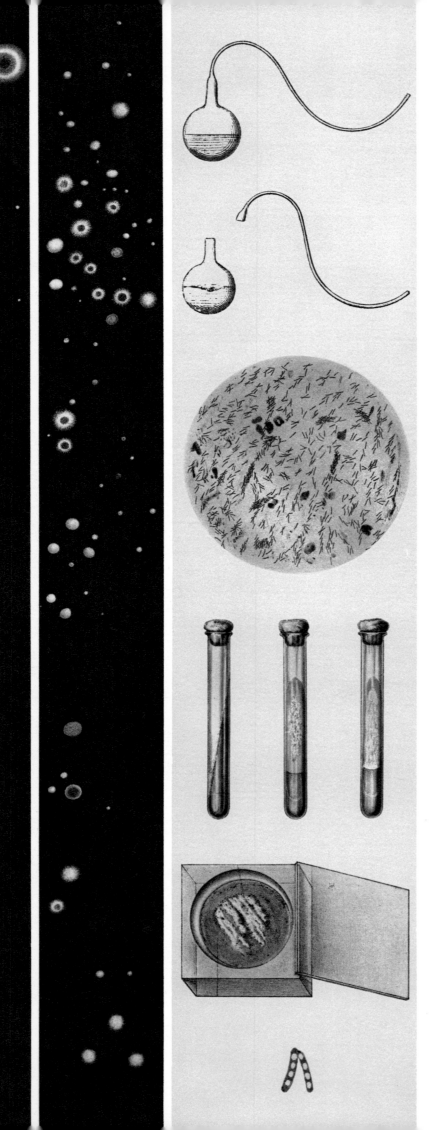

MICROBIOLOGY

Leaves decaying, milk turning sour, meat going bad—these have been familiar phenomena since the dim days of antiquity. No one would ever have dared to regard them as the work of minute invisible primitive plant organisms which hover everywhere in the air and propagate by division to such an extent in nutritive media that their 'colonies' become visible. The two long strips on the left show nutritive media covered with such organisms: gelatine solutions on the inner side of two sterilized glass tubes 16 inches long, exposed to air from a classroom in a Berlin school—before class (left), and after lessons (right).

This experiment made in the year 1882 was inspired by the work of the chemist Louis Pasteur and of the doctor Robert Koch, the two pioneers of bacteriological research. In the simplest conceivable experiment Pasteur proved in the face of resistance by many opponents that the cause of fermentation and decay was not to be found in the things themselves but in the air. A bottle with an S-shaped attachment (top) contains meat broth. The vessel is heated until all the bacteria in it are destroyed and it is then left standing for a long time with the S-tube attached but open at the end. The contents will not decay or ferment because the bacteria from the air stay in the lower curve of the tube and die off. But if the attachment is removed, then they can sink directly into the vessel from the air—in a few hours a scummy mass of microbes have covered the part of the nutritive area just below the opening. Pasteur also discovered that bacteria caused anthrax in domestic animals and fowl-pest in poultry and that a still smaller irritant which could not be seen even under the strongest microscope, a virus, was responsible for rabies in dogs. Never solely a scientist but always a saver of life as well, he found methods of inoculating a healthy organism with weakened microbial poisons and so immunizing it. Later generations have always remembered him as the painter Von Edelfeldt saw him in his Paris laboratory in 1885 (opposite). Pasteur holds in one hand a vessel with part of a spinal cord which has been infected with the germ causing rabies; he is about to obtain from this the inoculation material for immunization.

Robert Koch, who was originally an unknown German country doctor, waged the war against the bacteria at the place where they had so far been at work almost unchecked—in the devastating epidemics and illnesses in which they had annihilated patients from within. He was convinced that even tuberculosis was an infectious disease. For eight years he sought the germ which caused it. With new microscopic techniques and by using methylene blue solutions as a dye he finally forced the germ to become visible—a stick-like structure, which was first made public in pictures such as the round one reproduced here, in 1882, a time when many were afflicted with this disease. Koch provided conclusive proof, when he isolated the bacillus, bred it in 'pure cultures', and injected it into test animals, which after a time fell ill. His procedure was exemplary. He transferred tubercular tissue to a congealed serum obtained from animal blood. One can see in the three test-tubes and in the square glass bowl the small white scales of the colonies acting as parasites in an ideal nutritive medium. But again and again new bacteria seemed to be born by simply appearing out of the empty air—until Ferdinand Cohn discovered that with the so-called hay bacilli something remained behind when they disintegrated: bright, round, highly resistant spores, from which new bacteria hatched out (bottom picture).

188

THE CHURCH OF THE AUGUSTINES AT BRNO IN WHICH GREGOR MENDEL PREACHED

In the year 1843 the twenty-one-year old Johann Mendel, a farmer's son, entered the Augustine monastery at **Brno** as the novice Gregor. From 1853 onwards the young monk left his monastic cell at regular intervals to go to the secondary school, but only in the capacity of assistant teacher of natural history, because he never succeeded in passing the higher examinations in Vienna. In 1868 he became abbot, a position which caused him endless worries. The convent was the scene of a tragedy, for within the abbot and teacher lay hidden the naturalist who had succeeded in making important discoveries in the seclusion of the monastery. But the world paid no attention to his work, *Experiments with Plant Hybrids,* published in 1865 in a local journal. Mendel was shy and he made no efforts to make the world listen to him. After his death his work suddenly bore fruit. In the monastery garden below the wall with the arches were the beds which from 1854 until 1863 had been the centre of the happiest years of Mendel's life.

'A few bags of seeds were his tools,' wrote his biographer ▶
Ingo Krumbiegel. Mendel's purpose was to cross two
plants of the same genus, which differed from one another in
a few clear characteristics; he then tried, by studying the
way in which these characteristics were transmitted in the
following generations, to discover and define the laws of
heredity. He made his tests with the garden pea. He chose
the most suitable from three dozen kinds, tested their purity
for two years and then began to cross-fertilize them. By
using protective coverings over the blossoms he prevented
insects from pollinating them and so spoiling his work.
Mendel discovered, by crossing two kinds which differed
in one characteristic only, what he called the 'dominant-
recessive' hereditary principle. This differed clearly from the
'intermediary' hereditary principle, which seems to correspond most closely to the old conception of the 'mingling'
of inherited features in succeeding generations. Thus, for
instance, the result of pollinating a red-flowering Marvel of
Peru plant *(Mirabilis jalapa)* with the pollen of a white-
flowering plant is a first generation with pink flowers; it is
thus intermediary, occupying approximately a middle position
between the parents. In the second generation results are more
complicated.

On the other hand, where there was dominant-recessive inheritance Mendel obtained different results: for instance, in
his investigations into peas from yellow and from green
seeds. The result here was not a new generation 'between
the parents' with yellow-green seeds; on the contrary, all
the seeds were pure yellow. This first generation, however,
produced a second in which there was a mixture with green
seeds reappearing in a fixed ratio: one green to three yellow.
One characteristic (yellow) thus dominated over the other,
which in succeeding generations was sometimes lost (recessive), but sometimes reappeared. The sketch on the right
shows a pea-plant of the second generation. Its eleven pods
have a total of forty-two yellow (reproduced as black) and
fifteen green (reproduced as white) seeds, irregularly distributed amongst them. By counting exactly the characteristics
of the fruit of a large number of plants produced from
cross-bred seeds and observing the resulting proportionate
percentage, Mendel always arrived at the 3:1 ratio which
was typical of the second cross-bred generation. It reappears
in the proportion 42:15; in the second pod from the bottom
the 3:1 ratio is exactly reproduced. Thus the characteristics
of the two parents reappear from time to time in future
generations in fixed numerical proportions.

This mathematician of botany found his most difficult task
was to follow two pairs of opposed characteristics through
succeeding generations of cross-bred seeds. He selected
yellow or green pea-seeds with either a round or wrinkled
shape and he found here again that the characteristics were
divided up and reunified in the same fixed proportions.
This obedience to fixed laws he traced to divisions in the
inheritance system within the germ cells.

Three scientists, De Vries, Correns and Czermak took part
in research into the secrets of heredity; and they all, almost
simultaneously in 1900, came across the long-forgotten
Mendelian experiments and helped their author to achieve
belated fame. As a result of Mendel's discernment, it became
possible, in practice, to rear plants and animals with greater
knowledge and efficacy than before. And men soon understood why certain inherited diseases appeared and disappeared in succeeding generations. The discoveries of this
shy botanist in a monastery garden at Brno had results
which spread and continued to spread far and wide.

THE PARK OF PRINCE HERMANN VON PÜCKLER-MUSKAU (1834)

The goal of the park designer is 'the creation of a picture, not with paint, but with real woods, hills, meadows and rivers,' explains Prince Hermann von Pückler-Muskau, who brought from England to his estates in Lusatia not only the idealism of the well-to-do cultured nobleman, but also the ideal of the English park on the model of Repton. His park in Muskau, like the later one in Branitz near Cottbus, was nature enhanced twofold: in the first place, selected plants were cultivated there, for the most part in nurseries.

192

For millennia and long before any science of plant cultivation existed cultivation had meant only one thing: the creation of ideal forms, since nature seemed still to be a long way from the attainment of perfection. Hence Pückler-Muskau enhanced nature in a second way in his park by conjuring up artificial landscapes and combining trees, bushes, meadows and water into a perfectly harmonious picture. He laid out stretches of grass between the groups of trees, because in his view fresh grass played the same part in landscapes as the gilt background did in the old saint's images. Tall oaks, beeches and limes were planted, sometimes singly, sometimes in groups, to accent the landscape, meadows were softened by the addition of bushes which he planted in such a way that they cast beautiful shadows. Every park, he said, must have stretches of water to reflect the banks, the sky and quiet bridges. Thus the cultivation of plants as achieved by Pückler-Muskau became pure poetry. The picture is from his *Andeutungen über Landschaftsgärtnerei* (1834).

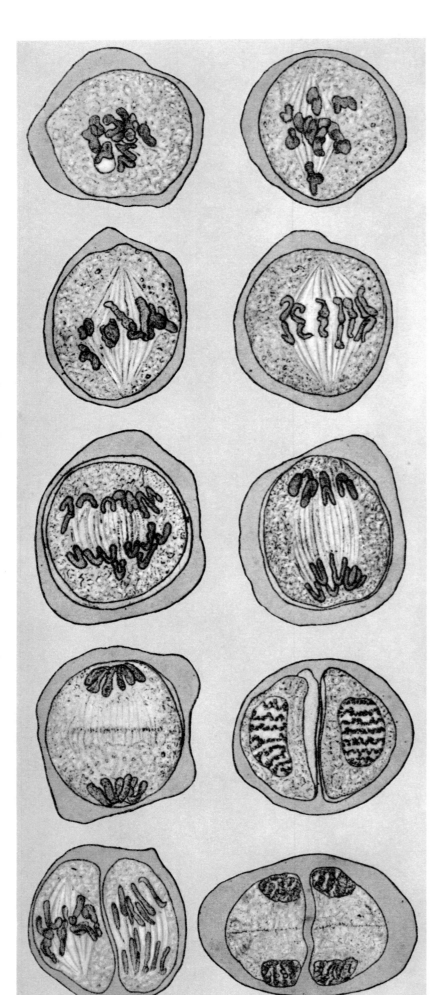

In the years after 1870 the vague and contradictory conceptions about the multiplication of that miraculous thing, the 'cell', which had obtained since the time of Schleiden and Schwann, were by degrees elucidated. The first botanists and zoologists who tried in those years to discover how the inside of the infinitesimally small cell nucleus was constructed, were men who freely risked their eyesight in the interest of their work. By disclosing the interior of the nucleus, which had to be measured in thousandths of a millimetre, they opened up a new world. To magnify with microscopes which were being continually improved was not enough; the thinnest cuts had to be made through tissues. But even then one could only make visible the invisible once it had been discovered that the substance forming the framework of the cell nucleus reacted vigorously to certain aniline dyestuffs recently brought to light. This is why the Kiel scientist Walther Flemming, in his research on cells, gave this substance the name of chromatin. The botanist Strasburger published these very early pictures in the year 1882.

'The division of the protoplasm occurs without any striking accompanying phenomena. But the cell nucleus, in dividing, follows a remarkably complicated process, a fact which indicates that its content has to be divided carefully and in a particular way between the two new nuclei as they form.' This is what the biologist Karl von Frisch said in 1952. This 'remarkably complicated process' was described by Strasburger as accurately as was humanly possible at the time when it was discovered. At the beginning of the process 'thread coils' built up, that is, the chromatin framework began to unravel itself into chromosomes: this name was introduced in 1888 by the anatomist Wilhelm von Waldeyer. The chromosomes folded together and moved (as we now know, they are at this stage already divided up lengthwise) towards the middle of the nucleus (top left) and arranged themselves in an 'equatorial plane' (second row, left). In the plasm of the nucleus there appeared at the same time from both poles 'spindle-threads'. In the equatorial plane the chromosomes divided up for the last time (not, as Strasburger wrongly assumed, in the middle, but lengthwise) and the new chromosomes resulting from this forced their way, bent into U-shapes and, as it were, pulled simultaneously by the spindle-threads, further and further apart to the poles (third row). As they neared the poles, they seemed to merge into each other (fourth row, left). They then converted themselves gradually back into the framework of the nucleus (fourth row, right—from this point onwards the scientist has turned the pictures through 180°). It can now be seen that the plasm is lacing itself together, a new nuclear membrane is forming; out of one cell nucleus, two have been formed. Strasburger followed the process still further: the new nuclei began to divide again. The thread coils built up again, a spindle again became visible (below left), the elements assembled again to form four nuclei out of two (bottom right).

Thus hair, plant leaves, butterflies, men grow from invisible cell nuclei. Every living thing grows, and it grows as a result of cell-division—after the work of Strasburger, the zoologist W. Flemming and others, this view gradually came to be accepted. Oskar Hertwig in 1888 took Harvey's sentence: *'Omne vivum e vivo'*: 'Only from living matter do living things originate', re-stating it as *omnis nucleus e nucleo*: 'Every nucleus derives from a nucleus'. The nuclei are the unusually big ones of the *Fritillaria persica L.*

A Quick-change Artist in a Horticultural Research Station

In 1886 the botanist Hugo de Vries, who came from the tulip town of Haarlem, found in an abandoned potato field a plant which brought him—and it—world fame. It was an *Oenothera lamarckiana,* a species of evening primrose. The plant had made its appearance from some neighbouring grounds and had bred a whole host of successors in the field. De Vries was astonished to find that these successors had produced all kinds of flower and leaf forms, seed capsules and so on different from the normal type. Two individuals were indeed so far removed from the original one that De Vries regarded them as species containing new elements. He transplanted three different kinds in the Botanical Gardens at Amsterdam and then, by carefully pollinating each with pollen from a plant of its own kind, he bred in the course of the years seven generations of successors from the three original kinds. There were about 5,000 individuals, and with more than 800 of them there had been 'mutation', that is, they showed new characteristics, evidently as a result of sudden changes in the inherited features. Some of these new forms are shown in the picture above. On the left, next to the stake numbered 35, and also between the fourth and seventh supporting posts, is the original form: *Oenothera lamarckiana;* to the right, next to the stake, is a new dwarf form; between them is an *Oenothera lata,* a species which developed only sterile flower pollen or none at all. The neighbouring plants which have grown to a great height (two have bags on them to prevent pollination from plants of a different kind) belong to a new long-leafed kind, whilst between the support posts 2 and 3 there is an *Oenothera gigas* and next to it *scintillans;* the first is a robust broad-leafed kind with large flowers, the second a weaker 'inconstant species'. Finally, on the extreme right, is an *Oenothera rubrinervis,* a brittle plant with many stalks and broad red stripes on its calyx and fruit. Nearly all these mutations from previous forms re-occurred in their own succeeding generations, and when cross-bred they behaved exactly in accordance with the Mendelian laws and were regarded by De Vries as constant species. Later, however, it turned out that they were no more than stable hybrids. All the same, De Vries had found a new answer to the question: how do new species originate? His answer provided vital support for the theory of evolution (*see* p. 371). The inherited tendencies did not automatically determine for all time the form and shape of a species; characteristics were lost unforeseeably, suddenly, but as a rule only seldom; similarly new characteristics appeared which could be inherited, as Karl Wilhelm Nägeli had already maintained purely as a matter of theory in 1844. The copper-beech tree, for instance, must be regarded as having originated by mutation from an ordinary beech. But the constant new form created by mutation is still subject, like all others, to those most powerful formative forces which along with those of heredity are at work in all living things: the influence of the place of origin, of the environment, and for plants especially, of the primeval elements—air, earth, water and the creative light from above.

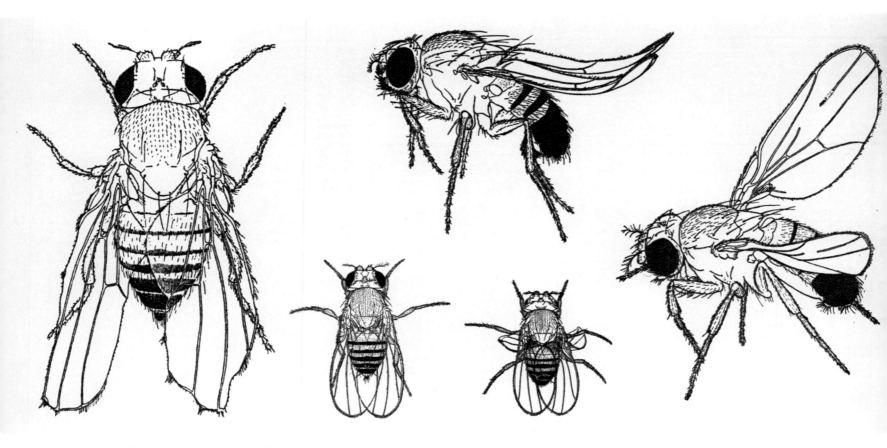

MORGAN'S EXPERIMENTS WITH THE DROSOPHILA

Why a picture of flies in the section on botany? Because the student of heredity can show by his experiments with this most important test insect to what extent the information obtained by the pioneer botanists about plants could also be usefully applied to other spheres. With the help of garden peas Mendel discovered the broad outline of laws of life; with the help of the equally useful *Oenothera* De Vries studied new aspects of the origin of species—and by using the *Drosophila* for his ingenious experiments the American, Thomas Hunt Morgan, examined the intricate structure of chromosomes, 'those small and wonderful containers of inheritable characteristics', as Karl von Frisch called them. The *Drosophila* fly is breeding in very large numbers and at intervals of only two to three weeks—the experimenter examined twenty-five or more generations in one single year. They were housed in a milk bottle, closed at the top with a plug of wadding, and at the bottom was a little purée of banana as food. As Morgan and his colleagues studied the thousands of offspring they soon came across the phenomenon which De Vries had discovered in plants: here and there sudden mutations appeared—inheritable changes in the wings, eye-colour, covering bristles and so on. In the group above, many anomalies resulting from mutation can be seen; left, the bristles are very thinly spaced across the whole of the fly's back; top, the ends of the wings are raised at an angle like skis; right, one of the wings is stunted and distorted. The small fly below on the right has as an appendage—a second thorax with stunted wings; its neighbour on the left has an excessive amount of hair.

The *Drosophila* (like all the flies and gnats related to it) has in its salivary glands cells with chromosomes, which are about one hundred times larger than normal ones. It was thus possible to see under the strongest microscopes large numbers of little disks arranged in rows inside the chromosomes; these are the genes which are regarded as the carriers of individual inherited characteristics. The proof for this was again provided by the useful *Drosophila*. In a series of extremely clever experiments Morgan was able to give factual proof that certain outward characteristics were determined by certain gene-disks; he thus succeeded finally in designing a 'map' of the genes in the chromosomes of the *Drosophila*. Up to the present, with the *Drosophila*, 650 'gene-points' have been seen to change—and this occurred in the case of an estimated 2,500 to 10,000 hereditary factors. The group of scientists working with Morgan used also chemicals of all kinds on the chromosomes, as well as X-rays, and they were able to demonstrate that the effect of these was a swift increase in the number of mutations. The more daring minds now asked themselves: would it one day become possible by exerting influence on the genes to produce changes in human beings? In the meantime, since 1950, biochemists like the Englishmen J.D. Watson and Francis Crick have discovered that the main chemical components of chromosomes are giant molecules of DNA (deoxyribonucleic acid). They consist of long chains of atoms and are regarded as the storing-places for the substances which through the genes govern the chemical structure of living things.

Plants in their natural Environment

Two powerful forces mould the scenery which forms the background to men's lives, namely the geological forces which pile up the earth's crust into mountains or flatten it into deserts, and plants which clothe the ground far and wide with their carpet of green. In these landscapes the animal is merely a passing guest. Organic life on earth means predominantly plant life; this rules the world. Here it constructs its mighty scenes before our eyes: the primeval forest, the tundra, the steppe, the swamp, or else, in the service of men, meadowland, ricefields and fields of corn. Here it takes its part in the great cycle of respiration. Here it appears as the unique source of vital force which combines decaying matter on the ground with part of the air so as to convert the whole into organic substance which provides food for man and beast. Once a year the peoples of the earth, otherwise so very neglectful, still commemorate this power in their harvest festivals.

The authors of the herbals, the systematists, the physiologists paid no attention to those gigantic plant communities. However, one or two botanists who travelled very widely and were thus able to compare one set of living conditions with another encountered new and fundamental problems of plant life. When, for example, Tournefort climbed Mount Ararat in 1717 he observed that at its foot he was surrounded by the vegetation of Asia Minor, halfway up by that of France and at the summit by that of Lapland. He realized, in Alexander von Humboldt's words, 'that the height of the ground above sea-level affects plant distribution just as their distance from the Pole affects it on flat land'. Thus a goal was already perceived for 'a science which was as yet not even named', that is, to determine the laws governing the distribution of plant communities throughout the world. Humboldt, the most universal of all naturalists, was the first to see the full scope of these questions raised in his mind by the landscapes of Central and South America, and shortly after his return he published his *Thoughts on a Geography of Plants,* dedicated to Goethe (1807). Through the volumes of his *Cosmos* runs a series of classic 'nature paintings' of different types of landscape. Almost half a century later M. J. Schleiden still regarded plant geography as a 'peculiar science, still young, displaying all the defects of youth and bubbling over with vigour'—in the same year, 1855, that Alphonse de Candolle brought out his *Géographie botanique raisonnée* in two volumes.

This young science was from the outset imbued with a Humboldtian tendency to the all-embracing universal approach. It attained maturity when botany was sufficiently systematized for most species of plants in the world to be distinguished and their distribution to be quantitatively noted. It also equipped itself with the results obtained in the laboratories of plant physiology, that is, an understanding of the respiration nourishment and cell functioning of the plant. But most of all it regarded the plant as a plant, as a complete organism living in the open air in a complex set of associations. Thus 'ecology' was born. It was found that individual species flourished or became extinct according to the presence or absence of an ideal set of ground, light, wind and water conditions and the close environment of certain plants and animals. By collecting, comparing and travelling naturalists elaborated the picture of floral zones spreading across the continents with their characteristic main genera and main species and the laws governing their relation to their habitat, as for example in the epoch-making book by the Dane J.E.B. Warming, *Manual of ecological Plant Geography* (1896), and in A.F.W. Schimper's book on plant geography (1898).

Plant sociology, in the same Humboldtian spirit as plant geography, was at work in clearings, in fern glades and alpine meadows and so forth in an attempt to investigate the laws of 'plant communities'. These were the smaller associations of genera and of species within the larger landscape; they had come together not by reason of affinity but because their common necessities of life were satisfied at quite well-defined places. One of the early masters of this mode of observation was Anton Kerner von Marilaun, an Austrian who possessed the requisite gifts for this type of overall plant observation. He had not only the researcher's eye for cell processes and the analytical sense of the systematist, but also the ability to see and feel on moors or in beech-woods the abundance of living things and to sense the rich interaction between habitat and plant communities.

This disciple of Humboldt did not overlook 'the relations between this diverse expression of landscape (plant communities) and the temperament of man'. The means he found best suited, not to giving a merely verbal picture of nature as seen by the ecologist, but to help man to find his place within nature so as to widen his mind, was a many-coloured 'prospect of vegetation'. In this he followed, as will be seen in the ensuing pages, some distinguished predecessors such as F.H. von Kittlitz or C.F.P. von Martius.

PLANT LIFE AT THE TIMBER-LINE

Prospects of Vegetation is the title which the explorer, Friedrich Heinrich von Kittlitz, gave in 1854 to the pictures of floral areas he himself painted on such a grand scale. This picture shows how he visualized the flora at about 5,250 feet above sea level at the beginning of June in the western Sudeten mountains. He saw with the eye of one whose aim is to examine plants within the whole of their environment. The dominant factors of the Alpine landscape are the thin, crystal-clear air, which permits the transmission of ultra-violet rays, the considerable difference of temperature between the hot hours of daylight and the nights which even in June are still cold (the snow has not yet quite disappeared), the fresh winds which often blow violently across the slopes, and the dry and drying air. The plant world which has come into existence here is one accustomed to storms and is deep-rooted, hardy and resistant to winter.

On the left, protected behind the conifers, is a last deciduous tree from the lowland; otherwise there are only firs with their drapery of needle leaves which equip them to stand up to the weight of the snow, the gales and the heavy evaporation. The tree stumps look as if they were victims of disasters. Around them are the low shrubs of the heather and the bilberry, with their hard, often very hairy leaves and woody stems to protect them against the main danger: evaporation. On the opposite slope, squat mountain pines and juniper bushes, shrub-like conifers, are growing well beyond the timber-line. Even on the slopes of boulders, drenched as they are with the trickling snow-water, forms of life continue to exist, from lichens and mosses to the cushions of saxifrage. 'The whole vegetation has been shifted towards the pole': this was the comment of the plant geographer A. F. W. Schimper on such landscapes in 1898.

TROPICAL RAIN FOREST IN THE PROVINCE OF RIO DE JANEIRO

Moritz Rugendas has included in his book *Picturesque Travels in Brazil* (1835) pictures of plant communities which are pure visual ecology. This is where nature has given plant life unlimited favourable conditions and the greatest luxuriance: in the tropical rain forest. In this sultry exuberance Schimper saw three main driving forces at work on the plants: the hunger for light, the warmth of the tropical air and the dampness caused by the heavy downpours of rain in these vast forests. The supreme need of this community was light. Three kinds of trees, all crowded together, here betray this need: below is the lower jungle of wild and rampant undergrowth with tree-ferns (right) and leaf-plants swelling with all their saps, then the medium-high palm trees, and finally the giant trees, which are trying to stretch their roofs of leaves high over the others, and, like the tropical fig-tree also seen here, are anchored in the ground by enormous buttress roots. Up through these three tiers of trees the liana climbs, carrying its leaves and flowers to the highest tree-tops and often literally strangling the giants. Then there are many epiphytes, which settle on the branches of the trees, without however becoming a parasite on the host-plant. In the barren brambles of the thorn forest in the same land of Brazil a deathly silence reigns for months on end, but in the rain forest Rugendas listened to the ear-splitting shrieks of the monkeys and parrots, the clapping of the beaks of the toucans, the groaning of the sloths, the croaking of the bullfrog, the buzzing and humming and gnawing of the tropical insect world.

THE THORN FOREST IN BRAZIL IN THE DRY SEASON

Where in tropical Brazil chalky sandy soil replaces humus, there appears in the rainless months the ghostly skeleton forest of the Catingas, a landscape of deathly rigidity and glaring light; it is inhabited by a plant community which in the bad season discards all the superfluous ballast which increases evaporation like leaves and flowers; it also stores as much of the vital moisture as possible in the thick cactus leaves, in the lumpy roots or even in the cylindrical trunks of the 'barrel-trees' (*Chorisia ventricosa*). With reduced energies they can hold out until the rain comes to relieve them. The Bavarian botanist C.F.P. von Martius, who in 1820 brought back 6,500 plants from his three years of travel through Brazil (his expedition is shown in the picture), described this prospect of vegetation in a masterly manner:

'It is with dismay and horror that the traveller penetrates this landscape in the dry season. As far as he can see, leafless stems, motionless, unfanned by breezes, stand rigidly around him; no green leaf, no juicy fruit, no fresh blade of grass on the burning barren ground; only strangely shaped cereus stems which rise like monstrous candelabra..., appear to maintain some trace of a fleeting life. But when rain suddenly loosens the fetters of this plant realm, there arises, as if by a stroke of magic, a new world. On the many branches of the stalks leaves of soft green shoot forth, countless kinds of strange flowers make their appearance, the skeletons of the menacing thorn barriers and creepers clothe themselves with fresh foliage.' (*Tabulae physiognomicae.* Vol. I of *Flora brasiliensis,* 1840).

ZOOLOGY

FERNS ON AN ICE-AGE MORAINE IN THE TYROL

In a clearing in the forest three of the polypodium family which are commonest in Europe have taken root on what used to be moraine. Right at the front are tufts of the male fern *(Dryopteris filix mas)*, behind this the fans of the bracken *(Pteris aquilina)* rise on tall stalks, and out of the cracks in the rock shoot the narrow leaves of the common polypody *(Polypodium vulgare)*. On the underside of three of them groups of brown spores can be seen. Anton Kerner von Marilaun had this wooded corner painted in 1890 by the painter Ernst Heyn to show that in a miniature botanical landscape the ground is usually covered with the plants of not only one group (like the ferns) but of several different kinds which form a community. In such a community, for instance, 'a thick mass of moss forms with its soft carpet the lowest layer on the ground; over this rises the foliage of the ferns and other leaf plants, and then as a third element the dark crowns of the pine trees, resting on their slender pillars, form their arch of shade.'

Aristotle, the first man in the history of scientific research to attempt a broad survey of the animal kingdom, did not restrict himself to drawing his information from nature and the writings of other scientists. He never tired of questioning hunters, fishermen and sailors, shepherds and peasants. These people were experts, potential colleagues, the last descendants of mankind's oldest zoologists, and we must not underestimate the wealth of animal lore they accumulated in remote pre-scientific times. The hunter was an ecologist when he observed the life habits of a beast of prey in his district, but he was also an anatomist when he skilfully disembowelled it. The Ancient Egyptian beekeepers or the Ancient Chinese breeders of fish and silkworm looked still more deeply into the creatures' mode of life, feeding habits and methods of propagation. The starting point of the natural sciences was found in bounteous nature. When in Ancient Greece a genuine scientific zoology entered upon this inheritance, it set itself, with Aristotle, extensive tasks which were not completed to any great extent until the centuries succeeding the reawakening of a strong autonomous urge to scientific research which characterized the Renaissance. The zoologist, a latterday Noah, had to classify every single creature living in earth, air and water. Besides this task of systematization he also had to be an anatomist and describe the internal and external construction of these creatures, and finally he had to elaborate and understand by means of comparison the common characteristics of every living organism. Thus zoology, during the centuries immediately succeeding the Middle Ages, consists predominantly of description of animals, systematization, anatomy and a marginal amount of physiology. These tasks assumed gigantic proportions because ever since the first circumnavigations of the globe both land and sea opened the floodgates of their immeasurable reserves of unknown forms of life, never to completely close them again. Sixteenth-century and seventeenth-century travel accounts written by the Portuguese about India, by the Spaniards about South America, by the English about North America, teem with zoological curiosities and read at times like zoological romances. Classic accounts of this sort were written by José de Acosta and Jean Chardin. When Linnaeus tried to classify the animal species in 1758, he reached a figure of 4,236. A century and a half later, 2,700 authors had reported more than 400,000 animal species of which 120,000 were coleoptera alone.

This animal kingdom, so unusually rich in species, almost disappeared in the green landscapes of the world, the face of which was entirely determined by the masses of silent plant life. But the animal introduced an active, dramatic, mobile element into this natural background. 'It wills, acts, is self-determining, functions and is linked through its senses with the most distant objects. Its individuality is a central point to which everything else is related, a speck which reflects the whole universe, a microcosm', as Buffon said. Every beetle climbing up a stalk, every frog jumping into the water, every bird migrating to other continents, resembles in this respect the active, struggling, victorious or defeated dramatic hero. In comparison with the calmer world of plants the animal kingdom is full of extraordinary happenings which give untold pleasure to children and readers of animal stories. The animal kingdom was also more productive of extreme, abnormal forms of life than the more uniform flora. A great problem of research was posed by the fact, for instance, that fish, which breathe, can move about in water without suffocating, or that creatures like birds exist, capable of rising into the air without suffering Icarus' fate, or that some insects lived through three widely differing states (see pp. 222–27).

This more active role (in comparison with the plants) was matched by an organism provided with its own complicated mechanism: a highly specialized musculature, keen senses, nerve fibres along which reflexes travelled as quick as lightning. As soon as scientists had the microscope at their disposal they began to probe the secrets of these amazingly delicate structures. In the nineteenth century the new physiology (see pp. 238 ff.) began to observe the concealed chemical and physical processes in animals. Even in the seventeenth century Swammerdam's microscope technique had meant an enormous advance on the honourable attempts of the medieval theologian Albertus Magnus to investigate with the naked eye the internal structure of a bee. 'I have been trying', he writes in about 1260, 'to make an anatomy of the bee. On the lower half of its body beneath the waist can be seen a shiny transparent sac and when this is tested by the tongue it gives a delicate honey flavour. The only other contents of the body are a thin, very slightly coiled bowel and tiny threads to which the sting is attached. Around this flows a sticky juice and the legs are set into that part of the body in front of the great indentation.'

In the nineteenth century Johannes Müller's *Handbuch der Physiologie* (1840) stands as a final monument to a spirit which could survey the life processes from the protozoon to man and could attempt to understand the unspeakably varied interaction between an underlying non-material force and the physical forces in beings which breathe, display metabolism, procreate and die.

Not until the turn of this century, after the specialized discoveries of physiology concerning the material aspect of animals' bodies, did animal psychology and research into animal behaviour lead back to profounder and wider concepts of the creatures saved from general destruction long ago in Noah's Ark (see p. 242). Today we can make a reasoned classification of the abundant forms of animal life and can trace them back through many millions of years. For this we are indebted to the great achievements of the theory of evolution.

NOAH'S ARK

The Noah's Ark picture-book is still for many children the best 'introduction to zoology for beginners': it offers a first chance to see the whole astonishing variety of forms in which those friendly living things, the animals, appear: there are those which fly in the realm of the air, those which swim in the sea, and those which live on the firm land, crawling, climbing, trotting or running with the speed of the wind. In this picture the illustrator of a Luther bible of 1564 has collected in front of the many-storeyed ark a gay throng of animals, nearly all of them in pairs 'to keep seed alive upon the face of all the earth'. The miraculous unicorn, on the other hand, the symbol of maidenhood in the Middle Ages, will climb into the refuge of man and beast without a companion (left). Apart from this newcomer out of the world of European fantasy, the animals shown are almost entirely those mentioned in the Bible. Amongst untamed animals the Bible gives in its list the lion and the hyena, also the leopard, the bear, the fox, the porcupine and the wolf—

and the serpent, burdened with the curse of God. Freely mixing with the wild beasts are those which man has taken into his service since time immemorial: the dromedary as beast of burden, the horse to carry him on his journeys and transport his goods, also those useful providers of food and clothing, the lamb and the cow and fowls of all kinds.

On the right Noah is kneeling, whilst some of his family climb the gangway to escape the Flood ordained by God in His anger. In the centre and background the Flood has begun to pour with annihilating force over the world. Men and beasts drown, only the ark floats, under the torrents of rain, on the waters which will at last begin to subside only after 150 days. The dove which was sent out (top left) returns with an olive branch in its beak: the earth with all its trees and plants is rising from the Flood, ready to become once again a home for man and for the beasts which the pious Noah took under his protection as ordained by the Creator—here is the archetype of man protecting nature.

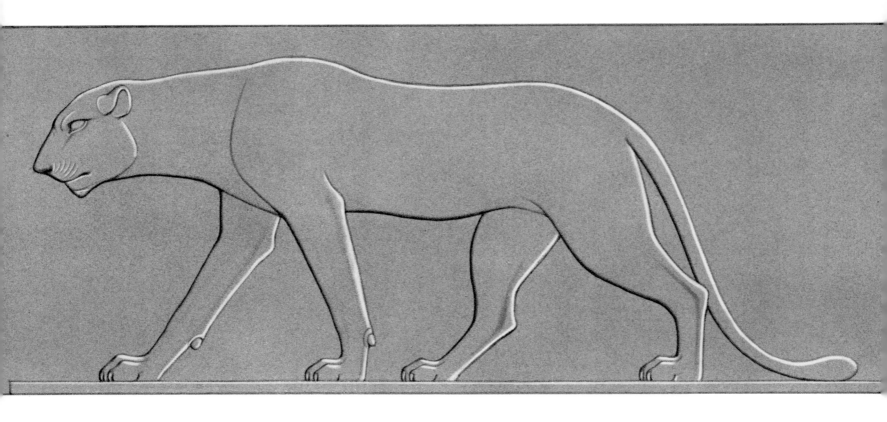

'The panther is the most beautiful of all the cats in this round world. As beautifully marked as he is supple, as strong as he is nimble, as bold as he is cunning; in the panther the beast of prey achieves perfection.' This passage from Alfred Edmund Brehm's *Animal Life* reads like a commentary to this 3,500-year-old bas-relief on the wall of the temple of Assassif, which portrays this animal with faultless stylization.

The painters and sculptors of the ancient peoples were excellent observers of animals. The typical characteristics are exactly represented: the broad nose, the thickly padded neck, the narrow pelvis, the carpal bone, which juts out at the upper end of the base of the forefoot, the heel-bone hump at the corresponding place on the hindfoot, and even the strongly developed third toe-joint which is higher than the others. The artist belonged to a people for whom gods and animals stood in close relationship. They had gods with the head of a falcon or a jackal, and animals which had become consecrated as gods, like the ibis, which became the god Thoth. Many belonged to a much revered intermediate realm, where the supernatural appeared in natural form.

FISH—2,400 YEARS OLD

This clay tablet was made in southern Italy in the fourth century before Christ. The four fishes and two mussels have been as perfectly preserved over the two and a half thousand years as were the insects in amber over thousands of millennia. Left, with the thick-set, ruggedly mailed head and the coarsely pointed back-fins, a gurnard *(Trigla)*, a name it derives from the noise it makes when it is taken out of the water. In contrast to this, below, the elegant slender spindle-shaped mackerel. On the extreme right, a member of the family of wrasse fish *(Labridae)*; above, a bass *(Labrax lupus)* with its two back-fins set closely one behind the other and its prickly gill-covers; it was the bass which Aristotle considered to be the most cunning of all fish.

This picture of fish in the Greek tradition is a work carried out in the spirit of Aristotle. The animal, like the plant, was becoming for the first time a subject for proper scientific study. The principal animal studied was the fish. Aristotle much preferred fish to domestic animals for his investigations, which were accepted right up to the sixteenth century as models to be followed by others. He surveyed a good five hundred animal species—more than any natural philosopher

before him. Thorough observation was for him valuable in itself; in some cases he could only acquire knowledge of the inner structure of the animals by dissecting them. He recognized that before an animal could be described, many questions had to be asked about it. What was its outward shape? What was its inner structure? What was its food? What kind of life did it lead? How did it originate? How did its organs work? How did it compare with other animals? What were its relations with its environment? These are all elementary questions of morphology, of anatomy, of physiology, of ethology, of classification, of ecology; it is true that the answers were sometimes clouded by unreliable observations or by hasty generalizations; nevertheless the bold spirit which led him to make this far-sighted research into the fullness of nature was an incentive to many who followed. For Aristotle it was an understood thing that nature created only things which had meaning and beauty and were intrinsically necessary. Darwin was so overwhelmed by the zoological writings of this Greek that he came to regard the much-esteemed masters Cuvier and Linnaeus as mere schoolboys when compared to Aristotle.

Animals have a great many things in common with man. The cunning foxes, the busy bees, the wise owls have inspired man to invent a variety of animal fables. Animal fables have much in them of the pre-scientific observation of the animal kingdom.

These three examples from the late fifteenth century are heroic tales in miniature in which the dramatic plots are unravelled with humour.

Above: At the end of the summer an ant is carrying out of its house the corn which it had collected for the winter, so as to dry it in the open air. A hungry cricket passes by and asks for food. 'What were you doing in the summer?' asks the ant. 'I was not idle,' replies the cricket. 'I skipped through the hedges and sang.' At this the ant laughs, locks its corn up again and says: 'You went singing in summer: now go skipping in winter.'

Centre: A thirsty crow has found a large bucket, but there is so little water in it that it cannot reach it. The crow is not strong enough to tip it over, so it begins to think out a solution. After some time, it takes some pebbles and throws a sufficient number into the bucket to make the water rise higher and higher. Thus it succeeds in quenching its thirst.

Below: A lion sees a goat grazing high up on a cliff. It makes his mouth water, but he is unable to bring the goat down. So he says: 'I ask you, sister, why do you live in these barren stony places and seek your food on such hard ground? Leave that desert and come down to the flowers and herbs in the green meadows: you can graze here happily and without toil.' The goat sighs when she hears this advice, but she replies: 'I can see that I would suffer mortal distress if I believed you. So stop giving me advice.'

In the Middle Ages there was an insatiable desire for a zoology of fantasy, like that found in popular works of the ancient world. The unidentified 'Maître de Charles d'Angoulême', an outstanding miniaturist, was enchanted with the idea of the wonderland Arabia (opposite, enlarged reproduction). This is where (according to Pliny, Solinus and others) a nomadic people lived in tents. The men tilled the fields. Months later they returned to reap the harvest of black pepper and red ginger. Snakes appeared and poisonous dragons; men went out to hunt these, for precious stones could be found in their bodies. The bird Synamolcos would build its nest on high trees from the twigs of sweet-smelling shrubs. The Arabs were said to bring down these much-prized nests with long stakes. The Middle Ages valued highest those animals which had their homes deep in this realm of miracles. Two of them may be seen here: the unicorn above on the right, and on the mountain-top to the left the eagle-like bird, the phoenix. According to Pliny it is supposed to grow old after five hundred years, and to fill its eyrie with incense just before its death: then it dies in flames. Out of its ashes comes a young bird. Christianity seized on the fine symbolism in this story and used it—it became the allegory of rejuvenation, and the phoenix became the symbol for Christ resurrecting from the dead.

PLINY'S FANTASY OF ARABIA

AN IMAGINATIVE PICTURE OF A CUTTLEFISH (1553)

At the beginning of modern times, zoology had no Galileo or Copernicus or Vesalius to persuade the people of that time to look with new eyes at an essential part of reality and so to start a new epoch. It was rather a case of a few well-read universal minds, personalities of this transitional period like Conrad Gesner and Ulisse Aldrovandi, carrying the science of animals into the new era on their broad compilators' shoulders. One of them was Pierre Belon, who had seen the countries of the eastern Mediterranean on his diplomatic missions, and like the others he lived in two worlds at once. On the one hand zoology existed for him in the form Aristotle and the other masters of the ancient world had laid down as binding for all time; on the other hand he was driven by his own irrepressible passion for discovery to search for new fields out in the country or on the dissection table. His dual nature becomes evident in two pictures: on page 212 is a carefully-drawn comparative picture to contrast the skeleton of a human being with that of a bird; in the picture above, which comes from his book

on fish of 1553, he is seen as the faithful successor of the ancient authorities.

Nowhere but in the sea was there such amazing variety of animal life, wrote the famous Pliny the Elder; there one could even see horses' heads rising from shells of snails (the sea-horse). But the most remarkable monster was the *Argonauta*. Belon depicted the female fish with some of its characteristics realistically drawn: the eight 'arms' with the suckers, the mouth with the parrot's beak so suitable for the cracking of mussel-shells, the thin spirally formed shell, and even the folds in its so-called mantle (top left). But the rest is fantasy learned from the book of Pliny who in turn relies for his knowledge on Aristotle: 'When the fish swims on the surface, it bends back its two front feet and spreads out its thin covering. In this way it is able to sail, and it rows too with the rest of its legs. This is the way the cuttlefish swims across the deep sea—like a little ship. When it is frightened, the skin covering fills with water and the fish submerges.'

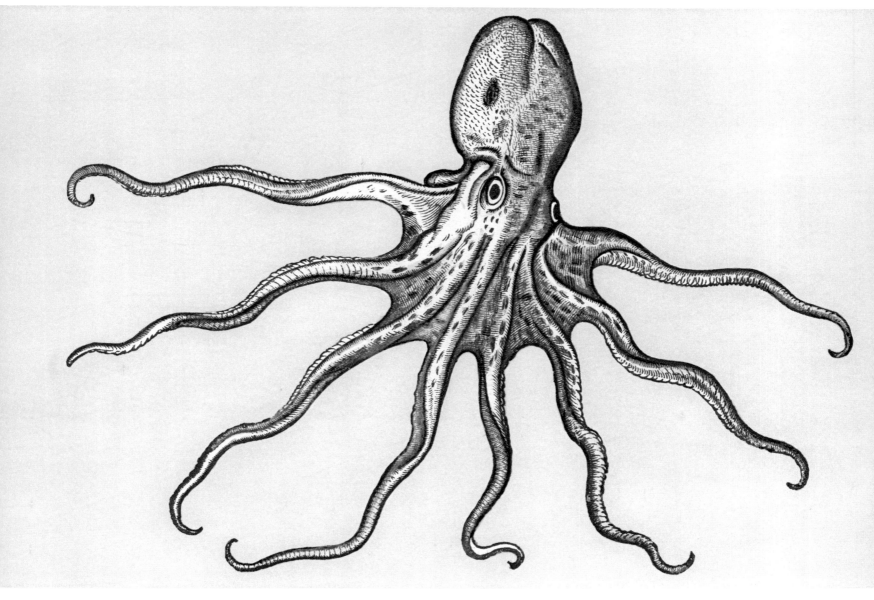

A MORE REALISTIC PICTURE OF A CUTTLEFISH (1563)

Conrad Gesner was the most important of these Renaissance zoologists. Whoever wanted information about animals or plants would find in his house, so he said, 'a whole library contained in one book' on each of these two subjects. He described the two books as the main objective of his life. And he achieved it in the form of a positively gargantuan volume on animal natural history (it appeared in Latin in 1551 and in German in 1563) and of the unpublished material he left behind for a similar volume on plants. In this animal book with its uncertain classification there is everything that this impassioned but constantly overworked Zurich city doctor was able to collect: his notes on almost all the writings available at that time of the ancient and a few medieval classical authors, the knowledge he had obtained as a student in Basle, Paris and Montpellier, the information sent to him in letters by scholars from all over Europe, and also his own observations of the animal world in his native country. In his richly illustrated work he interwove the same two worlds as Belon did. With Gesner as with Belon,

evidence of this may be provided by his description of a representative of the cuttlefish family, this time an *Octopus vulgaris*. The French doctor and expert on fish, Guillaume Rondelet, had sent him a fairly realistic drawing of the fish. As Gesner was compiling the relevant notes on it, there fell on his paper not only the light of Rondelet the expert, but also the shadow of the fanciful animal pictures of an older period. The 'hideous fish without bone or blood like so much tripe', he explained, used its arms for crawling and seizing prey, and spat out the water it had sucked in with great force along a tube. So far he was fairly on the firm ground of reality. The octopus, he continued, likes to crawl long distances on land at night; there was one, for instance, which scented the barrels of salted fish in a merchant's store, crushed the containers with its powerful suckers, and so greedily gulped down those sea fish which had come such a long way from the sea. Here we are in the realm of fascinating 'curiosities', of which Gesner is one of the most likable addicts.

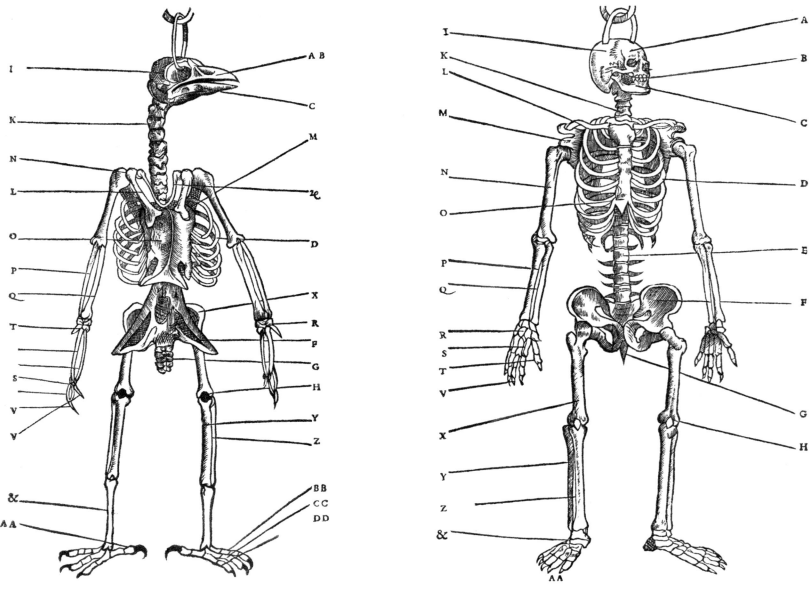

EARLY COMPARATIVE ANATOMY: SKELETONS OF A MAN AND A BIRD (1555)

'We tried to dissect every bird which fell into our hands.' This is the voice of that other Belon, who created his natural history not out of the writings of the ancients, but as a result of the conscientious observations he himself made of nature. He found wonder upon wonder in the inner structure of birds' bodies. Above all, he discovered that as soon as he removed the birds' coat of feathers, which enables them to be distinguished from each other so easily, and also their muscular system and inner organs, he was left with a little *homunculus* of bone, and he found that between the skeletons of the higher vertebrates and of man there were in fact astonishing similarities. Belon displayed these to the world by placing a human skeleton and that of a bird side by side for comparison, giving the appropriate parts of each skeleton the same letters. It did not escape his sharp eye that the wing structure of the bird was built like a hand. Similarly he compared the joints of the feet by showing the lowest part of the bird's leg (&) as equivalent to the human heel. He did not overlook the points which were dissimilar (for instance the many neck vertebrae in the bird) and explained these as resulting from the totally different functions these parts had to perform. Belon had started on the

road which led finally to the triumphs of comparative anatomy achieved by Cuvier, Owen and others.

A century after Belon's bird-book of 1555, a brilliant observer of animals from Paris, Claude Perrault (*see* p. 216), penetrated deep into fields previously unknown. He chose gazelles and bears, dromedaries and beavers for his anatomical experiments, but he preferred to all others that favourite subject of ancient animal descriptions: the chameleon (opposite). This laterally compressed animal with the angular head was like a skin which had come to life, he said; it had the strange characteristic of being able to change quickly both its colour and its shape; this change of shape was due to the working of its very large lungs which with the lateral extensions almost filled its whole body (P, Q, upper diagram); the very convex eyes, protected by deep cavities, can be moved independently of one another (top left, he has tried to show their connection with the optic nerve and the brain). The tongue is thick at the front and sticky; it serves as an instrument of capture, on which the seized insects stay lodged. By means of the muscular system of the middle part (V, Y) it can be shot out like lightning and aimed with precision at the prey, since it is extensible 'like a stocking'.

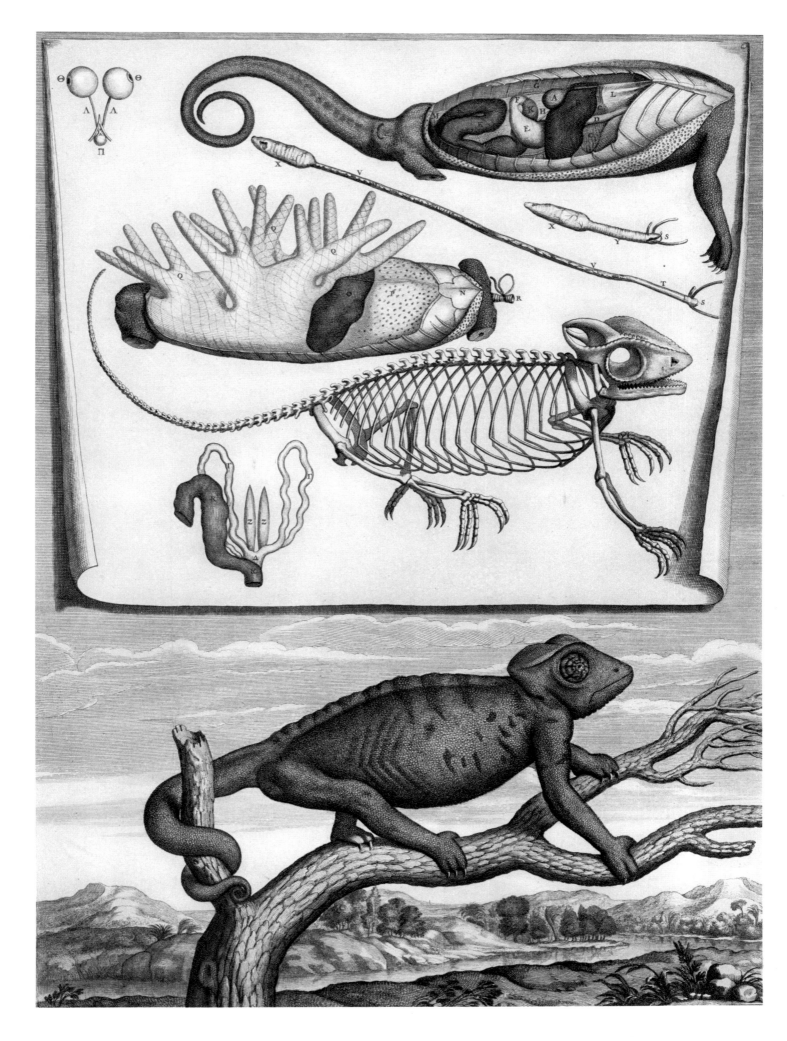

213

COMPARATIVE ANATOMY WITH HUMOUR

In 1733 the London surgeon William Cheselden, Newton's doctor, published the well-known *Osteographia, or the Anatomy of the Bones*. The masterly copper engravings in this work show how sure of itself anatomy had become since Vesalius, in that it was able to comprehend the skeleton down to the smallest bone, and to explain its structure in accordance with its functions. A few engravings show this in a humorous way too, like the reproduction above of an encounter between a dog and a cat in which the whole contrast of character between the animals has been worked into their skeletons. The dog is the roamer and runner with long strong legs, solid fixed claws, and a stiff vertebral column which steadies the body when in swift motion. The cat is a climber of trees, equipped for lying in wait. The very long back legs are suited to the spring-like act of jumping, equally mobile is the vertebral column, which here is arched up into the deterring likeness of a feline hunchback. The paws are not designed for walking long distances, but for the seizing of prey; hence the sharp and movable claws. Both animals are quick of hearing; the dog has in addition a highly developed sensory organ, a nose perfectly adapted for picking up the scent and strengthened with a solid bone structure; the cat has forward-looking eyes sunk into great cavities, and a jaw with thirty teeth, exactly differentiated into varying shapes and sizes; beside these the dog's jaw with its forty-two teeth looks almost like some clumsy organism from prehistory.

The science of anatomy, in particular the study of the osseous structure
of animals, had reached a high level by the middle of the nineteenth century.
Men had learned the art of 'reading' animals' skeletons as if they were
animal biographies.

Belon had already pointed out the way when he used the word *corre-
spondances,* correlationships. Some naturalists, who followed in his footsteps and directed their research towards comparative anatomy, made an
important discovery. Birds, mammals, reptiles and many other classes of
animals had organs which were somehow similarly shaped; this seemed
to suggest that they had originated from a common prototype but now
fulfilled quite different functions in the body. Were not the wing of a bird
and a horse's fore-foot related in some strange way, both being built as
'hands', though in one case the organ is adapted for flight and in the other
for movement on land? To describe these relationships the expression
'homologous organs' coined by Aristotle was adopted; but it was two
brilliant and creative 'readers' of skeletons, Cuvier and Owen, who first
gave the Aristotelian phrase its full significance. The coining of terms
with precise and distinctive meanings was not one of Owen's accomplish-
ments, but two of the most comprehensive collections of his day were
freely available to him for scrutiny: these were the animal collection of the
Hunterian Museum in London, which he catalogued, and the natural history
exhibits at the British Museum.

The three volumes of his *Anatomy and Physiology of Vertebrates* (1866–68)
derived a great deal from this abundance of material. It is from this work
that the pictures (right) of homologous organs are taken, with the exception of the second from the top. One can see various forms of the hand
which have structural similarities but which have to fulfil totally different
tasks. At the top is the heavy, thickset three-toed sloth with powerful
sickle-shaped claws on the forepart of the hand (two of its joints have
become stunted)—a climbing animal, which often hangs for hours by its
four extremities from the branch of a tree. Below this is a bird-like flying
mammal, the bat; it has four extensions at the ends of its forearms splayed
out into something like very long fingers, and these are used to spread out
the thin membrane of the wings, whilst the shortened thumb with the claw
on it enables the animal to grip tightly when climbing.

The flamingo, shown here with its beak in the water in the feeding position,
spreads out its wings with the help of a supporting osseous structure; this
consists of the upper arm, the forearm and hand-bones which are arranged
in one straight line and have been partly stunted.

After the four-footed and flying mammal and the bird comes the reptile
with wings. These are fossilized remains of the long extinct pterodactyl
with a crocodile skull. The carpal bones of the hands end in four fingers
with claws, but the fifth is far longer—the crawling animal has become
a flying saurian. The small reconstruction at the bottom shows the pterodactyl
with wings spread out sailing through the air.

When Owen returned in 1830 to London after a study period with Cuvier
at the Jardin des Plantes, he decided to devote himself to the acquisition
of material for examination, so that he would be able to answer the basic
questions of comparative anatomy which had been raised and passionately
discussed in Paris. Was the great variety of form in living creatures for
functional purposes or not? Had the higher forms gradually developed from
the lower ones or had each made its appearance without any earlier stage?
And as far as the homologous organs were concerned: was there not some
hint in their thousand shapes of an archetypal form like the prototype leaf
of Goethe in the plant realm? Or a hint in the hand of a prototype hand?
'For everyone who wishes to understand the unity in the diversity of any
group of organisms, the acceptance of the principle of an ideal type is
indispensible.' Owen stood by the idea of a mysterious vital force which
produced an inexhaustible supply of creatures, all of them modifications
of ideal types. He still did so at a time when Darwin's theory of evolution
was finding quite a different significance in homologous organs—here
they were variable parts of organisms which changed their functions and
rose like the pterodactyl step by step from a lower to a higher state.

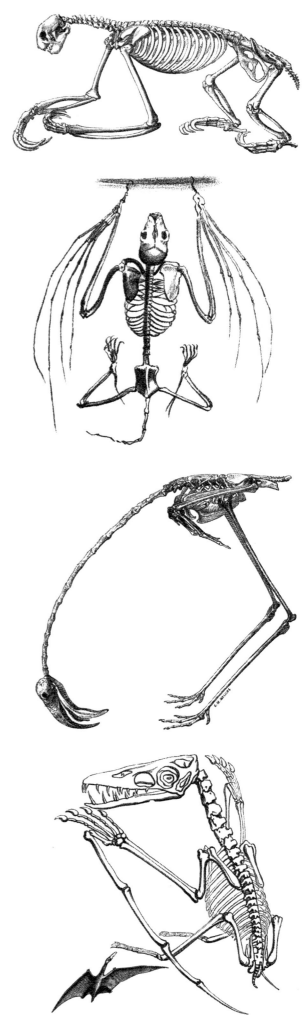

BETWEEN BELON AND CUVIER: STUDYING ZOOLOGY AT THE JARDIN DES PLANTES (1669)

In this scene, which the copper engraver Sébastien LeClerc has recorded, every detail reveals the pride of a science which knows that it has come of age. In front of the table Claude Perrault is sitting and pointing at a manuscript of one of his animal monographs. According to their author, these, like all work from the circle of Parisians engaged on this research, ought always to give evidence of 'assured and recognized truth'. They had been verified by 'people who had eyes in their heads'. In this circle observation was everything and tradition was only of value in so far as it was confirmed by observation. The fanciful cuttlefish of the past were brought, so to speak, into court for detailed judgment to be passed upon them; the works of masters like Aristotle were calmly examined and the admissible information was separated from the inadmissible; the new tendency was to follow Descartes and Borelli in regarding the animal body as a perfectly functioning mechanism. The task of

zoology was this: to portray with precision the outer and inner structure of the animal, to collect as much material for scrutiny as possible, and finally, after making comparative checks with the evidence already established by others, to classify the animal realm in such a way that the whole of it could be surveyed at a glance like the formal garden outside the window. The skeletons on the walls give some idea of their collecting activities. The men engaged on research with magnifying glass and microscope seem determined to make their observations as precise as possible; so do the two zoologists, who are preparing for study the inner organs of a fox. At the left-hand end of the table the secretary J. B. DuHamel is keeping the Minutes. Words are inadequate for the scientific description of their material, illustrations are needed to complete the picture—this is why the illustrator LeClerc is standing behind Perrault and showing the very elegant anatomist Du Verney a plate

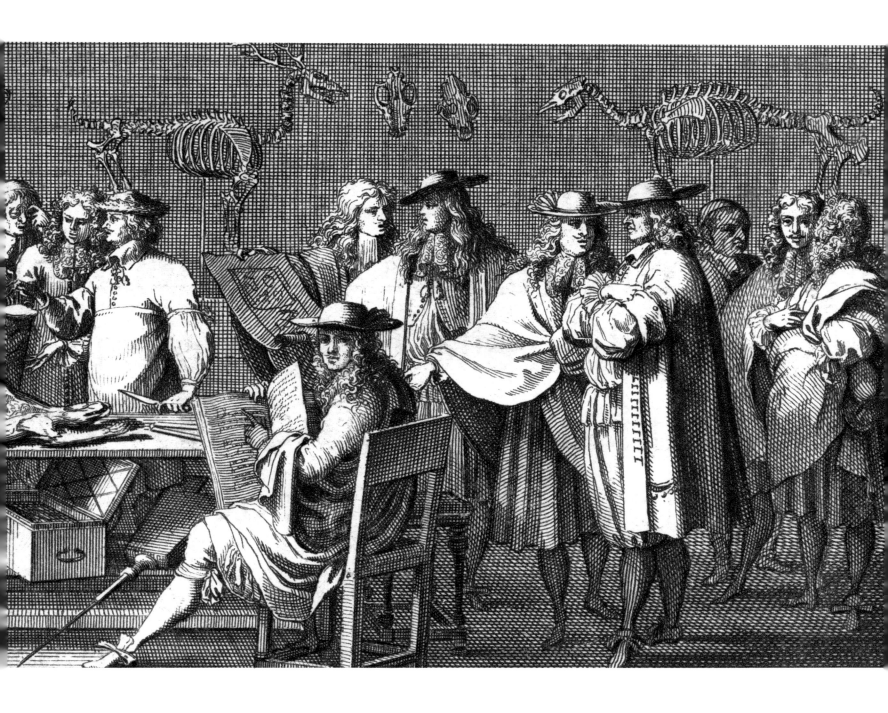

from the great joint work which this circle of men is bringing to fruition: *Mémoires pour servir à l'histoire naturelle des animaux et des plantes* (Memoranda to promote the natural history of animals and plants). The man on the right with his arms crossed looks, according to Franck Bourdier, like Cureau de la Chambre, who introduced zoological research into the Jardin des Plantes in 1635.

In 1626 only a herb garden for the benefit of doctors had been planned here. Very soon, however, the Jardin des Plantes became the home of an independent and far-seeing form of natural science—a form which took delight in observation and experiment, and far surpassed the traditional and more academic science taught at the Sorbonne and the Faculté de Médecine. It made vigorous strides, and attracted important scientists and collectors who donated their valuable collections; it won world fame as a place where bold attempts were being made to create great comparative surveys of the whole plant and animal kingdoms. It was in this spirit that many famous scientists worked here: the botanists De Jussieu and Vaillant, the zoologists Buffon, whose brilliantly written *Histoire naturelle* was read throughout Europe, Lamarck, the classifier of the invertebrates, Etienne Geoffroy Saint-Hilaire, the expert on vertebrates, and the classifier and palaeontologist Cuvier (*see* p. 249). Mineralogy, physics, and chemistry were brought in to help the main scientific work, and between 1640 and 1907 there grew up here a unique branch of the fine arts: the most notable illustrators of France painted on 6,000 large sheets of vellum thousands of plants and animals, a systematic pictorial encyclopedia, a beautiful and faithful record of nature which will never be forgotten. Examples of pictures from this work, which can still be seen in the library of the Jardin des Plantes of today, are to be found on pages 163, 219 and 224 in this book.

The tortoise is one of the many unusual forms of life which are found in the animal world. Conrad Gesner gives this dramatic description of the most amazing characteristic of the tortoise: 'Nature made the tortoises in such a way that they are covered and protected with a hard stony shell; this means that they are not broken in pieces even when run over by a fully laden carriage.' Aristotle in his animal classification placed them not far from the snakes and the batrachia among the 'egg-laying scaly quadrupeds'; Linnaeus classified them with the salamanders and frogs amongst the amphibious animals; Constant Duméril in his *Erpétologie générale* (1834) placed them finally with the reptiles. This well-known Paris classifier and comparative anatomist also made use of the well-known collection on vellum in the Jardin des Plantes in his attempts to distinguish the many varied types of tortoises. His contemporary Nicolas Huet, an impassioned discoverer of beauty in the animal world, produced many masterly works such as this water-colour, approximately actual size, of three examples of the marsh tortoise, which Duméril called *Emys reticulata* (today it is the *Deirochelys reticularia*). The plates of the back-shell are humpy and full of small wrinkles; the pattern which these make against the green background have earned the genus its Latin name, meaning 'covered with a small net'. The neck and head are unusually long and have distinctive red stripes, the tail is short, triangular in shape and pointed. It is a guest from the lakes of North America, clumsy on land but very skilled in swimming and diving; the webs for swimming can be seen between the toes. It has downward-looking eyes, so that it can search for prey on the river-bed. Just as Duméril described with such accuracy the exterior of the American *Emys reticulata,* so did the anatomist and physiologist Martin Rathke make the most subtle examination of the inner structure of the corresponding European

animal, *Emys europaea,* in 1848. He sought amongst other things an answer to the question: how did the tortoise get that strange form which made it the subject of so many fables? He succeeded in opening eggs and removing from them embryos in about the middle stage of development (below). When enlarged six times, a wide navel opening showed clearly on the underside of the embryo, leading towards the yolk-sac. A part of the integument of the embryo lies like a ring round the navel opening, on the left can be seen a piece of the allantois, a bladder which takes off the urine from the embryo. The stomach and back shield have already begun to grow, and in such a way that the skin of the rump is thickened, or to be more exact, that part called the cutis which lies under the epidermis. On the underside of the animal the two halves of the future stomach armour have partly joined together from left and right along a centre line which is still visible. This shield stretches from the area of the collar-bone to the sexual organ, whilst the back shield which is also forming out of the thickened skin is already providing a protective covering for the first neck vertebra at the top, and at the bottom for the growing tail vertebra. Plates of bone will later strengthen this shield. On the upper shield the epidermis, which extends over the thickened cutis, has already developed a very delicate pattern: the top layer of skin has begun to divide up into as many sections as there will be horny plates on the adult animal. The head with the humped crown is an enormous size, but the lower jaw is not yet fully grown. And so it was that a tortoise embryo from the region of Königsberg (now Kaliningrad), standing, so to speak, for the whole varied family of its kind, revealed to a naturalist who worked on it with precision and devotion, how what 'could not be broken in pieces even by a fully laden carriage' began its formation from soft and delicate skins.

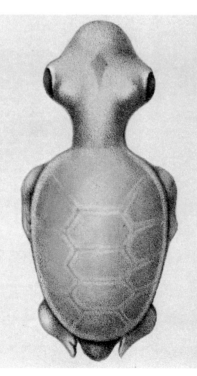

The Deirochelys reticulata, as seen by Nicolas Huet

Left: 'How the Shells of Tortoises are formed'

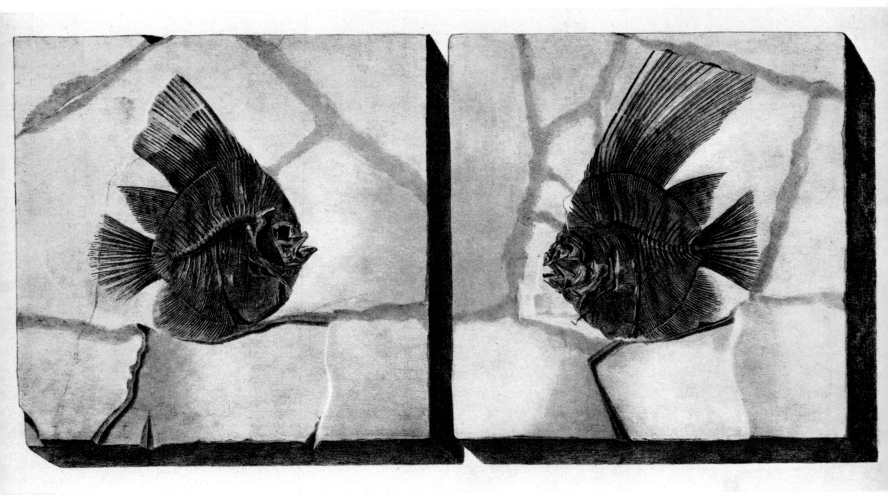

FISH FROM PRIMEVAL SEAS

In the 'epoch of the first manifestations of life on earth' the only vertebrate amongst the many invertebrate inhabitants of the sea was the fish. So says Louis Agassiz in *Recherches sur les poissons fossiles* (Research into fossilized fishes) (1833–42). This statement still holds good, in the light, too, of the fossils found in the earth's crust since Agassiz, although today one has to regard those early creatures which lived hundreds of millions of years ago as rather primitive forms of fish, being jawless like the river-lamprey or, in later forms, more like the shark. The more distant the geological periods this natural scientist from Neuenburg had to study, or the more insoluble his problems seemed to be, the happier he felt. He was equally at ease when he had to show his contemporaries, in a sumptuously illustrated publication, all available fossils of that time as evidence of prehistoric fish-life, or, when later as lecturer in geology and zoology at Harvard he found himself carried forward by the progressive spirit of a young country to probe the depths of the sea along the coasts or to build up for his university a vast museum of comparative anatomy. In order to fill his book with pictures of fossilized fishes he went to Paris to see Cuvier, who generously put at the disposal of this intrepid young man of his own ilk, both his own collections and the preparatory notes for a similar book which he himself intended to write. Agassiz searched through English and other collections as well. For seven years the Munich painter Dinkel drew the pictures for the *Recherches*. When Agassiz, who for twelve years had brought fame to the little university of Neuenburg by his natural history lectures, went to America in 1846, he had sacrificed the whole of his paternal inheritance for the sake of his *Recherches* which became an indispensable publication for naturalists. The division of fishes according to the shape of the scales, as suggested by Agassiz, was not continued, but he did succeed in displaying to an astonished world fish forms embedded in the rock, some of which died out long ago, whilst others—in later modifications—continue to swim the seas today. Following the example of Cuvier, he examined every fish-scale he obtained and every fish-bone. Now and then a discovery revealed at how astonishingly early a date fish-forms were perfectly adapted to their element. Here (above) are examples only very little affected by the passage of millions of years: two specimens of *Platax papilio* with the large cavities and the long flowing fins on the compact body. Agassiz even found traces of colour on the scales of these fossils from the famous Paris collections.

Page 221: Marcus E. Bloch published his *General Natural History of Fishes* (1782–94) in many volumes with 343 selected pictures

THE 'BROAD-FINNED' AND THE 'BLACK-FINNED' FISH IN THE INDIAN OCEAN

on European and exotic fish. At the age of nineteen he was still unable to read a word of that same German language in which he was later to describe very precisely all the beings which inhabit sea and river. He came from a poverty-stricken Jewish family in Ansbach. Later he freed himself from the misery of his childhood and with the support of relatives became a doctor in Berlin. There he directed his whole passion for research, collecting and analyzing towards the many varied forms of the creature 'fish'. He was a very gifted successor to Ray and Willughby, the English founders of the systematic classification of fish. In addition to the European kinds there were, in the century of Cook's voyages, more and more exotic varieties, like those shown above, which had to be brought into the general picture. What Bloch, his French colleague Lacépède and their predecessors had collected and classified, became later merged into something much more ambitious: an attempt to produce the most comprehensive survey ever made of the form, anatomy and way of life of fish; this was the *Histoire naturelle des poissons* by Cuvier and Valenciennes. Still later a refined physiology, working with the microscope and following in the wake of Johannes Müller and others, described the fish as *the* prototype of a living creature which was fully harmonized with its medium. As early as 1679 Borelli, with

the eye of the physicist, saw in the fish simply a weightless creature suspended more securely in the water than a bird in the air. The air-filled swimming bladder was in his view the organ which equalized 'quickly, easily and exactly' even the smallest variations between the specific gravity of the water and that of the animal. Borelli also repudiated the opinion of the ancients that the fins were the oars of the fish. He saw the pectoral and side fins rather as organs for steering and stabilization; the forward movement of the fish on the other hand depended on the strength of the tail fin. In the case of the two *Chaetodon*-forms pictured above, the whole flattened-out body (see the cross-sections) together with the strongly developed back and stomach fins have become something like one single tail fin. Both have the same type of gill-covers; they are semicircular and look as if they were covered with a silver skin. Under these, the vital element, the water which streams in through the thick-lipped mouth, performs its work and provides oxygen for the gills. Both of them have along their sides a line which rises in a high curve—that row of tiny holes in the skin which directs the water into a subcutaneous canal, where sensitive nerves register the slightest change in pressure of the water around it. Thus, even if the fish were blind, they would not collide with obstacles in their way.

Bees have earned the love of man from time immemorial. In the Middle Ages there was a charming legend that Christ himself created them, and that when Peter tried to do so, wasps appeared instead. Virgil, the Roman poet who died nineteen years before the birth of Christ, extolled them in the fourth book of his *Georgics*. He can be seen above with his patron Maecenas standing behind the beehives. The man on the left is giving the 'swarm warning' on a cymbal, a means used by ancient peoples to intimidate a swarm of bees in flight so as to be able to bring them in more easily.

Virgil says that at the head of the bee-state there is a warlike king and bees are not born but 'gathered' by the others 'with their mouths from friendly herbs'. Such conceptions settled the question of the reproduction ob bees until the seventeenth century. It was assumed that the spawn formed on flowers or olive-trees or that the working bees were fertilized by the drones; it was also thought that the female working bees originated from the 'king', and the drones from the females.

It was the cleverest of all the early microscopists, the Dutchman Jan Swammerdam, who discovered the ovaries of the queen bee and the genitals of the drones and brought to an end all the earlier erroneous ideas. Swammerdam with his unquenchable thirst for knowledge revealed things never before imagined. It was only in 1737 that Boerhaave published from the papers left behind by Swammerdam at his death in 1685 the *Bible of Nature* with its unique copper engravings. On page 223 (far right), can be seen the ovaries of the queen bee (*a, c*) filled with eggs, with the oviducts and the bag containing the sting poison (*z*). The eggs which are ready for laying are fertilized as they pass by the seed-bag (*t*). This bag, as we now know, is filled with so many seed-cells as a result of one act of union of the queen with a drone that fertilization is assured until the death of the queen, that is, for three to five years. 40,000 to 70,000 bees belong to a single colony!

In the centre is Jan Swammerdam's drawing of a bee-sting, showing the barbed hook (*h*) which is thrust into the victim—'a work of art by the Great Master.' The dreaded poison is pressed by a muscle out of the little bag (*b*) into the channel of the sting; Swammerdam regarded *l* and *m* as tiny cartilages, *o* as four muscles which set the sting in motion. When Swammerdam later became a chiliast, he did not know whether he ought to publish or suppress these discoveries which by then seemed to him almost sacrilegious. It was he and Malpighi who first started the science of entomology in great style. It progressed from strength to strength through René Antoine Ferchault de Réaumur and Jean Henri Fabre to Karl von Frisch's discovery of the sign-language of the bees in our time.

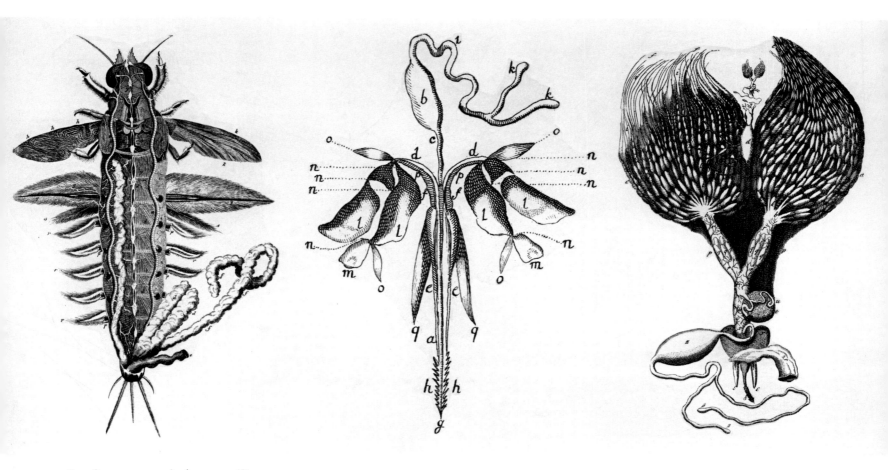

JAN SWAMMERDAM'S AMAZING DISCOVERIES

With astoundingly delicate feats of micro-dissection, both Malpighi and Swammerdam enlarged men's knowledge of invertebrate anatomy. The larva of the may-fly (left), from
Swammerdam's *Ephemeri Vita* (1675), is a drawing of a creature no more than a quarter of
an inch long. The dissection shows how two air-tubes on each side of the centre run through
the tiny lungless body, how the little air channels at *p* (here cut through) lead to the outside and to the gills (*r*) and into the wings, how the nervous system, arranged in ganglia,
collects sensory messages, and how the intestinal system operates. *Bottom right*: Not long after
the appearance of Swammerdam's *Bible of Nature* a highly gifted observer, Charles Bonnet
(*see* p. 176), inspired by Réaumur, began in Geneva his work on caterpillars, grubs and butterflies. In May 1740 he succeeded in proving the existence of a method of reproduction which
had until then only been a subject of conjecture by very few men: parthenogenesis, the birth
of new living creatures without fertilization and without sexuality. Bonnet set a small flask
filled with water into the earth of a flowerpot, put into it a small branch of a spindle-tree,
after inspecting its leaves very carefully; then he put on the branch an aphis which had just
been born before his eyes. Finally he turned a glass jar upside down over the plant, so that
his prisoner was completely cut off from the world. From four o'clock in the morning until
ten at night he observed it continuously with a magnifying glass, kept a diary on its movements and the casting of its skin, drew up ten stages of its growth and discovered on 1st
June that he must 'now call her mother aphis'. From this day until 21st June she produced
ninety-five offspring by means of clearly proven parthenogenesis. In the same year Bonnet
established that the aphis reproduced itself in the autumn by sexual copulation, and thus
undergoes an annual cycle in which there is variation in the reproduction method. Hardly a
decade later the research work of this Calvinist, who loved nature like a Rousseau, came to a
sudden end. His eyes, overtaxed by the microscope, ceased to render him any further service.
The pictures are from his *Traité d'insectologie* (1745).

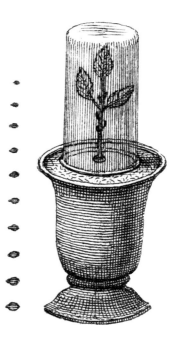

The butterfly provided the natural historian with the greatest of all his puzzles: transformation. One and the same creature appeared in what seemed to be three totally different forms, one after the other. The first great entomologist, Aristotle, described the larva, the form it adopts when young, by a word which means 'mask': the caterpillar is the butterfly but still in the shape of a worm. It is within the concealing and protecting cocoon that this great transformation occurs: a land creature (in some cases even an aquatic one) grows wings and flies into the air as a butterfly. It took men many centuries to discover the secret of the hidden transformation of all the insects, for instance from larva to chrysalis and from chrysalis to cockchafer or from fly-maggot to fly; and there are countless other instances. Decisive research was undertaken by Swammerdam who classified the insects according to the extent of their transformation. But it was William Harvey who first used a term which he nevertheless at that time did not clearly interpret: metamorphosis. Claude Aubriet, in one of the most beautiful plates he painted for the Jardin des Plantes (opposite), recorded the metamorphoses of the swallow-tail even to the extent of showing the changing of colour within the maturing chrysalis; in the middle row of his picture he placed the male butterfly, as seen from above (top), and as seen from below (middle); below that, the female. At the bottom, left, are a few butterfly's eggs (bottom right, slightly enlarged). It was not until more precise research was carried out in the nineteenth and twentieth centuries that the whole transformation process within the chrysalis was understood; that is, how the organs of the caterpillar disappear and the butterfly's organs, which up to this point appeared only in rudimentary form, become fully developed.

'If the scholars like to think bees are formed from dead decaying oxen, or hornets from dead horses, or dor-beetles from dead donkeys, I leave all this, as far as I am concerned, to others to decide on its worth or its worthlessness. I do not want to blame anyone for it; let anyone believe it who will!' declared the Berlin scholar Johann Colerus in 1592. These were mild doubts felt about the prevailing views on the formation of insects, views which had been laid down as authentic by Aristotle, and were seldom challenged until the invention of the microscope. According to the evidence of the naked eye, maggots and larvae seemed to be brought to life by the friendly warmth of the sun, and then to creep out of compost heaps or corpses. There were no signs of their having been begotten or born of another animal—therefore insects did not come out of eggs. The inference was rather that dead matter could produce life. Buffon, Lamarck and even Fouchet, who died in 1872, supported this theory of 'spontaneous generation'; Swammerdam, Francesco Redi, and Lazzaro Spallanzani opposed it. As time went on, scientific research was devoted not so much to the question of the formation of insects out of nothing, as to those micro-organisms, the bacteria, which, invisible and seemingly born out of the air, were suddenly there. It was Pasteur's experiment, shown on page 188, which finally demolished the theory which taught that living things on this earth could appear out of nothing as if it were the result of some sorcery on the part of nature. With the discovery of viruses in the twentieth century the question was again revived.

Opposite is a metamorphosis of insects in a comfortable lodging. They are larvae of the carpenter-bee (*Xylocopa*), as they were first observed with great precision by the man who was perhaps the most important entomologist of all, R. A. F. Réaumur. He described these larvae in his *Mémoires pour servir à l'histoire naturelle des insectes* (Memoranda to promote the natural history of insects) (1734–42). The inventor of the famous eighty-degree spirit thermometer has uncovered a place where carpenter-bees are hatching out (*aa* to *hg*); it is inside a round stake which is supporting a sun-baked apple espalier. At *o, s* and *r* are entrances. The insect, similar to a bumble-bee, has opened these up with its sharp jaws and in the interior it has gnawed out from top to bottom four tube-like passages (*f*), (*g*), (*h*) and (*i*). Right at the bottom it has laid an egg amongst a mass of honey and pollen; the supply of food will last long enough for the larva to turn into a bee. Each wood-cubicle has been sealed at the top with a cover of concentric rings; in this way the passages have been filled to the top with cubicles for the offspring. Réaumur stood in wonder before this minute creature the 'carpenter-bee' which seemed to be endowed with such foresight.

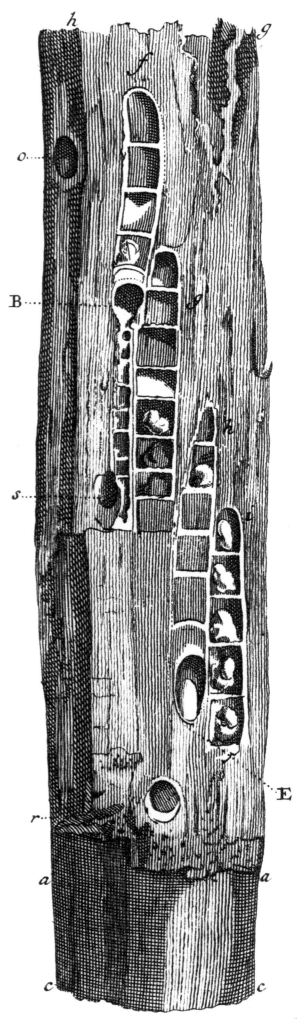

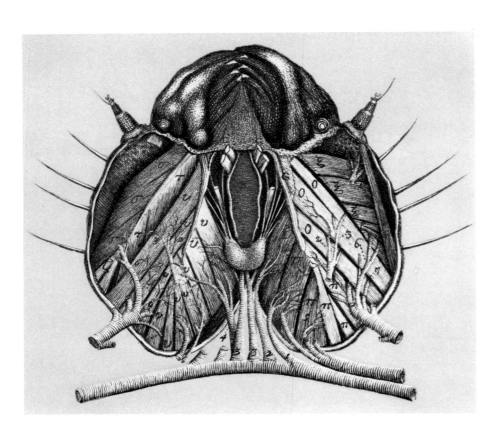

The lively race of insects with their many species has from the earliest times attracted the amateur naturalist. They comprise a miniature fauna; they are comparatively easy to catch and to observe and they stand not too high and not too low in the great hierarchy of living creatures. All over the world their observers still behave as if they belonged to a secret society; the leading principle in their worship of nature is the sentence formulated by Pliny: 'Nowhere does nature seem so wonderful as in the smallest creatures.'

Some of these amateurs achieved in their research more lasting results than many of their long-forgotten academic colleagues. The Dutch solicitor Pieter Lyonet and the Nuremberg miniature painter Johann Roesel von Rosenhof were typical of such men. Lyonet, who was a second Swammerdam as far as the art of microscopic dissection was concerned, published in 1762 an anatomical monograph illustrated by his own hand on the caterpillar of the goat-moth. Seventy pages of text are devoted solely to a description of what, to his astonishment, he found in the head of the caterpillar. He counted no less than 228 muscles in it. One layer after another he removed, working from below—a monster apparatus of muscular fibres in miniature, all designed to set in motion the crunching mechanism of the mandibles (above). The symmetrically arranged fibres (*o, n, v*, etc.) can be clearly seen in the round shell of the head. On the right close behind this runs the muscle which can withdraw the smaller joint of the feeler into the larger one. The gullet has been removed from the long dark cavity in the middle. The cushion-shaped structure at the bottom end is the ganglion of the head, which has nerves running away from it to the front and sides; from the body come strong (here partially dissected) breathing-tubes (*1,2,*

3, etc.) which branch out into the muscular fibres, to distribute the oxygen which, in the case of many other animals, is brought along by the blood.

Right: Roesel von Rosenhof describes in detail in his *Diversions with Insects* (1746) the activity of the 'cunning and skilful ant-brigand', the ant-lion. The Nuremberg painter searched the fringes of the forests with great care for the small ditches where the larva of the ant-lion lies in wait, half buried, with only the mandible showing (*a*). At *c* it prepares to close its mandible to make it into a scoop and pelt with sand an intruder, an ant, so that it slides down into the sand funnel. Figure 5 shows a victim making ineffectual efforts to escape; it is going to fall straight into the jaws of the highwayman. Figure 6 is a masterly achievement of observation: 'Once the insect is caught, our cunning fox, hidden in the sand, usually holds her high above him (*f*) and sucks all the juices out of her.' Later entomologists established with the microscope that the mandible has a concave groove incorporated in it. Through this the 'cunning and skilful ant-brigand' pumps into its prey digestive juices, which dissolve everything digestible in it; this is then sucked into the jaws along the groove. Digestion thus takes place in front of the mouth as happens with the spider. The gut of the ant-lion has a very narrow bore. Finally the enthusiastic painter watched the ant-lion building its trap. He saw it crawl close under the surface of the sand (Figure 7) and at a suitable place it began to make a spiral of sand (*h*), working always inwards towards the centre. It thus formed a round hole with very uneven slopes surrounding it. In order to level these out, the insect closed its mandible, covered itself—including its broad head—with sand, and hurled it in the air so that it covered the walls evenly (*K*).

Fig. 2.

Fig. 5.

Fig. 6.

Fig. 7.

Fig. 8.

227

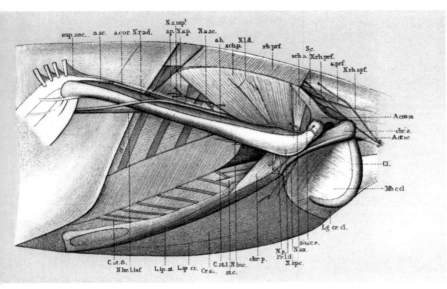

SECRETS OF BIRDS' FLIGHT

PETRUS CAMPER'S DISCOVERIES IN BIRDS' BONES

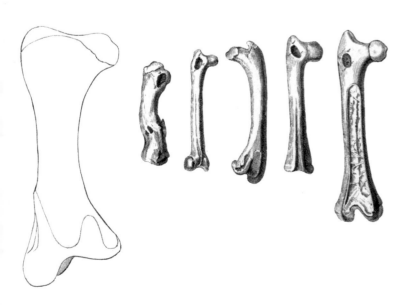

Birds puzzled the physicists as much as they did the zoologists. How was it that the law of gravity which bound men and animals to the earth like stones did not appear to operate in the case of birds? Were birds lighter than air? Galileo had noticed that birds' bones were light, hollow and thin and Borelli's sharp eye had detected how birds, like gliders, allow themselves to be carried aloft by flying into the wind, and to be propelled through the air by the impetus of the varying air currents. The Dutch anatomist Petrus Camper, basing himself on Galileo, discovered an astonishing natural phenomenon in 1771. He opened up the marrowless upper thigh-bone of an eagle (bottom, extreme right) and saw how several little bone supports strengthened the thin wall and how the covering of the bone was intersected by blood vessels—but he also saw to the left of the top of the joint a strange oval aperture. This also occurred in the stork and the capercaillie (second and fourth figures from the right); even the massive-looking bone of the ostrich (extreme left) was found on closer scrutiny to have this aperture at the back. Tests revealed that part of an air channel system ran through these bones; the bird could fill not only its lungs and spacious air-sac with air, but also some of its bones. In this way it reduced its weight. On examining birds which flew and ran badly—a domestic fowl (third from the right) and a sparrow—he found the hollow parts of their bones were filled with heavy marrow.

The two cross-sections of the shoulder of a wild goose (above) show how the morphologist Max Fürbringer, laid bare in 1888 the inner mechanism of the flying apparatus itself. One might be looking at a technical drawing with countless clearly labelled individual parts—muscular fibres, sinews, bones and thin nerve-cords, together making up the faultless structure which carries the great birds of passage high over the lands of men.

Opposite: The humming-bird, the lightest of the light inhabitants of the bird world. Here are the male (left) and female of the *Phaëthornis intermedius:* they have a greenish and brownish colouring, and can therefore live hidden in the undergrowth of the Brazilian primeval forests without drawing attention to themselves. They collect the nectar from the tropical flowers with their long beaks. The English painter and ornithologist John Gould included a description of the bird in his magnificent *Monograph of the Trochilidae.*

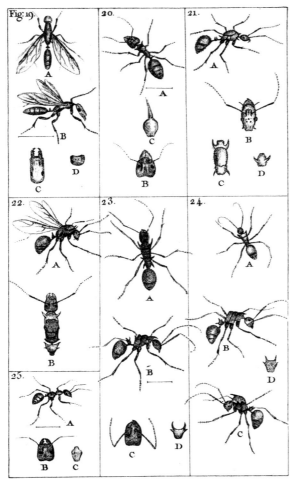

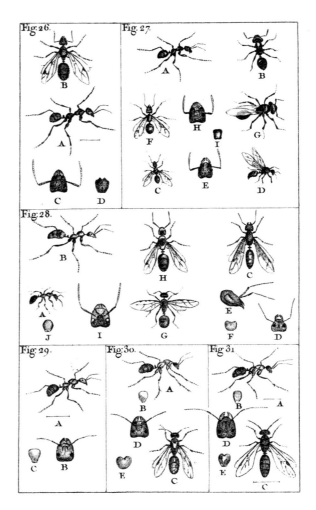

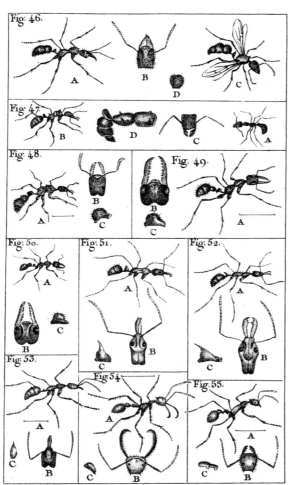

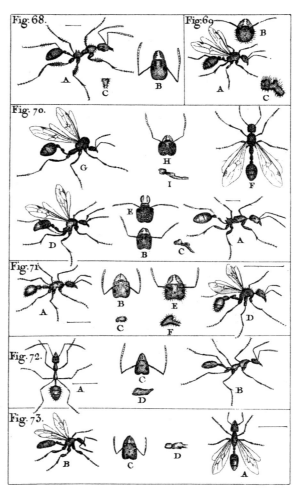

Embryology

The human body consists of billions of cells, all of which fulfill their varied and differentiated tasks and help to produce the living miracle of a breathing, growing, seeing, thinking man. When life departs from him his body becomes the scene of billions of dying cells. Only a few individual cells of one single type escape this death. These are the reproductive cells, the egg cells measuring roughly 0.1 millimetre, and the motile sperm cells or spermatozoa, three million of which, according to Hermann Linder, occupy about the volume of one bean. In this sphere of minute dimensions the species wins its victory over death by the union of the sperm cell with the egg cell and the continuation in a new living being of both substances, mysteriously laden with the inheritance of generations. This is the picture drawn by modern natural science of the basic pattern of a process which is similar for all sexually reproductive animals (and generally speaking for all plants too). It was only in fairly recent times that any firm evidence was obtained. In 1875 a researcher was the first to see with his own eyes a spermatozoon penetrate an egg-cell, and only since Pasteur has it been shown that no form of life, not even the most primitive, can proceed from dead matter, but that everywhere and in every type of birth life proceeds from life.

With the growing tendency to specialization during the nineteenth century a particular science of emerging life arose, embryology. It created an increasingly detailed picture of ontogenesis—the growth of the individual from the embryo to full development—which is one of the most precious gifts science has conferred on modern man.

'Take twenty or more hens' eggs and give them to two or three hens to hatch out. From the second day onwards remove one egg daily, crack it open and examine it.' This passage, from a work ascribed to Hippocrates, gives the earliest known directions for the first experiment in embryology. Aristotle followed them too. His observations raised a question in his mind which still evoked passions in quite modern times: was the future animal at the very beginning of its life already contained in the egg, entirely formed in every detail, even though not completely visible? Many thinkers inclined to this theory of preformation right up to the eighteenth century. Or did the organs appear within the egg one after the other? The Greek thinker favoured the second hypothesis. This idea of epigenesis, as it is called, was one of the great insights he handed down to posterity just as the assumption of spontaneous generation and his picture of fertilization in viviparous mammals and in man were among his errors. Did not menstrual bleeding cease after sexual union? Therefore, he deduced, after direct contact with an active male principle, this blood henceforward nourished the developing life until birth.

The long road leading to the discovery of the hidden origins of life is signposted by the great names of Harvey, de Graaf, Wolff, and von Baer. William Harvey (*see* p. 282) tested his skill in observation

Today we can distinguish over 5,000 species of ants. The road which led to the wide surveys of species and genera of animals was paved with centuries of work by the classifiers. This work, at least in the early periods, often resembled that of the Danaids ceaselessly trying to fill their sieves with water. Everything they achieved was soon out of date, because new discoveries continually broke up the system. The born classifiers never allowed themselves to be dismayed by looking into the future; they found themselves rather urged on by the thought that the systems worked out before them were quite inadequate. The Frenchman, André Latreille, for instance, despite Swammerdam and Linnaeus tried in his *Histoire naturelle des fourmis* (Natural History of Ants) of 1802, to classify all the ants he had found in the south of France and later, working under Lamarck, in the abundant collections of the Jardin des Plantes. It was not 5,000, but only about 100 species, which he gathered together in nine families. The illustrator Oudinot drew them, slightly enlarged, displaying as he did so an obvious delight in crawling insects. Latreille's task was made more difficult by the fact that with ants as with bees there has to be a distinction between the egg-laying queens, the males and the hordes of female workers. All three 'castes' can be seen in Fig. 27, one of the twenty-nine groups reproduced here. In this group the classifier has placed the *fourmi fuligineuse*, the 'sooty' ant, a branch of the family of the 'arched ants'. AB is the female worker, CD the male, winged, ready for the act of fertilization, FG is the queen, also winged in readiness for the marriage flight; B, D, G are slightly enlarged specimens; E, H, I are parts of the head and armour, displayed in this way so as to make it easier to distinguish them from other forms.

by Hippocrates' original experiment. His discoveries about the hen's embryo went beyond the somewhat earlier researches of Volcher Coiter, Hieronymus Fabricius and the rather later work of the microscopist Malpighi. He found in the egg the place, known later as the embryonic disk, where the embryo's life began; he observed that even before the egg hatched out certain organs moved within the foetus as if in a dream, that they arose successively and that the whole creature certainly did not exist already preformed 'with bones, claws, feathers and flesh'. And so he came out strongly in favour of the epigenesis theory and in 1651 threw out the most challenging statement in the whole of embryology: *Omne vivum ex ovo,* every living creature comes from an egg.

Harvey's great century of natural science came near to a solution of these problems. In 1677 Jan Ham discovered human spermatozoa while his master Leeuwenhoek made a similar discovery about various animals. In 1672 a doctor friend, Regnier de Graaf, who was attempting to find the ovum of mammals and of man, thought, like Nicolaus Steno and others, that he had made the great discovery. He had in fact found what he later named follicles, not ova but vesicles in the ovary containing the ova. Not until 1827 was Karl Ernst von Baer able to show that man and viviparous animals grow from an egg cell, and in no other way.

Harvey's bold assertion *Omne vivum ex ovo* was thus confirmed over a wide field. An important discovery had meanwhile been made, namely that animal life could also be propagated asexually by budding and division as Leeuwenhoek had observed, or by partheno-genesis as Bonnet had observed. A twenty-six-year-old naturalist, Caspar Friedrich Wolff, had finally settled the stormy century-old argument over the idea of preformation by his dissertation *Theoria generationis* (1759). Neither in the plant germ nor the hen embryo nor that of any other living creature was there the slightest trace of a preformed organism; the animal's organs developed successively like the roots, leaves and blossoms in plants. Wolff's bold intuition actually anticipated the findings of embryology a century later, namely that physical organs developed from quite specific embryo layers of the developing ovum.

Do we know the origin of life today? Despite all the biochemists' Faustian attempts to create the moment at which life first begins to pulsate within highly complex synthetic combinations of albumen, we do not really know how any one fertilized cell, escaping the mass death of all the cells of an organism, begins to take shape and to form a new living creature.

A POND NEAR NUREMBERG

The artist Roesel von Rosenhof has written his initials on the two posts on the left. If one ignores the two menacing ducks just drawing near and concealed frog-killers like crows, storks and large fish, this is precisely the kind of place a frog really loves: calm water, a few water-lilies, reeds and bulrushes on the bank, in which he can hide, tree-trunks and boulders, on which he can sun himself in comfort for hours, a soft bed of mud where he can dig himself in for his winter sleep, an open space where sound will carry to the neighbouring village for the gayest of spring singing contests: 'In the cool of the evening the song begins on every side; it continues with greater persistence than any other song of the night; only towards morning does silence return to the ponds, though one or two, still blissfully conscious of the champion performance they have just given, will treat their audience to one more half-suppressed croak' (Brehm).

It is mating time for the water-frog. For other kinds it is over; the large eggs of the grass-frog, rolled into slimy lumps, are already lying in the water near the banks. Tadpoles have slipped out and move round in the water in all stages of development: there is the wriggling larva, the two-legged swimmer and the four-legged swimmer. A toad has put her string of eggs into the water. On the tree-trunk the male water-frog sits in mating position on the back of the female, like other pairs which mate as they swim in the water. The white voice-pouch of the male can be seen below the eye. The elephant cow brings six calves into the world during her whole life, a female herring lays about half a million eggs. The higher rate of propagation amongst animals which run the danger of becoming prey to others is their main weapon against mass destruction. The same applies to the plants. It is this which accounts for the little orgy of fertility in the pond near Nuremberg.

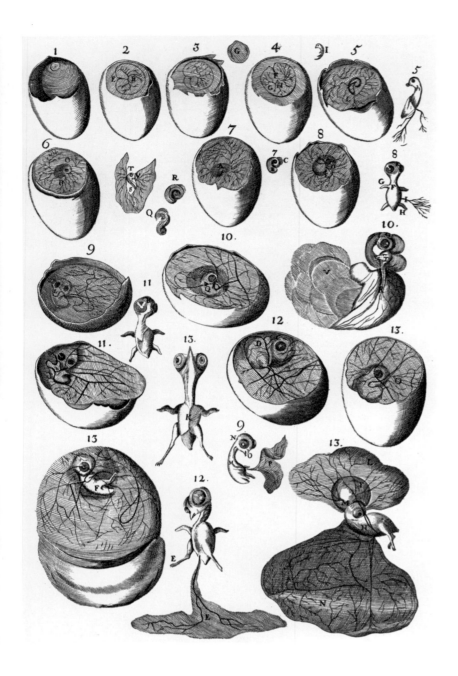

The series of pictures of the development of a hen's egg reproduced above is the earliest of its kind. This draughtsman's work is derived partly from a rather inadequate book-knowledge and partly from personal observation: it is thus reminiscent of much of the work of the Renaissance naturalists. He realized that the white and yolk of the egg served as nourishment for the embryo, but he thought the fine sinuous cords under the top arch of the egg, the *chalazae,* were the seat of the forces which formed the developing animal. Hieronymus Fabricius, professor of anatomy at Padua, did not use a microscope, so he often saw more in the embryo than was actually there. He observed correctly the development of the head and the large eyes, but he also indicated (in *5*) the whole shape of the embryo a little too early (in fact on the second or third day). He thus gave strong backing to the supporters of the preformation theory, according to which a new creature develops in the egg with its shape already cast from the beginning and with all its organs maturing simultaneously.

Right: 'Every living creature originates from an egg,' announced Harvey boldly in 1651, but without sufficient evidence. It was only in 1827 that K.E. von Baer closed the widest gap in the chain of evidence. Before his time direct observation had supported the view that the viviparous mammals did not originate from the basic cell 'egg'. But this German-Baltic scientist saw the 'first beginnings of the egg of the mammals and of man in the ovary', and the evidence he produced was like a collection of specimens from the realm of fantasy. With large Arabic figures *1* to *7* he marked the egg of a bitch at different stages of maturity. At the beginning it is so small 'that it could not be drawn properly by the copper engraver' (*1*). Below this he placed the tenfold enlargements of his discoveries with Roman figures, and the thirty-fold enlargements with Roman figures and asterisks. IX is the Graafian follicle (which many had taken for the egg of the mammal up to that time) of a pig with the actual egg (8). XIII shows the human egg, XIV the corpus luteum of the bitch, and in the black segment at the bottom von Baer has placed in a row for comparison, the embryonic cells of a few of the lower animals: of a snake (XVI–XVIII), of a lizard (XIX–XXII), of a frog (XXIII–XXVI) and of a river crab (XXVII–XXX).

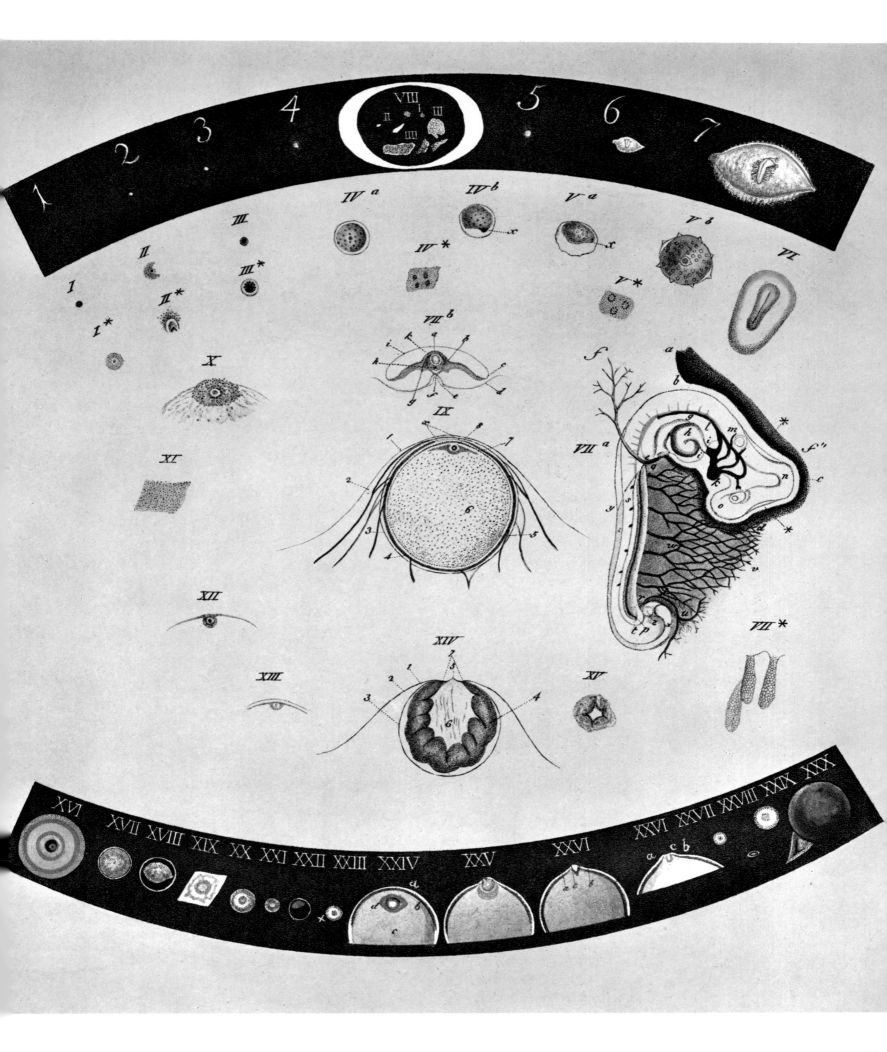

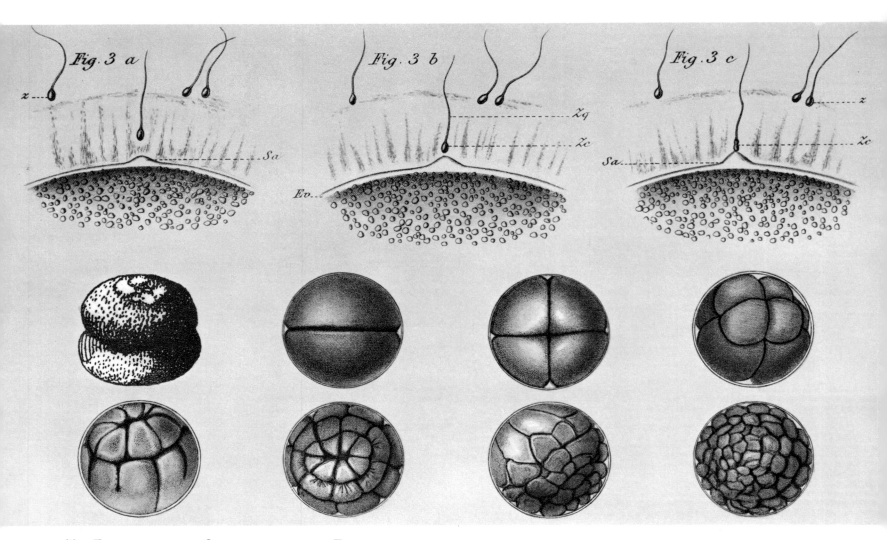

THE FERTILIZATION AND SEGMENTATION OF THE EGG

Great events in the history of embryology occurred in the years 1875, 1877 and 1884. In 1875 the twenty-six-year-old German anatomist Oskar Hertwig observed for the first time the process of fertilization: the object of his observation was the egg of a sea-urchin. Two years later the Swiss Hermann Fol took these observations further by examining the egg of the starfish *Asterias glacialis*. And in 1884 the botanist Eduard Strasburger, when examining a flowering plant, followed for the first time the passage of the pollen nucleus into the egg-cell (*see* p. 174). In both realms of nature new life originates as a result—if one ignores the simplest creatures and some special instances—of the uniting of two embryonic cells, which carry hereditary substances and preserve a strictly constant number of chromosomes, as Eduard van Beneden demonstrated in 1883. These discoveries answered questions which had been asked for thousands of years. In the top row is a picture by Fol of four spermatozoa, 600 times enlarged; they are being propelled by a tail thread (zq), and making their way towards the ovum which is far larger in size. (The fertilization takes place in the water outside the animal's body.) The egg is covered by a soft integument. A minute '*cône d'attraction*' or cone of fertilization arches itself opposite the approaching spermatozoon, according to Fol, and then

just at this point the spermatozoon makes a sudden entry. Immediately a little skin forms round the egg, which cannot be penetrated by any other spermatozoa.

The lower rows show the first visible stirrings of the creative forces in the fertilized egg. It is a slightly enlarged reproduction of an egg-cell of the brown grass-frog. With frogs' eggs the segmentation process can be followed very clearly. Malpighi discovered this when for the first time he observed the beginning of segmentation under the microscope (extreme left). The series of phases which follow were drawn in 1851 by the physiologist Alexander Ecker. Between two phases there is an interval of half an hour to an hour. During this time and in accordance with strict numerical laws a one-cell structure turns into one with many cells; the egg is divided into 2, 4, 8, 16, 32, etc. cells. At the lower, brighter-coloured vegetative pole which is rich in yolk (in the seventh figure it is turned upwards to the left), the formation of cells is hindered by the yolk in the egg-cell, and so fewer cells are formed here than at the opposing, animal pole which is weak in yolk. In the last figure the animal pole is in the centre; the 64-part 'raspberry form', as K. E. von Baer called it, can be seen. It is a hollow sphere built up from cells, the blastula, in which the creative forces will cause the first forms of future organs to appear.

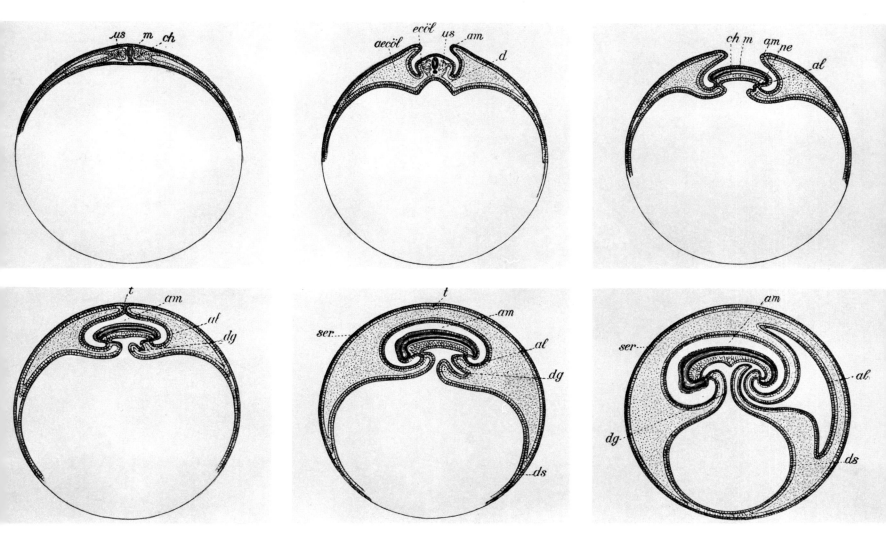

FORMATION OF GERM LAYERS AND ORGANS

The earliest phases through which a living creature passes as shown here in schematized form, are in accord with the views of Caspar Friedrich Wolff expounded in his ingenious *Theoria generationis* in 1759. But it was in the first half of the nineteenth century that their meaning was really understood, mainly as a result of the work of Heinrich Christian von Pander and Robert Remak, a Poznan doctor who later became a professor in Berlin. Here it is possible to see the development of a germ-disk swimming on top of the yolk mass of a fertile hen's egg. (The first two pictures are cross-sections, the rest are longitudinal sections through the back-stomach axis.) Whereas with the frog's egg the 'raspberry form' folds itself into the egg from the vegetative pole and thereby forms a double-wall (it is called a gastrula at this stage), on the egg on the left above there appear two layers, called germ-layers, pressed down almost flat by the mass of yolk, and kept apart only by a third germ-layer (which is seen to be in two parts), the mesoderm. The outer germ-layer, called the ectoderm, will, as would be expected from its position, produce the protective covering of the body. From it also will originate the highly differentiated communication system of the senses and the nerves. The neural tube, the future spinal cord and brain, has already separated itself from the germ-layer. In the inner germ-layer, lying directly on the egg-yolk, that is the endoderm, other formative forces lie dormant. These are to build up out of fast-propagating cell-groups the intestinal canal, the liver, the bladder and also the lungs. In the middle germ-layer there are at *ch*, the chorda dorsalis, the beginnings of the vertebral column; at *us*, the original segments, there are the first signs of the future muscular system, bones and blood-vessels. The dotted space in between is the abdominal cavity beginning to form. In this way the forces in the three germ-layers create the foundations for the main parts of the awakening organism, and these parts give the creature its form and cause it to breathe, feed itself, feel and, before it dies, to create life in its offspring. And in these offspring the same delicate processes, in which the organism seems to envisage its future structure, will repeat themselves and so create, in turn, the main component parts of their bodies. In the sixth figure the yolk-sac *(ds)* has already become smaller, the cavity of the body (dotted) and the growing structural appendages of the organs take up more and more space. At *ser* the serosa, the protective outer skin, is visible, at *am* an inner membrane covering for the embryo, the amnion, whilst *al* indicates the urine sac (allantois); this collects the urine which forms as a result of the metabolism taking place within the embryo.

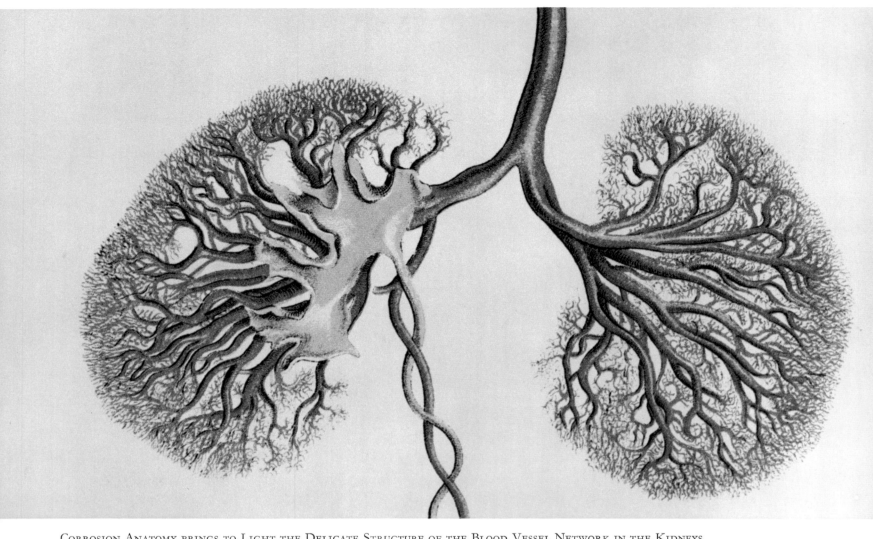

CORROSION ANATOMY BRINGS TO LIGHT THE DELICATE STRUCTURE OF THE BLOOD VESSEL NETWORK IN THE KIDNEYS

Before the middle of the nineteenth century there was no very clear division between anatomy and physiology. When the anatomist examined the structure of an animal's skeleton, or its muscular or nervous system, he was usually also seeking an answer to the physiological question: how do the skeleton, muscular and nervous systems work? And when Albrecht von Haller, working in the spirit of his master Boerhaave, raised physiology to the status of a separate science, it was found that there was room here for contributions from anatomy as well. Those who in the nineteenth century with Claude Bernard, Johannes Müller, Carl Ludwig and others disciplined themselves to confine physiology strictly to questions of the vital functions of the organism, took over a science which had already created a rough and ready structure of its own. After thousands of years of error, blood circulation was broadly understood, thanks to Harvey and Malpighi; similarly the chemistry of breathing was known, thanks to Lavoisier; Lazzaro Spallanzani, an eighteenth-century man of all-round interests, had proved by drastic experiments on himself that the food in the stomach is neither ground down by any mechanism nor forced into a state of decay or fermentation, but subjected by the stomach juices to definite chemical disintegration processes; the Viennese Georg Prochaska made

public about 1800 some reasonably clear ideas about the reflex mechanism of the central nervous system. The physiologist was much helped by the highly refined methods of preparation used in anatomy. These allowed him to recover whole and even bring under the microscope the most delicate vessels which lay concealed deep down in the organs. In his 'Atlas', published in 1873, the Viennese anatomist Joseph Hyrtl presented some real works of art in the field of corrosion anatomy. His work represented the culminating point of a development which began with Swammerdam, who injected the air-tubes of insects with coloured wax to make them visible, and with Ruysch (*see* p. 286), went on from there to the resin injections of the Berlin naturalist Nathanael Lieberkühn (1748) and finally saw the technical refinement of Hyrtl himself. He worked with coloured liquid wax and caustic corrosive mineral acids. In this way he was able to prepare the two separated halves of the kidneys of a gnu-antelope, reproduced above; it is a very delicately ramified net of blood vessels, through which liquefied waste products and surplus water are carried into the kidneys. The excretory duct or ureter where all the tubes run together from all sides is coloured in yellow. The internal spermatic artery is wound round it in spirals, a method of display well-known in anatomy.

CLAUDE BERNARD ENGAGED IN PHYSIOLOGICAL EXPERIMENTS IN HIS LABORATORY

The new, fully independent physiology of the nineteenth century established itself first in France. It was here under the direction of François Magendie, that those first burning questions were asked about the most delicate chemical and physical processes in the organs of the animal body; it was here too that countless new kinds of apparatus were invented for experiments on animals, and it was these that brought a surgical atmosphere into the physiological laboratories; and it was here in France that the most distinguished mind of the Paris school, Claude Bernard, applied himself to the great basic question of physiology: what exactly holds the innermost parts of a living organism together? These men, as they studied the functions of an animal body within the new physiology, applied their knowledge at the same time to the human organism and vice versa.

Bernard can be seen above, holding a lancet connected with an electric wire above a rabbit, in the corner of the cellar of the Collège de France which he had converted into a laboratory and furnished with experimental equipment largely made by himself. From left to right are pupils and colleagues: Gréhant, Dumont-Pallier, Malassez, Bert, d'Arsonval, an assistant (behind), Bernard, Lesage and, directing the proceedings, Dastre. The most primitive physiological workshops produced the most important results. The man whose first professional attainment as an apothecary's apprentice in Lyons had been the manufacture of a tin of shoe blacking, succeeded as doctor and later as lecturer in Paris in clarifying by thousands of experiments the rôle of the digestive juices in the mouth, the stomach and the intestines. The appearance of sugar in the urine in cases where the blood had a high sugar content led him to suspect that the kidneys were the organ which controlled the mineral content of the blood. He discovered glycogen, studied the effects of poisons on the organism and in 1878 he introduced the concept of the 'milieu intérieur', which led to the acquisition of more knowledge in physiology than most other ideas of this kind. He meant by this that astounding interplay of the inner controlling system of the body, which causes it to react intelligently as a complete entity to changes in its environment. Too high or too low temperatures are automatically adjusted to those in the outside world, and the supply of moisture is regulated accordingly; the nerves and the blood act as stabilizing media of a most delicate kind. Only one thing escaped Bernard: an 'inner vital force independent of outward chemical-physical influences'. A few years after his death the research into hormones went forward in the direction he had indicated. It is still breaking new ground.

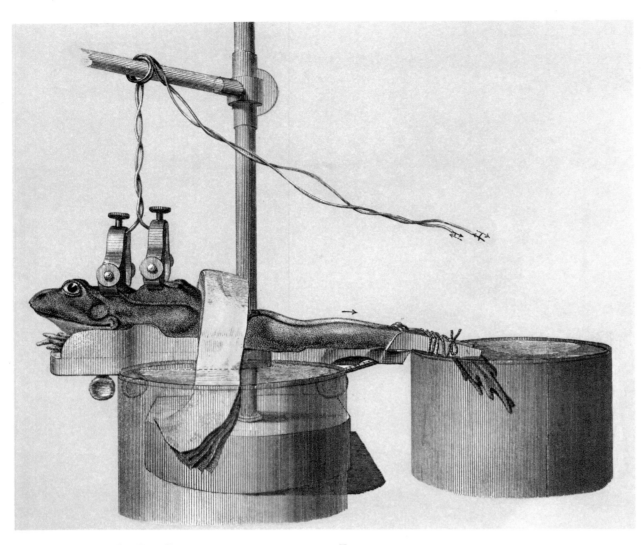

HOW EMIL DU BOIS-REYMOND EXPERIMENTED WITH FROGS IN 1848

Emil Du Bois-Reymond, a professor in Berlin, was the Edison of the physiological laboratory. He devoted himself with great enthusiasm to the invention of one apparatus after another for the examination of physical forces in animals. The main theme of his research was animal electricity, which he investigated in the active nerve. In order to obtain a reliable measurement of the very weak current in the animal he used a frog for his experiment, and to establish beyond doubt what effect electric shocks from outside had on the muscles and nerves, he had to bring the animal through the experiment alive, undamaged and in a state of complete immobility. He tied it firmly with non-conducting silk cord on to a platform made of old dry mahogany and placed this on two vessels filled with a saturated solution of salt. These were connected to a sensitive recording apparatus. Two brass clamps led in the current; the grips of these had blunt teeth, and they were placed on the folds of the frog's neck. Strips of wet blotting-paper, folded together like a compress, led the current away into the solution. To Du Bois-Reymond such apparatus proved not only the existence of physical forces, but also the universal applicability of his philosophy. 'Ernst Brücke and I have sworn to prove the truth of the statement that there are no other forces operating in the organism but the physical-chemical ones': this passage comes from a letter in which Du Bois-Reymond, ignoring the weakness of his logic, challenged contemporary thinking. He was worlds apart from the subtlety and conscientiousness which a Claude Bernard would display as he resisted enthusiastic but unproven interpretations; he furiously attacked everyone who held the view that chemical changes and physical forces did not alone suffice to explain the life and working harmony in the organism. When Liebig dared to name this other missing element 'vital force', Du Bois-Reymond flew into a rage and called him a 'scourge of God'.

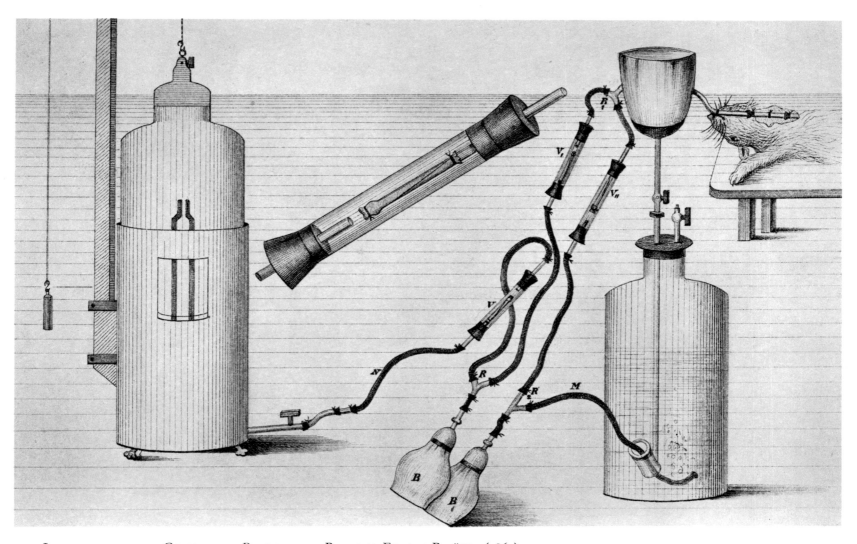

INVESTIGATIONS INTO GASES IN THE BLOOD BY THE PUPILS OF EDUARD PFLÜGER (1865)

In 1878 Eduard Pflüger, who was then aged forty-nine, opened his new physiological institute in Bonn. It was equipped with several physical and chemical laboratories and was one of the many similar establishments which opened their doors at that time in Europe; they were places where new ground was often broken in experimental work on the subtle chemistry and physics inherent in living matter, as E. Pflüger called it. Carl Ludwig, whose studies dealt in an exemplary way with urine secretion, the rôle of oxygen in the blood and several other questions, had founded his own institute in Leipzig in 1869, his pupil Ivan Petrovich Pavlov followed his example in 1890 in St Petersburg (Leningrad). This was the splendid result of the work which Magendie and Bernard had begun in Paris. An experiment, executed by Pflüger's pupils gives an idea of the intellectual atmosphere of this refined physiology of the nineteenth and twentieth centuries. The young medical student, Wilhelm

Dohmen, starting from the research undertaken by Isidor Rosenthal, set himself the task of establishing what influence the gases in the blood—oxygen and carbon dioxide—exercized on respiratory movement. What was the motive force behind breathing? Autonomous orders from the nervous system? Or did all respiratory movement in human and animal life follow the most basic of all laws: that is, was the impulse to breathe brought about by the accumulation of carbon dioxide or the urgent need for oxygen? The answer (according to which both factors have a stimulating effect on the nerve centre controlling the respiratory muscles) was discovered with the help of the apparatus pictured above.

It is a highly complicated network of hose-pipes, air-bags (B) and equipment to collect and measure gases from the blood, which are extracted from the living organism by means of tubules inserted into the wind-pipe of the animal.

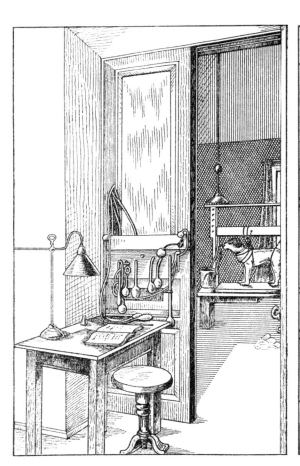

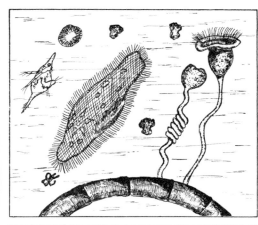
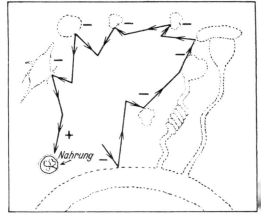

The Animal as a Mechanism or as a Being with a Soul

The drawing on the left above shows two rooms in Pavlov's 'Tower of Silence' at St Petersburg (Leningrad). This house was built in 1910 and so designed that the animals brought there for experimenting on would be cut off as far as possible from disturbance and noise from the outside world. Even the scientist himself was only connected with the room from behind the door through the cable of the recording apparatus by his writing desk. The task was to examine the extraordinarily complicated signalling mechanism of the cerebral cortex of the dog. The animal stands on a trestle wearing a light belt; the saliva, which it immediately secretes on seeing food, is drawn off through an artificial passage in its cheek into a baby's bottle. The experimenter can read off the amount secreted on a calibrated horizontal tube. Pavlov proved the existence of so-called 'conditioned reflexes' in addition to the innate ones. If a metronome was allowed to tick when food was shown to the dog, on a later occasion it would secrete saliva simply when it heard this familiar ticking—a centre in the brain has responded to a new stimulus and this has led to a new automatic reflex action. The wily Pavlov came to the conclusion that the brain was nothing but an automatic telephone exchange; the purely mechanical character of all so-called mental processes seemed to be proven.

This kind of thinking on psychological matters prevailed until about 1900, but opposition to it was soon to arise. One of the leading protesting thinkers of that time was a land-owner-scholar from the Baltic named Jakob von Uexküll; he brought into science a broad and courageous mode of thought; it was also one which was close to nature. He used

to say that the leading physiologists treated nature like a man who, when reading a book, examined the form of the letters and the printer's ink, instead of grasping the information it provided. If an animal was to be understood, it should not be artificially isolated in some Tower of Silence, but its reactions examined in relation to its particular environment; and, as scientists of similar views added, the animal should be regarded as a complete being with very many sides to its individuality and not simply as a mechanically functioning object. Uexküll explored the environmental relations of birds and bees, dogs and earthworms, even *Paramoecia* (slipper animalcule). This creature is shown (above right) in the minute environment where it lives. Its cilia make undulating movements as it dashes through the water. Everything uneatable around it against which it knocks represents for it something like a negative signal in its environment—it is simply 'obstruction'. Such obstructions always cause the minute creature to move quickly away. 'Only when it reaches its food (decay bacteria), which alone of all the things in its environment is not an irritant, it comes to rest.' Today in many countries the science of ethology has clarified broad, previously unknown aspects of animal life, through the work, for instance, of W. Craig in America, of Konrad Lorenz in Austria, of Karl von Frisch in Germany, of Heini Hediger and Adolf Portmann in Switzerland, of F. J. Buytendijk and N. Tinbergen in Holland, and of E. Howard in England.

In close relationship with the new concepts of ethology stood the animal psychology which began to blossom at the turn of the century. It boldly enquired what independent

Paleontology and the Theory of Evolution

Few natural phenomena have caused man such boundless amazement or occasioned such strange conjecture as the remarkable fossilized remains of animals and plants encountered in the earth's crust. Dwarfs, giants, mandrakes, two-headed calves, all seemed less mysterious than the fact that, far removed from any seas, mussels in stone were found on high mountains, while fishes were seen in quarries or even stones bearing drawings of comets found in mines. Mention is made of them in Chinese and Greek writings of the last pre-Christian centuries and Xenophanes and Strabo give the correct interpretation of them: fossils are remains of extinct creatures. But well into Renaissance times the study of fossils was directed not by sober logic but by a spirit of speculative fantasy or by belief in miracles. Like Aristotle and Avicenna, men postulated a 'formative power' in the earth with an unlimited capacity for producing the most amazing effects. They imagined that cosmic light penetrated minerals and produced pictures of the stars, or they believed in a kind of sport of nature, or they supposed that germs of plants and animals drifted in the air and then grew in the soil into subterranean flowers or insects. These formations were particularly revered as displaying the creative hand of God.

One of the founders of a scientific paleontology, Johann Jakob Scheuchzer, had as it were adopted these interpretations in historical sequence until he announced the prevailing interpretation current in Christian circles in the seventeenth and eighteenth centuries: 'And my eyes had been so far opened during my search for truth that I now clearly perceive that the source of those fossilized fragments was the Flood.' With Leonardo da Vinci, Girolamo Fracastoro and Bernard Palissy he is one of a series of pioneers who saw in fossils evidence of the history of plants and animals. As early as 1669 the most important of these scholars, Nicolaus Steno, distinguished forms which were 'as like as two peas' to extant creatures from others belonging to extinct forms of life from past ages. The great era of paleontology was the first half of the nineteenth century when, in the Jardin des Plantes, Cuvier, Lamarck and Geoffroy Saint-Hilaire collected and organized their abundant finds, determining their age in close collaboration with the geologists. To them 'species long extinct owe their scientific resurrection' (Goethe).

The conclusions drawn by generations of scientists from fossilized plants and animals had unusually powerful after-effects. Despite the violent resistance of theologians, paleontology overthrew accepted ideas of the age of the earth and discovered in quarries and mines a new picture of the development of living things—the concept of evolution. Man in his short life perceived around him landscapes that changed with the seasons. But the species of plants and animals, the elements and the earth appeared to have stood unchanged and unchangeable from the beginning of time. Martin Luther in accordance with Christian tradition estimated the age of this eternally constant creation to be six thousand years. But anyone studying fossils found this span of time as inadequate to explain

behaviour occurred in the animal, since it was able to experience things, to reach after things and to 'think'. Among the earliest experiments in this field were the intelligence tests which Wolfgang Köhler carried out on chimpanzees in 1913 in Teneriffe. In the middle picture, the bait, the much-desired banana, hangs high up on the plaited wirework over the experiment room. Three boxes were placed on the ground far apart from each other. The chimpanzee Sultan tried to reach the banana first by making gigantic leaps—but in vain. Then with great zeal he pushed up the biggest box, put the second on top of it, and, standing on top of this, tried to snatch the banana. This failed. He then discovered the smallest box, carried it carefully up, and by jumping from the top of this breath-taking tower he finally brought down the tasty morsel. Now he can be seen sitting and watching one of his less skilful colleagues at work. Köhler, as well as I. Meyerson who worked with greater discrimination, and a number of others, found in countless tests that the higher animal possessed within fixed limits the ability to behave 'judiciously', and to use reflection and deliberation, and that there was considerable variation in intelligence level between each individual animal. It is no longer frivolous to say as Hans Driesch did in about 1900: 'The soul is an elemental factor in nature,' both in animals and in man.

them as did the geologist for his primeval seas. Aristotle had referred vaguely to very long periods of the earth's history, Buffon's calculations yielded the figure of seventy-five thousand years, Lamarck assumed that nature 'surveyed unlimited tracts of time, thousands, millions of centuries.' Haeckel in about 1900 thought the age of the earth to be a hundred million years, and subsequent methods of determining the age of rocks based on radioactive processes yielded a figure of 2.3 to 3 thousand million years. Luther's six thousand years, in contrast, seem not much more than a second of time in the earth's history.

Paleontology and geology between them have revealed to man a temporal abyss never before suspected. He has learned painfully to think, not in thousands but in millions of years. He has filled them with pictures of the ice age, the throwing up of high mountain chains, primeval landscapes, eras four hundred million years ago when 'life climbed out of the sea on to *terra firma.*' The oldest fossils known today show organisms which may have lived more than five hundred million years ago. The concept of non-historical nature has totally disappeared, taking with it many inadequate notions. We now know that nature has her own infinitely long, slow history, just as that of the human species is short and swift.

The idea that the species were not created once for all to remain invariable throughout these incalculable ages was not original to Lamarck and Darwin. As early as 1685 the English lawyer Matthew Hale dared to write this revolutionary sentence: 'We must not imagine that all genera were created in the form in which we see them today,' and Robert Hooke in 1705 anticipates the visions of later paleontology: 'There were in past ages whole countries which sank beneath the sea... There were countries which rose from the water... Many species of things were completely destroyed and became extinct, while others underwent change and variation... Though it is indeed very difficult to read nature's handwriting, to establish a chronology from it and to determine the intervals of time at which particular catastrophes or changes took place, it is by no means impossible.' It is as though earlier paleontology already contained the seeds of the idea of a gradual evolution of all life before this concept expounded by Lamarck, Darwin, Huxley, Haeckel and others in the nineteenth century profoundly modified current ideas of natural history.

JOHANN JAKOB SCHEUCHZER DISCOVERS TRACES OF THE FLOOD IN THE SWISS MOUNTAINS

In 1716, Scheuchzer, a Zurich doctor, published a catalogue of his unique collection of fossils under the title *Museum diluvianum;* it contained 528 items. He was the first to go on systematic searches for fossils in his native Alps and in particular in the limestone slopes of the Jura mountains. He made countless excursions there. In the picture opposite a few outstanding specimens from each main group in his fossil collection lie at the feet of their discoverer like game laid out in front of a huntsman; ammonite, snail and mussel shells, fish and even a few remains of fossilized plants. Scheuchzer used to take with him on his expeditions students who were living in his household. One of them can be seen on the right working with a pick in the hope of making new discoveries. The draughtsman has placed the scene in the Alps instead of the Jura. The path leads up to cloudy regions; a refuge, perched like Noah's Ark on a hilltop, makes the scene look like Mount Ararat, but in a Swiss setting. The picture is in complete harmony with Scheuchzer's views on geology: 'The mountains have, so to speak, two kinds of epoch from which the calculations of their age must begin. One goes back to the time of the Creation; the other to the renewal of the earth during and after the Flood.' The Flood crushed the original landscape of the earth into a 'liquid mass', covered it with mud, boulders and rocks; when the waters receded, the new landscape appeared as it was to remain after the Flood, just as we see it in this picture; but hidden within it lay the objects which bore witness to the Creation which came before the Flood, those forms turned for ever into stone, which were once living animals and plants. Scheuchzer had worked his way through all the errors of the early make-believe paleontology, before John Woodward's *Essay toward a Natural History of the Earth* (1702) taught him to regard fossils as a completely natural phenomenon. At the same time he found this new knowledge thoroughly satisfying, because it was in keeping with his instinct to see a revelation of God in every work of nature.

Truth and Faking in Paleontology

In the spring of 1725 three youths brought to the physician-in-ordinary to the prince-bishop of Würzburg and dean of the medical faculty a quantity of most unusual fossils; they said they had found them buried in the ground on a nearby hill which was evidently a real happy hunting ground for the fossil collector. There were low reliefs on stones as big as plates, of primeval spiders spinning their webs, of wasps flying towards flowers, and of fourteen-legged insects of a species never seen before. Beringer was not in the least suspicious; on the contrary he became passionately interested in the promising young science of paleontology. He put in hand further excavations; stones with stars on them came to light, and comets, and so-called *lapides litterati* with the name of Jehovah on them in characters which approximately corresponded to Hebrew! The dean of the medical faculty still noticed nothing unusual, threw discretion to the winds and in 1726 announced to the scientific world his unprecedented finds in 200 pictures. 'Is this Franconian hill the only one to produce such treasure? Is there anything like it in the whole of Europe?' he asked proudly. He was unable to explain the origin of the stones; in the accompanying text he presented all the reasonable explanations so far produced and alongside these the more absurd ones; and he then left the reader to judge for himself whether they were buried talismans and works of art or fossilized works of nature. By the time the book appeared, the truth had been discovered. Beringer had been the victim of an academic intrigue. Ignatius Roderique, professor of geography and algebra, and Georg von Eckart, university librarian, had themselves made the fossils and bribed the youths to present them to the unsuspecting Beringer, whom they envied and hated, so as to provoke him to bring out a publication which would make life impossible for him. It is said that Beringer first became suspicious when one day a stone was brought to him which had his own name written on it. The perpetrators of this malicious hoax were the losers. They had to leave Würzburg; Beringer remained. He lives on today in people's memory as a tragic

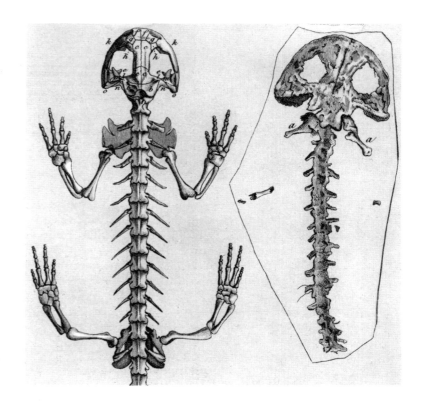

figure—the gullible scholar who was so blinded by his passion for a new field of science that he failed to discern deceptive things—or people.

In 1726, the same year in which Beringer's ill-famed *Lithographia Wirceburgensis* appeared, Scheuchzer amazed the world by finding a skeleton of 'antediluvian man' (top right) in the marly limestone quarries at Öhningen on Lake Constance. He thought he had found the yoke-bones, eye-sockets, frontal bone and dorsal vertebra of *Homo sapiens;* his frequently stated belief in the Flood enabled him to account for the rest. A century later the remains of this '*Homo diluvii testis*' reminded the knowledgeable Cuvier of a similar well-preserved skeleton in his own collection. This is what he established: the finds were the bones of a giant salamander—he spoke ironically of the 'frog of Öhningen'. But posterity has continued to respect the discoverer—even though he was wrong—and gave the giant salamander species the name *Andrias scheuchzeri*.

Below left: An undisputed relic, much reduced in size: part of the jaw-bone of a primeval colossus, the megatherium, first shown in 1856 by Owen.

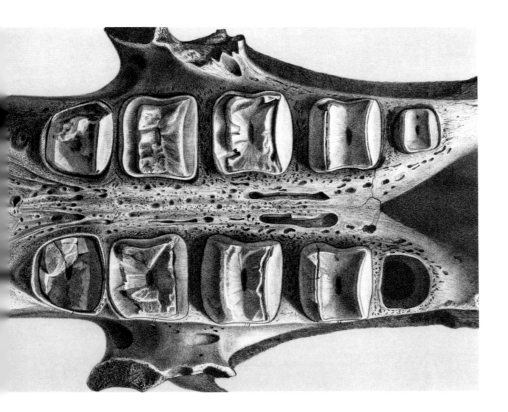

'And the bone structure of our animal has been completely reconstructed': this is how Cuvier, as adroit as a conjuror, closes his commentary on the drawing reproduced below of a model of an animal belonging to an extinct species. The bottom picture shows how the remains looked, before the scientist applied his logical mind to their assembly: they are bones of *Anoplotherium commune,* a mammal about the size of a pony and with a long tail, which was found in Antony in the Seine area; Cuvier had compared its bones with those of an example preserved in a similar condition from the gypsum of Montmartre in Paris where many fossils were found. For Cuvier had a very sharp eye for the possibilities of combining several elements into one and his technique consisted in making up one animal out of the remains of two or more. In the case of the skeleton found in Antony, for instance, this provided a number of missing dorsal and lumbar vertebrae as well as the head for the Paris specimen. Cuvier also drew on his knowledge of the anatomy of animals still living—an inexhaustible supply—in his search for forms to complete the structures. The third and most adept step in these magnificent reconstructions of extinct creatures was of a purely intellectual nature. Cuvier's first principle was that every living creature is a whole which coheres as the result of an inner synthesis, and in which each separate part enables one to draw certain inferences about the whole and similarly the whole suggests certain conclusions about the parts—the so-called 'principle of the correlation of parts'. 'If the intestines of an animal are so constructed that they can only digest meat—and only raw meat at that—then its jaw must be adapted to eat it, its claws to grab it and tear it apart, its teeth to cut up the prey into small pieces and masticate it; and its whole system of organs of movement must be built for pursuit and the hunting down of its prey; and its sensory organs must be attuned to detect it in the distance.' By applying the law of correlation Cuvier saw in his mind the *Anoplotherium* grazing in the primeval swamps and crunching water-plants and roots with its set of teeth specially designed for this kind of feeding.

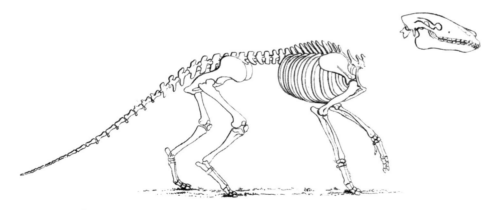

A Paleontological Gallery is opened in Paris in 1885

In the Jardin des Plantes, where Cuvier had worked, a new paleontological collection was opened in 1885. The greatest draw for the Parisians were the extinct colossi of the animal world, those skeletons dug out of the ground which seemed like the remains of a race of giants long since departed. Here are two examples: a mammoth-like elephant found near Le Gard, and the plump megatherium, the giant sloth. It was found near Buenos Aires and Cuvier devoted to the monster hours of conscientious study. Head and shoulders are like those of the sloth, the fat three or four-toed feet with the sharp-cutting nails designed for digging suggest the anteater. The slanting pelvis and the powerful upper thighs are far heavier than the bones of even the largest elephant still in existence.

GEORGES CUVIER LECTURES ON PROBLEMS OF PALEONTOLOGY

Under Cuvier and some of his colleagues, the Jardin des Plantes (or *Muséum national d'histoire naturelle* as it has been called since the Revolution) reached the culminating point of its long and famous history. Young people streamed from every land, eager to learn, amongst them L. Agassiz and R. Owen—to the brilliant, many-sided, eloquent Cuvier, who also served French education as a councillor of state. Cuvier, the comparative anatomist, classifier and paleontologist, based his thinking on the concept that every organism was built as a unit with special functions; the function conditioned its structural plan, and its classified place in the animal world depended on the structure of its most important organs, that is, its nervous and circulatory system. All species were for him variations on a few proto-

types; these had not originated from each other by evolution, but were laid down at the Creation as separate orders; some species had disappeared again as a result, perhaps, of great natural catastrophes, and different new ones had made their appearance afterwards. This part of his philosophy was superseded by the discoveries of Darwin and others.

The finding of any well-preserved fossil of a plant or animal must be regarded as a stroke of good fortune, when one considers the many destructive forces which sweep away the remains of organisms and blot out the traces of earlier millennia. This did not, however, deter Cuvier, Adolphe Brongniart, Lamarck and others, as they worked in Paris, from introducing their conception of the prehistoric world like a new dimension into zoology and botany.

On the Staircase of the Old British Museum

In the second half of the nineteenth century, in particular, scientific expeditions left Europe for the unknown areas of the world in very large numbers; it was as if they wanted to fill, before the end of the century, the gaps left by earlier discoveries. The draw of the scientific research expedition was as powerful as the expansionist desires of the nations which were now becoming world powers or developing world-embracing economies. The material available for study to botany and zoology surpassed all that had previously existed and provided practical opportunities for far-sighted investigations, in which the great abundance of living matter could be mastered. The concept which had the most important results was the theory of evolution.

Like the rising tide approaching the high water mark, the increasing flood of scientific material poured in to swell the stocks of exhibits in the leading European museums. Their history in the nineteenth century is one long tale of museum buildings which overflowed, were extended and then overflowed again. This was the case with the world-famous British Museum. It was opened in 1759 in the select Montague House, its contents at first consisting mainly of natural history exhibits. This watercolour by the elder George Scharf gives a very vivid impression of the situation as it was in 1845, a time when a new building was going up. This in turn soon proved too small, with the result that in 1882 the natural history exhibits were taken to the vast building in South Kensington which still houses them today, a veritable palace of comparative natural history.

THE JAMES CLARK ROSS EXPEDITION DISCOVERS AN ERUPTING VOLCANO IN THE ANTARCTIC

In the years 1839 to 1843 the English explorer J.C. Ross led the most important expedition into the ice-world of the Antarctic since the journeys of Cook. One of the most amazing of their finds was a smoking volcano which towered up to 13,000 feet. It bears to this day the name of the flag-ship *Erebus* (in the foreground), and a smaller, extinct crater that of the accompanying ship *Terror*. The explorers brought home with them an abundant collection of botanical and zoological specimens. They studied among other things the penguin, observing its way of life in greater detail than ever before. These birds have moved from the realm of the air to the water—the realm of the fish—but they return to the land for the hatching of their young. Their wings have turned into fins, the feathers are short, dense and stiff; those on the wings are like scales; three of the four forward-jutting toes are webbed. The body is heavy with its paddings of fat under the skin, but even in a rough sea it is superbly suited for swimming. The picture (opposite) of the species *Eudyptes* (today *Megadyptes*) *antipodes,* which a zoologist in the expedition drew, shows not only the body structure of several birds from a close vantage point, but also in the distance masses of them drawn up in almost military files, assembling as they do every year in their familiar mating areas.

THE BEAGLE AT THE FOOT OF MONTE SARMIENTO IN THE TERRA DEL FUEGO

H.M.S. *Beagle,* a brig of the Royal Navy, was under orders from 27th December 1831 until 2nd October 1836 to chart the coastal waters of Patagonia and Chile and also some groups of islands in the Pacific. On this ship, cooped up in a very narrow space with his collections, notes and books, lived Charles Darwin. Darwin was largely self-taught; he gave up the theological studies which he had undertaken in a half-hearted way and joined the expedition as member responsible for natural history research, on the recommendation of the botanist, Henslow. During explorations lasting several weeks, mainly in South America, Darwin collected an immense amount of material for study, and he showed his genius in creative comparative work on plants, animals and stones throughout half the world. 'In earlier times this district must have been full of giant animals' he noted down in his diary when he made a rich discovery of fossils on South American territory. Darwin compared the skeleton of the giant sloth and of the giant armadillo with its far smaller successors now living. He also compared species of finches on the Galapagos islands six hundred miles from the coast with those on the South American continent. These were evidently descendants of ancestors which had once strayed off to the islands, and had then developed beaks of many different shapes, evidently to suit the different conditions of life there. As a result of these observations by Darwin traditional views on the immutability of species began to waver. While on the *Beagle* Darwin arrived at the first outline of his theory which was to prove that the species is variable. He felt compelled to design a new and rich picture of 'this magnificent wonderful world'. This was far removed from the Christian myths about the Creation, and the prevailing ideas about the constancy of the species. He saw the abundance of the animal and plant species as the result of a drama lasting millions of years in which living things had come into being, changed, and disappeared. (Detail of a watercolour by the painter Conrad Martens.)

Three years after his return from his adventurous world tour, Darwin, now thirty-three, moved with his wife to the peaceful atmosphere of his country house in Downe, Kent (below, the workroom), where he worked indefatigably until his death forty years later. He made no further tours abroad, except in his mind which ranged through all the periods of the earth and through all the flora and fauna of every continent. The tone in this household was set by the great spirit of kindness shown by its members to each other and particularly towards the scientist, suffering as he did for decades from crippling neuroses. He made his seclusion into a way of life; cut off from everyone, yet connected with the whole world through his correspondence, he lived on, refusing all distractions, amongst his books, his simple experimental apparatus, his testing beds and his all-embracing thoughts. On the left can be seen one of his many bookcases; on the right, in the niche, shelves and chests in which he amassed a whole collection of carefully treasured oddments, bottles full of preparations, boxes of flower-seeds and all those files in which he collected extracts from books and journals, all neatly arranged according to subject. In front of the niche to the right, the large easy chair in which he used to sit writing letters and manuscripts; in front of the fireplace, to the right of the coal-scuttle, like the true animal lover that he was, he has put a round basket for the dog. The trees of the estate can be seen through the window. From the peace of this country house went out works which spread the light of knowledge in a wide range of subjects, from the power of movement in plants to the formation of coral reefs, from the breeding of animals to the workings of cross-fertilization and to the expression of the emotions in men and animals. But the name Darwin is above all associated with *The Origin of Species,* which appeared in 1859 after twenty years of preparation. The central theme is this: species have not been created in an unalterable form; on the contrary living beings have developed over long periods of time from lower simpler forms to higher ones with a more complicated structure. He said in 1844 it seemed to him as if he was confessing to a murder—the old idea of the immutability of species had been so deeply engrained in him. He did not create the concept of evolution, but he supported it with so much material out of his own experience that from this moment the evolution theory, though strongly challenged, was taken into the storehouse of confirmed knowledge like a 'Newton's law' of biology (see fold-out next to page 368). Darwin strove to ascertain the causes of evolution. Two seemed to him the most important: the variability of living creatures, which continually caused forms of all organisms to appear with new inheritable characteristics in future generations (today we call them mutations); and selection, determining which forms are to prevail and which are to disappear—natural selection or 'the survival of the fittest' in the battle for existence amongst the superabundance of creatures on earth. Darwin formulated his own theories far more cautiously than did his less scrupulous successors.

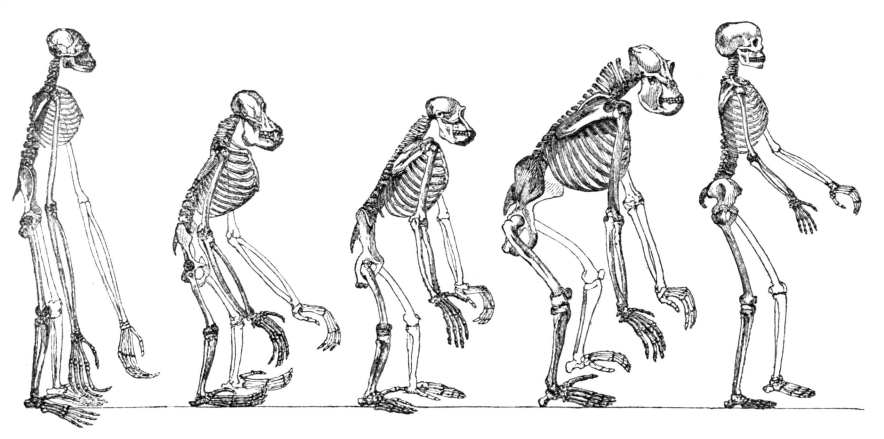

THOMAS HENRY HUXLEY EXHIBITS A CHALLENGING ROW OF FIGURES

In 1758, the God-fearing Linnaeus, for the first time in science, classified man alongside the apes in the family of primates. Thereby a problem was set which caused much emotion and excitement a hundred years later. When in the nineteenth century a sufficient basis was found with the help of Lamarck and then of Darwin and others to accept the slow development of higher from lower animal species, a new question soon came up for consideration: Was man the only exception to the laws of evolution? Even before Darwin published his book *The Descent of Man* in 1871, the geologist C. Lyell and the biologists T. H. Huxley, A. R. Wallace and Ernst Haeckel had already taken up the theme, considering it from the viewpoint of the evolution theory. Huxley made a comparison of five skeletons (above), from left to right four anthropoid apes: a gibbon, an orang-utan, a chimpanzee, a gorilla and then a man (the gibbon, which we today no longer count among the anthropoids, he made twice its natural size in comparison with the others). He then announced the similarities and differences he had found when he compared the body structure and organs. The apes showed the same number of teeth as man, a narrow nasal septum, similar hands with a thumb which could be freely moved, a half upright stance, no bony tail, and the ape's embryo went through the same stages as that of man. In contrast to this, man walked upright, had shorter front extremities, a far larger skull casing with an unusually heavy and differentiated brain, and a clearly recognizable profile. Darwin drew cautious conclusions from such comparisons: 'We must not fall into the error of assuming that the common ancestor of the *Simiae* (apes), including man, was identical with or even very similar to any ape existing today.' He placed

the 'branching off' of man from the common, entirely unknown original form in the Eocene period; according to today's view the *Oreopithecus,* the oldest man-like form so far known, belongs to a period some ten to twelve million years ago. Nothing is so far known of that early form, from which it is believed—we do not know how or when—man developed further and higher, whilst the ancestors of the apes as we know them today developed to a markedly less advanced stage. The fact that since Darwin's day fragments of primeval or intermediate forms seem frequently to have been found, has brought us no nearer the truth about our common origin.

Does the assumption that man has developed organically from the animal realm 'involve the brutalization and degradation of man?' asked Huxley provocatively in an essay in 1879 and set the expected affirmative reply of the orthodox against the negative of the evolution theorist. We also hear of Du Bois-Reymond proudly announcing in 1878: the '*reasonable animal* man travels by steam, writes with lightning and paints with the sunbeam.' A more subtle way of thinking today sees great importance in the truth that man is closely related through his body to every living thing. It will come to interpret more clearly with the help of Fairfield Osborn, Alexis Carrel, Adolf Portmann and others this special species man; in so doing it will show that this species both in its destructive and constructive capacities transcends the boundaries of the animal world; it will show too that the species is not comprehensible in purely biological terms.

Left: PAINTING OF A MONKEY *(Simia sinica,* TODAY *Zati sinica)* FROM THE JARDIN DES PLANTES, BY J. B. AUDEBERT.

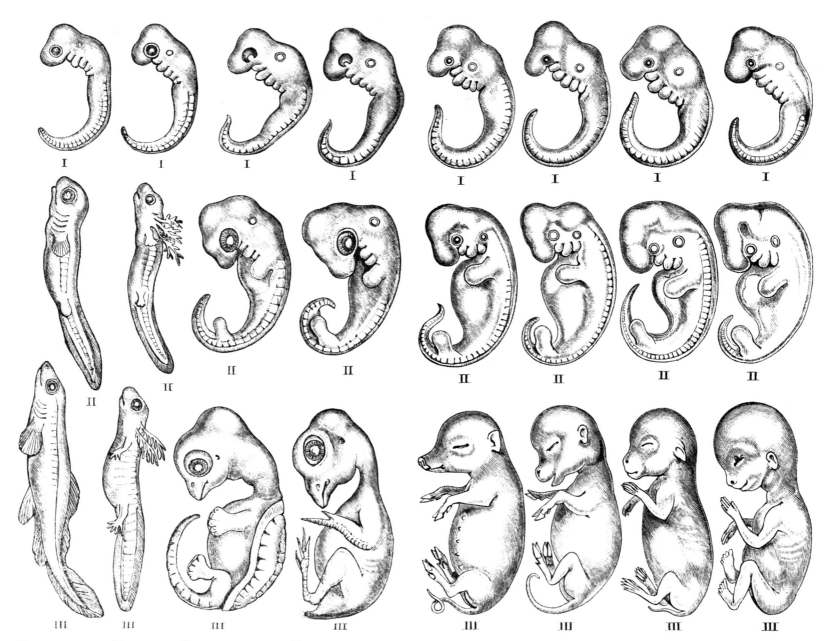

THE MYSTERIOUS MESSAGE OF PREHISTORY IN THE EMBRYO

Geoffroy Saint-Hilaire assumed that there reappeared temporarily in the embryo something like traces of far earlier phases in its ancestry. We find others holding the same view; it was given its most logical and distinctive form in 1866 by Ernst Haeckel, Darwin's turbulent champion in Germany. Haeckel envisaged a cast-iron law which laid down that the development of each individual embryo recapitulated the history of its ancestry. He was a gifted draughtsman and he illustrated his 'biogenetic basic law' in a persuasive manner. He chose the embryos of two lower and two higher vertebrates (the four left-hand sequences), a fish, a salamander, a tortoise and a bird, and he added those of four 'mammals', a pig, an ox, a rabbit and a man. He drew them all enlarged up to the same size and in three approximately equivalent stages of growth (I–III), leaving off the embryos' skin covering. In the top row the embryos show in a strange way the characteristics of fish: to the right of their eyes where one would expect to see the ear, they all have a gill-like structure—as if something lived on in them of those distant ancestors, whose vital element was water. At a later stage the embryos grow limbs; at first

they are small stumps. The gills are still present. Only in the third stage do the differences become clearer; the embryo of man is now already quite different from those of the higher mammals and the gills have disappeared. Haeckel was thus more radical than Darwin and Huxley and did not concern himself with the gaps in his theory of the 'recapitulation of ancestry' or with the special peculiarities of embryo development; and he incorporated embryology firmly into the evolution theory.

Left: CHARLES DARWIN IN 1881, A YEAR BEFORE HIS DEATH

This is the picture of Darwin which is most firmly imprinted on the memory of posterity. With eyes under their bushy eyebrows looking keenly and enquiringly into the world, the broad-brimmed hat pressed down over the deeply wrinkled forehead, the coat rather like a pilgrim's cloak covering shoulders and arms, the scientist is leaning against a tree; he looks almost like some spirit of the earth, which for a few decades took on the form of a man, quiet and retiring yet possessed of a great new concept of nature, and answering to the name of Charles Darwin.

The Chemical Laboratory in the Expeditionary Ship 'Challenger'

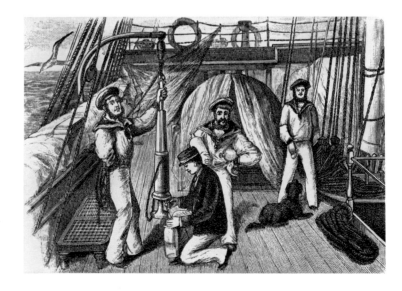

Water from the Depths of the Sea is brought up to the
Deck of the 'Challenger'

Natural scientists have gathered together almost as much reliable knowledge about the animal world in the upper levels of the oceans as they have done in the woods and marshes. The dark depths of the sea, however, remained for a long time inaccessible, as did the two poles. It was only in the nineteenth century that technicians, spurred on by the laying of the first cables, learned the art of sinking trawl and drift nets, valved vertical cores and dredges on mile-long ropes down to previously inaccessible depths. It was then that the first great biological deep-sea expeditions went out to find the answer to many vital questions: Did life exist at the bottom of the sea? What was the sea-bottom made of? What was its history?

The most noteworthy expeditions of this kind were those of the British research ship *Challenger* between 1872 and 1876 under the scientific direction of the biologist Wyville Thomson, and of the German steamer *Valdivia* (from 1898 to 1899), which explored the Indian and Atlantic oceans under Carl Chun. Dozens of experts devoted dozens of volumes to the enormous number of finds. The Englishmen handed over their collections of Radiolaria to the German, Ernst Haeckel; the Germans passed the results of their probes into the sea-floor to the Englishman, John Murray, for examination.

The laboratory shown opposite was one of the scientific workshops on board the *Challenger*. This is where sea-water raised in the vertical cores (bottom left) was examined. Mud from the sea-floor was brought up in the iron pipes which are ranged in threes on the right of the picture. The room is full of fragile articles and they are all secured against falling; the test-tubes, distilling cylinders, bottles of testing materials, even the salts and other chemical identifying agents in the drawers on the left are made fast. Nevertheless some of the tools on the long narrow table in front indicate that the glass-blower was often busy after storms. In the background there is a large bottle of distilled water standing high up on a three-legged stand. On the left in front of it is an apparatus with a copper condenser and some glass vessels elaborately connected with each other. This apparatus analyses the sea-water and extracts from it the carbon dioxide. To the right of the casement window are an inkstand and a quill pen for notes, which will one day become the common property of the scientific world. They provided information about the different kinds of sea-bottom, of depths in which there were neither currents nor seasons of the year, and about the microscopic flora of the water; but the most important discovery these oceanographers made was that the sea was a vast breeding ground of unicellular creatures, the foraminifera. The *Challenger* expedition alone discovered about 10,000 new forms of the calcareous shell of these creatures; when they die, their shells sink down like a shower of dust and in the course of millions of years they build up layers often hundreds of feet deep.

The picture above shows a 28-fold enlargement of a minute sample of this foraminiferous sand, which was brought up from a depth of some 475 feet by the cores of the *Valdivia*. It was found near Cape Bojador off the African coast. It is greensand over which the chemists of the expedition have poured diluted hydrochloric acid. It consists of stone-cores of foraminiferous shells in all kinds of different shapes, and fragments of these. Mixed in with them are greensand grains which look like shot or particles of metal; these originate from the African continent near by. There are also some stone-cores of the quills of sea-urchins and corals.

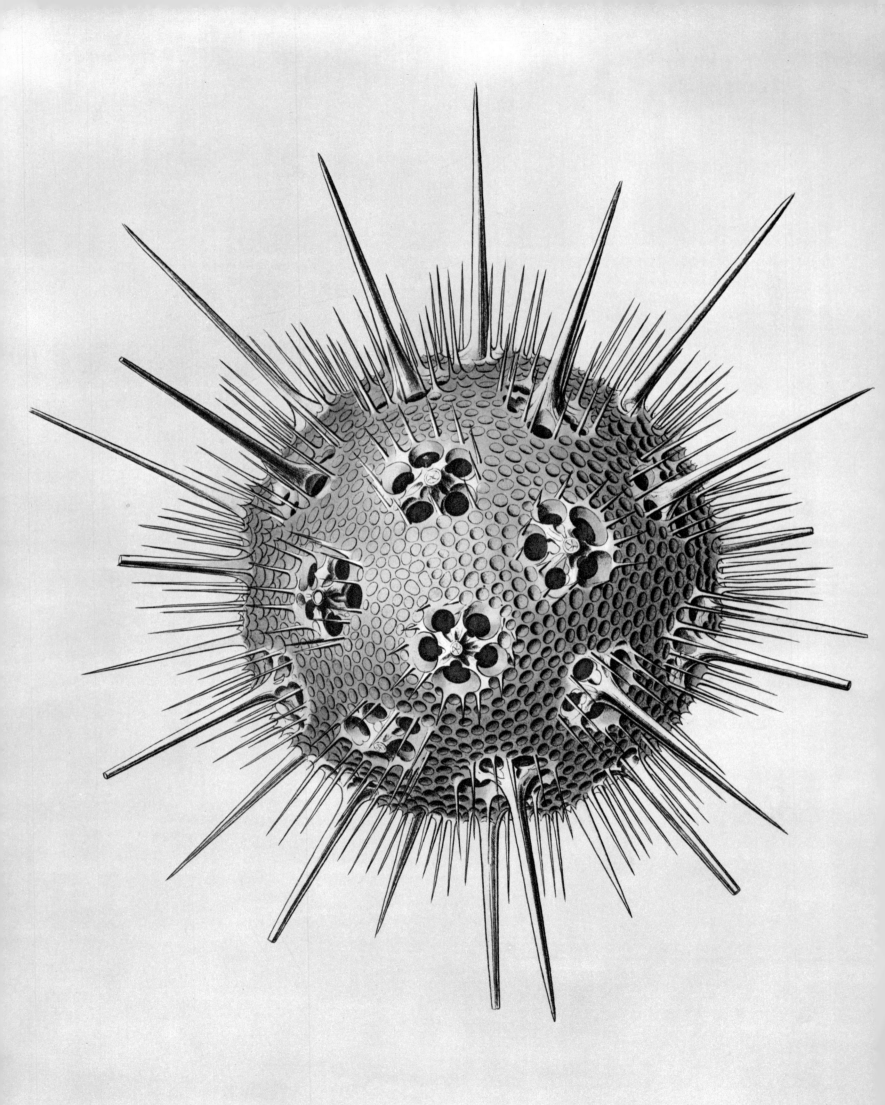

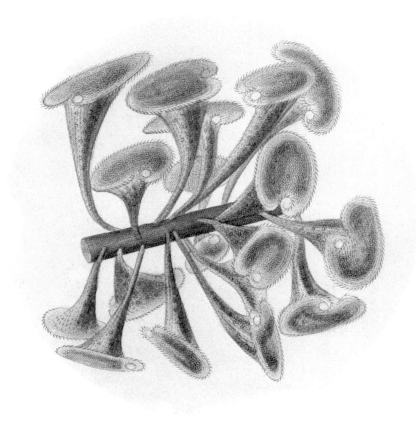

Left: AN 'ART-FORM OF NATURE': THE RADIOLARIAN
'Haeckeliana Darwiniana'

When the biologist John Murray, who published the reports
of the *Challenger* expedition, wanted to give some mark of
distinction to one of the most beautiful radiolaria and also
to the man who worked on them, Ernst Haeckel, he named
it after him but added the name of Darwin as well. It was
Haeckel who in his earlier years had broken so much new
ground in his research on the Radiolaria. Out of the object
which to the naked eye was nothing but just a speck of
sandy sea-mud or a drop of water, Haeckel with his artist's
eye saw one perfect 'art-form of nature' after another emerging under the immersion microscope: he discovered, for
instance, minute unicellular organisms, which build wonderful structures around themselves, all quite invisible to the
naked eye. On the page opposite is an example: a spherical
shell the size of a grain of sand, which is covered on all
sides with little round dimples. The outside of the sphere
is pierced at evenly distributed points by round pores
arranged five together in circles. From the central point of
these a sturdy spike rises radially; smaller spines stand
round the pores and at some other points. It is a fortified
house for a defenceless inhabitant, for inside there lives a
creature consisting of a single-cell nucleus and a covering
of slimy plasma. It puts out through the openings little
pseudopodia which look like beams of light (not visible
here); with these it poises itself or sweeps food along. At
the age of twenty-six Haeckel had described 144 new kinds
of these Radiolaria. On 10th February 1860 when he had
caught no less than twelve of them with a fine net in the
sea outside Messina he wrote to his fiancée: 'I fell on my
knees in front of my microscope and cried out with joy as I
offered my most heartfelt thanks to the blue sea and the

kindly sea-goddesses, the gentle Nereids, who continue to
send me such wonderful gifts: I promised too to be good
and behave well, remain worthy of this good fortune, and
to devote my whole life to the service of glorious nature.'
Above: Haeckel was inspired to carry out research on these
creatures by a pictorial work which has become a classic
and by Johannes Müller's studies on Protozoa. The illustrated
volume, which extolled the Protozoa to far greater heights
than anything else before Haeckel's writings, was part of
the treatise published in 1838 with the title *The Infusoria
as Perfect Organisms,* a work by the Berlin professor of medicine, Christian Gottfried Ehrenberg. Using a relatively
weak microscope he had made many observations of *Paramoecia* and other very small creatures. He had even 'fed'
infusoria with finely powdered carmine and indigo, and as
the colours collected at certain points in the transparent
bodies, he felt certain he could recognize intestinal canals,
nerve-fibres, masticatory and other highly developed
miniature organs. Ehrenberg was astonished at the miracles
which occur in myriads of the minutest living creatures. It
was soon discovered, however, that he had often 'seen' far
too much in his dyed preparations. Up to the present time
even the most powerful microscopes have shown up no
real organs in these unicellular animals, but only the rudimentary beginnings of such organs, so-called organelles,
which provide for the taking of food, excretion and so on.
The group of trumpet-shells reproduced above from Ehrenberg's work are no exception. They have swum through
the water and fastened themselves with their stalk-like
tips on to a minute stem. The cilia round the broader trumpet-
shaped front ends sweep water and all kinds of food inside.
These creatures have the most elementary possible metabolic
processes, but they do possess excretory organs; this is the
function of the minute whitish blisters.

THE OTTER IN ITS ELEMENT

In zoology, as in botany, there is 'ecology', the science which takes the animal out of the laboratory and experiment cages and tries to study it in its entirety against the background of its whole environment, and to discover how it finds food, protection and opportunities for reproduction, and in particular how it reacts to this environment. Long before scientific ecology existed there was the ecology of the huntsman. The picture of an otter reproduced above comes from a hunting book, *Illustrations of Game* (1740), by Johann Elias Ridinger.

The otter is shown close to a sparkling fishing stream, its own element; it has webbed toes to make swimming easier. It likes to build its earth in sloping banks which have been washed clean by the water like the one on the right. On the opposite page, a remote mountain forest of the Carpathians,

as it was drawn in 1887 for the publication *The Austro-Hungarian Monarchy in Word and Picture*. Four animals which make their homes in this neighbourhood—all eagerly hunted by men—have been set in the landscape: the brown bear, the wild cat, the adder on the warm stone, and the capercaillie on the lowest branch of the pine-tree.

Amongst the zoologists who studied the animal in its habitat were Alfred Edmund Brehm, author of the classic *Animal Life;* a man who had an uncommonly lively descriptive style, Alfred Russel Wallace, the explorer of the Amazon and the Malayan archipelago, who independently of Darwin produced a selection theory simultaneously and became one of the founders of animal geography; and the draughtsman and zoologist Ernest Thompson Seton, who studied the animal world of North America.

PHEASANTS AT THE TIMBER-LINE IN THE HIMALAYA

After the First World War, William Beebe, the head of the research department of the New York Zoological Society, undertook an expedition to the homeland of Asiatic pheasants. He observed some species which were little known up to that time or had never before been described, such as the *Catreus wallichii,* a species which is found only in a limited area of Nepal and Garhwal. Beebe climbed up with his tent to the summer home of the bird, at a height where there are a few remaining deodars and where the steep slopes, streaked with rocks, begin. They are covered with alpine flowers and beds of dry brownish grass. These are the breeding grounds of the *Catreus wallichii,* the Cheer Pheasant, far removed from those areas close to human habitation, into which it is later driven by the snows of winter. It lives usually close to the ground, feeds on insects, roots and berries, and is an undoubted expert at camouflaging itself. The breeding places are hidden in the grass, often in a hollow which they dig out. The birds themselves are often hidden too since both the male and the female, the latter with a smaller tuft on its head, have golden-brown feathers sprinkled with yellow, and the long narrow tail has a pattern of broad stripes across it—a complete camouflage. The American explorer observed carefully the perfect inter-relationship between animal and environment; what could not be described in words was incorporated in the pictures drawn by the draughtsmen of the expedition. Beebe's four magnificent volumes, *Monograph of the Pheasants* (1922), is a unique ecological memorial.

MAN

Our knowledge of the human body rests mainly on the discoveries of the anatomists who observed its structure and the physiologists who observed its functions. The history of this scientific discovery of the human body, which can to some extent be surveyed as a whole, goes back about as far as Hippocrates in the fifth and forth centuries BC. It would be absurd to suppose that previous centuries lay plunged in blackest ignorance, but they constitute the pre-scientific age whose picture of man was largely independent of anatomy and physiology. In all ancient civilizations the people who guarded and added to the mainly oral store of rudimentary medical knowledge gained by experience were the mothers and the doctors. They have been to this day in the forefront of those who know the human body because they tend and care for it. To obtain some idea of a highly developed empirical knowledge of the body before the days of systematic anatomy and experimental physiology, before the microscope and the scalpel, one need only consult the *Corpus hippocraticum,* writings partly attributed to Hippocrates, which came from the medical school flourishing on the island of Cos between 600 and 350 BC. Up to that time the healing doctor and the healing priest were one. The knowledge of early doctors was gathered with no more than an observant eye, hands skilled to feel, commonsense and the most delicate perception of man as a psychosomatic whole, occasionally supplemented by observations of animals. There are traces in ancient Egyptian papyri to show that before Hippocrates other civilizations must have possessed medical knowledge of a similar though less developed type.

But the decisive step beyond these beginnings could only be taken when a science arose not merely of the exterior but of the interior of the body, that is, when the dissection of corpses became possible. This happened for a short time in neo-classical Alexandria. The main field of research for anatomy and physiology lies concealed within the body. The crucial importance for the history of science of the possibility of such inspection is shown by the achievements of Herophilos and Erasistratos alone, and by the strength of their example which inspired Vesalius in 1500, when it was imperative to strive for similar privileges.

'If you cannot go to Alexandria it is still possible to inspect human bones. I have often had the opportunity to do so when graves or monuments were opened. Once a swollen river flooded a grave, tore away the putrefying flesh of the dead body, and carried the skeleton a mile away. There it lay on the bank as if set out for the investigating student of medicine. ...Even if you are not fortunate enough to see something of that kind you can still dissect an ape...'

It was on shaky foundations like these occasional gifts from swollen rivers or not absolutely valid comparisons with animals, above all on the collective medical traditions of antiquity, also rich in uncertain findings, that Galen, in about AD 200 constructed his science of the human body which carried throughout the Middle Ages the authority of a gospel. Not until the late thirteenth century did his influence weaken, in North Italy. Mondino de' Luzzi, the head of the Bologna medical school, wrote a manual coloured by Galen's thought but already with only a superficial bearing on the human corpse. His style of lecturing and that of his successors provoked Vesalius' scorn: 'Up there at their desk they croak out facts [while below at the dissecting bench a demonstrator points out on the corpse the parts under discussion] about things they have never experienced at first hand but have only crammed into their heads from other men's books.'

But this new science did not encounter a full spate of unsolved problems until about 1500. The picture of the human body has been largely set up in the few centuries since the epochmaking achievements of Vesalius. What are the component parts of the skeleton? How many muscles can be distinguished and what tasks does each one fulfil? Which paths does the blood follow throughout the body? What material changes occur in breathing? How does the chemical laboratory of the digestive organs work? What is the difference between nerve cells and skin cells? How are the tissues nourished? What is the funtioning of the system of information and command between the organs of sense and the brain? How is the plasma of the body cells nourished? How does a human being come into existence? Where are the seeds of death in the ageing man? Such questions led the scientific researcher deeper into the mysteries of the human organism, from the bone structure to the delicate structure of the capillaries, from the circulation of the blood to the haemoglobin of the red corpuscles.

The science of man is still faced with countless unsolved problems, and the questions continue: 'How do cells organize themselves by their own efforts into communities, such as the tissues and the organs? To what extent does willpower modify the organism? How is the mind influenced by the state of the organs? What is the relation between consciousness and the cells of the brain? In what manner can the organic and mental characteristics, which each individual inherits, be changed by the mode of life...?' That is the beginning of a long, creative account of unanswered or hardly answered questions in Alexis Carrel's book *Man, the Unknown,* a work which sees the human body as the 'point of intersection' between mind and matter, which is also the view held by the more refined psychosomatic science of this century, which, having inherited the great answers of the past, is grappling with the still greater questions of the future.

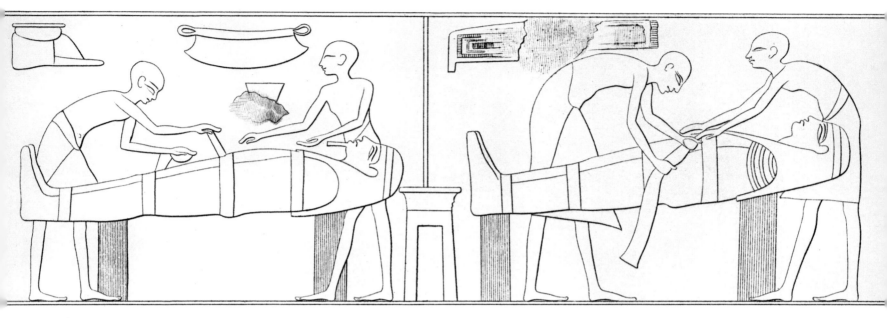

A Dead Man being Embalmed

If we are to judge by the large number of mummies found in the Nile valley in later ages, the Egyptians must have had a much more profound knowledge of the human body than any of the other ancient civilized peoples. But that would perhaps be a rash conclusion, for the dead in those days were not embalmed by learned anatomists but by expert 'Mummy-makers' who were but little concerned in their work with finding answers to the problems of man's questing mind. What they did was to extract, rather clumsily, the entrails and various organs through a smallish opening in the dead body and afterwards place them, and the body, into an antiseptic solution for seventy days. Then the organs were preserved either in special jars or put back into the body stuffed with shavings or pieces of cloth; this was followed by the final stage of embalming illustrated above, the whole body being tightly wrapped in bindings. The first person to examine the embalmed organs four thousand or more years later may be a modern paleo-pathologist, using every resource of historical, medical, and natural scientific knowledge. From the preserved tissues of the body he may be able to diagnose, with the aid of a microscope, the disease from which this ancient Egyptian died.

But in addition to specialists on embalming there were Egyptian doctors who were called to the sick in many parts of the world. Their diagnoses must have been based on considerable practical knowledge of the human body and their prescriptions show that they had much experience with drugs. Medical papyri testify to that: 'Vessels lead from the heart to each organ, and when the physician places his hand or finger on the front or back of the head, on the hands, over the heart, or on the arms or legs, he can feel something of the heart; for vessels lead into every organ, and therefore the heart 'speaks' at the end of the vessel in each member.' This is how they described the pulse. The Greek physicians combined some of this knowledge with their own findings, and it was passed on to posterity.

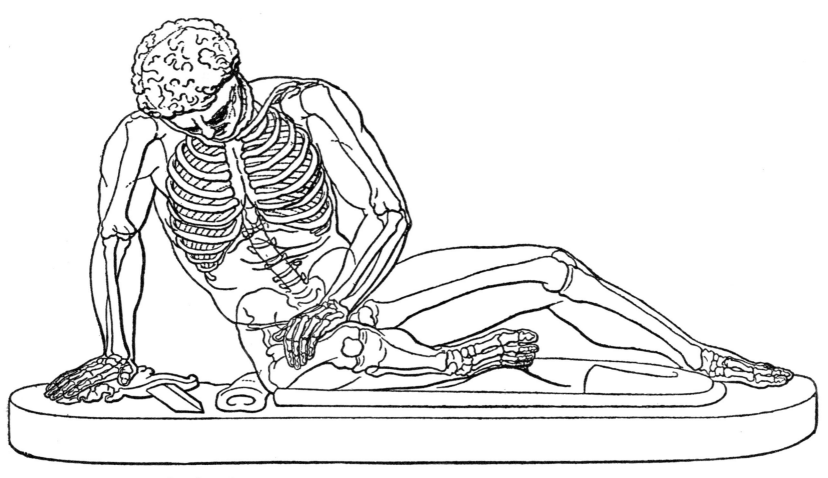

ANCIENT WORKS OF ART, SEEN ANATOMICALLY

Writings about the human body which have been handed down to us from ancient times are fragmentary, and the illustrations are even less complete. But the fine arts of antiquity allow certain conclusions to be drawn as to what progress the science of anatomy had then made. Knowledge of the muscular system, in particular, has been preserved in statues; and in this form it has stood the test of time superbly, better than any lost treatises on anatomy could have done. Some of these masterpieces of antiquity are so perfect that, especially after the Renaissance, they served artists, laymen and anatomists as models of the essential features of the human body. Thus in 1850 in a volume designed for artists, the physician Burkhard W. Seiler found it easy to sketch into a picture based on the famous *Dying Gaul* a skeleton in perfect harmony with the anatomical knowledge of the master of ancient Rome who had produced it (above). In 1844, Charles Bell, looking at the same figure with the eye of an anatomist and physician, said: 'His posture is that of a man seriously wounded in the chest who seeks relief in that anxious and oppressed breathing which attends a mortal wound with loss of blood.' He is looking for a place on which to rest his arm so as to be able to expand

his chest. He is struggling for breath, while more and more blood is ebbing from his heart and lungs. His shoulders, which are rigidly keeping their position, support the muscles of his ribs and arms, and together they seem to combine into a single muscular breathing system so as to hold the escaping life, if possible, for another instant.

More than 150 years earlier, Bernardino Genga had shown in the *Borghese Warrior* (right) that the sculptor of ancient Greece had excellent knowledge of the muscles and their functions. On top is the mass of the shoulder muscle which raises the arm up to the horizontal position, then the twin-formation of the biceps which bends the forearm, while the contrary motion of straightening the arm is carried out by the triceps. The numerous elongated muscles which govern the hands and fingers are clearly shown. The forward bend of the man's trunk is sustained by the abdominal muscles which run down from the chest either side of the navel. Man's walk and upright posture are regulated by a complex lifting, stretching and bending mechanism; as Genga sees it, with the eye of an anatomist, a single forward thrust of the fencer's fist requires the harmonious interplay of every individual fibre of the body's muscular system.

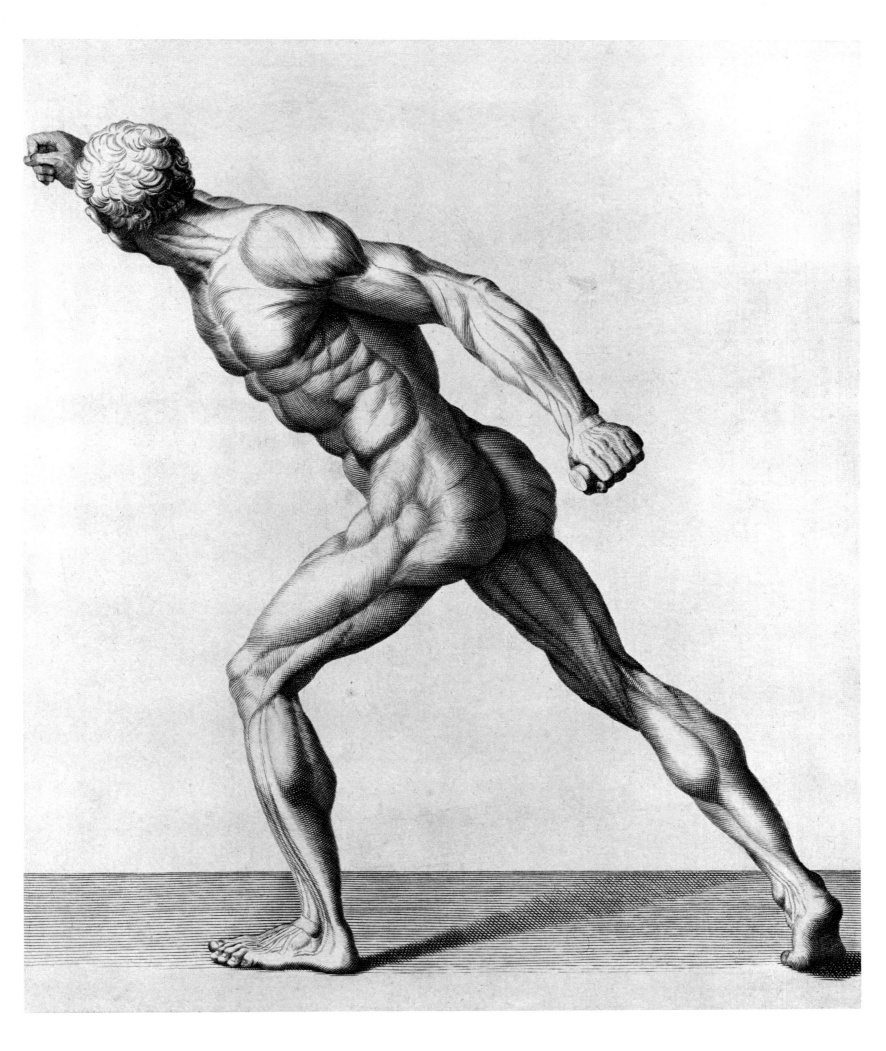

·GALENVS· ❖ ·AVICENA· ❖ ·ⲨPOCRATES·

THE THREE GREAT TEACHERS OF MEDICINE OF THE MIDDLE AGES

Here they sit, solemn and venerable, almost like three gods of medicine whose wisdom decides between life and death for the sick. Hippocrates is on the right. He taught that the human body must be regarded as part of nature and that it blends into nature through the four elements. A master of the art of prognosis, which involves careful observation of man as a whole, he conquered age-old superstitions in medicine. In his hand he is holding a glass to observe a urine sample—a pointer to his theory about the fluids of the body. On the left is Galen who coordinated the medical knowledge of antiquity, and therefore also the science of anatomy, and passed it on, with the addition of his own observations—some of which were right, others wrong. The books symbolize the teachings propounded by the three masters. For nearly fifteen hundred years some of them were considered sacrosanct and gradually hardened into dogma. They were held to be definitive and this is illustrated by the imperious figure of the Arab physician Avicenna holding the insignia of a king. He included the teachings of Galen, Hippocrates and Aristotle in his systematic *Canon of Medicine* and his version was the one that was passed on to the Middle Ages.

'It is true that Hippocrates accomplished a few things, indeed he has laid the foundations, but it is I who paved the way and made it usable as Emperor Trajan did with the military roads of the Roman Empire,' Galen declared with his characteristic vanity. A provincial Greek who came to Rome from Pergamum, Galen was personal physician to the Emperor Marcus Aurelius. Towards the end of classical times he collated everything that had been written up to then about the human body in sickness and health. He widened knowledge of the topography of the body by his exact description of three hundred muscles. The scholars of medieval Europe and Islamic countries found in his writings not only a greater wealth of information than in any other source but also praise of God. For Galen saw in the ingenious mechanism of the human body a mirror of God's perfection, and in his view anatomy proved God's existence more conclusively than the sacred mysteries of old. For fifteen hundred years people were convinced that Galen's was the last word on anatomy and medicine.

But Galen's knowledge, compiled with such passionate devotion, was only a beginning. This is clear from the two sketches of the system of blood vessels (right; the sketches are greatly reduced in size here). *Iecur venarum principium* is the inscription on the five-lobed liver which Galen had observed in dogs and inserted into his conception of the human body. Galen assumed that the vena cava begins at the back of the liver (the right kidney appears beneath one of the lobes); there it receives the blood which is produced by the liver from nutritive fluids flowing into it from the intestines through the portal vein. At the same time, the liver imparts to the blood a spiritual force, called *spiritus naturalis* which exists in all living substance. The vena cava distributes the blood all over the body, including the right ventricle of the heart. A side vein at a point above the liver, indicated by an oval contour line, branches off to the heart. Galen was ignorant of the existence of auricles. The blood, he says, remains for a while in the right chamber; its impurities pass through a vein, now known as the pulmonary vein, to the lungs to be exhaled. Then the venous blood flows back from the right chamber into the veins which take it in numerous ramifications to the arms and through two branches to the head. Downwards, the blood is distributed into the kidneys and the abdomen and finally flows into the legs and feet.

But from the right ventricle of the heart, a tiny amount of the venous blood from the liver follows a course of its own. Through minute apertures in the longitudinal wall of the heart (one of Galen's inventions) it trickles into the left chamber. There it takes up *pneuma,* essence of the World Spirit, which had entered the body through the lung like the air we breathe. And then there is formed the *spiritus vitalis,* the force which enters into the arterial system via the mighty aorta (lower picture), which distributes it throughout the body as the venous blood does the *spiritus naturalis.* Several arteries also take it to the head where it is distributed into delicate little channels by the disk-like *rete mirabile*—another of Galen's inventions. Here is found yet another *pneuma,* the *spiritus animalis;* this reaches the rest of the body via the nerves, which must be imagined as hollow tubes. As yet the concept of the circulation of the blood had not been born; according to Galen the blood trickles off into the body through thousands of delicate little veins. Many of these fanciful concepts contain the glimmer of awareness that the blood is the vehicle which transports vital substances from the centre of the body to its extremities. It was Andreas Vesalius who in 1538 drew these two 'artery men' and included the sketches in a small anatomical atlas for his students of anatomy at Padua. At the time he was a staunch supporter of Galen, but five years later he produced his own anti-Galenic illustrated work on the fabric of the human body which made him the founder of a new concept of anatomy.

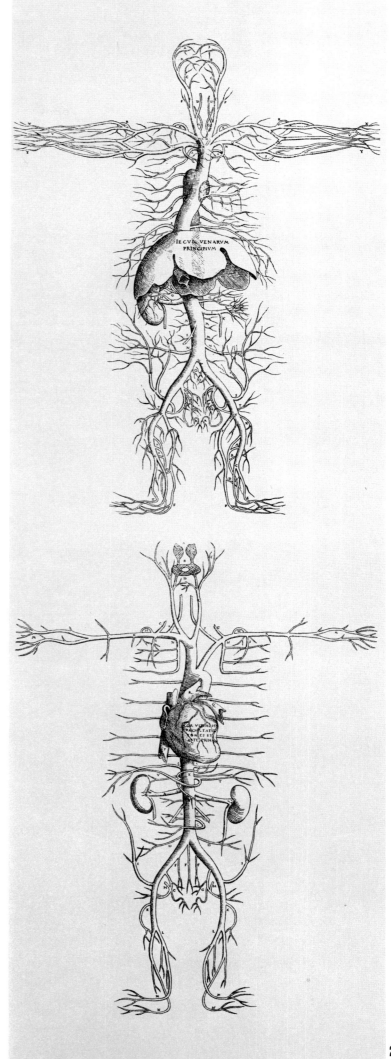

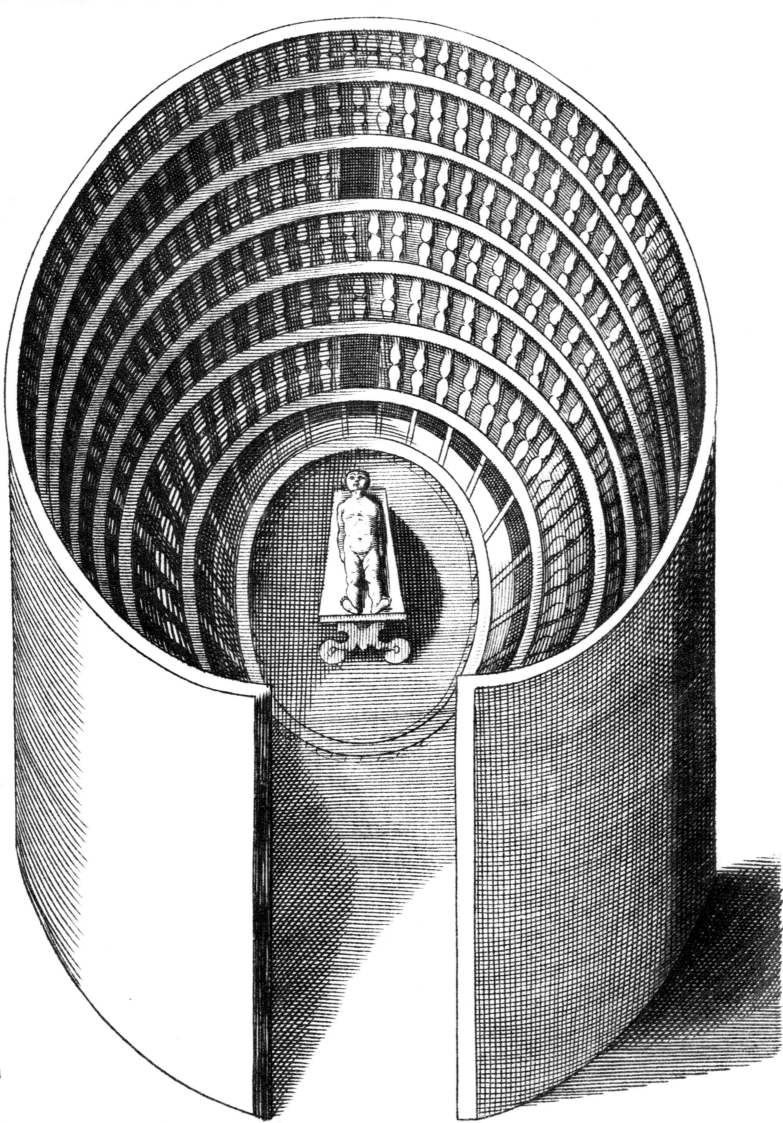

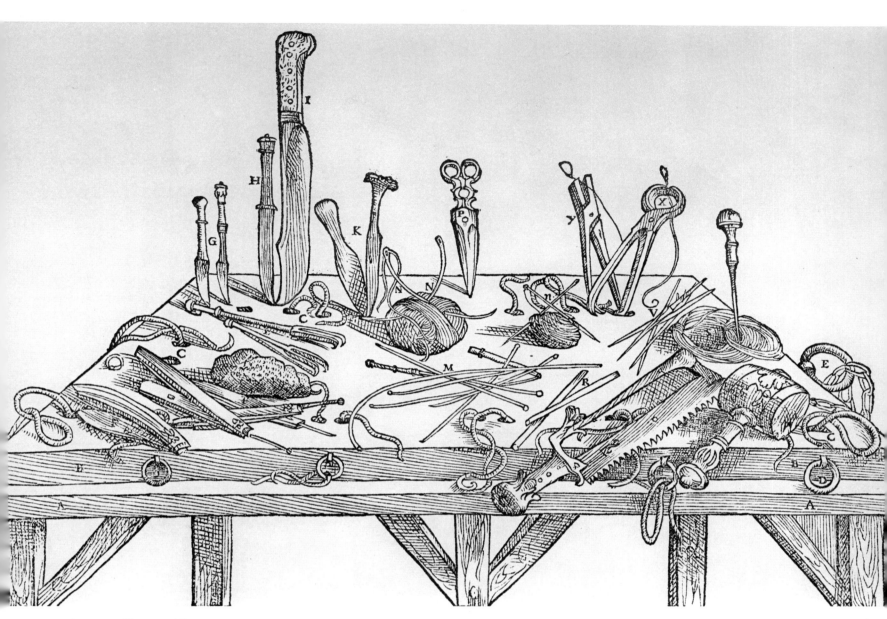

ANDREAS VESALIUS' INSTRUMENTS

Left: THE ANATOMICAL THEATRE OF PADUA UNIVERSITY

Well into the Middle Ages (if we except a few bold advances in antiquity) it was considered a repulsive and sinful undertaking to carry out post mortem examinations in order to discover what the inside of the human body looked like. It was not until the late thirteenth century that several medical faculties in Northern Italy lifted the ban on such operations. They attracted scientists from everywhere, who were prepared to undertake what others had omitted to do for thousands of years, the radical rediscovery of the human body, for the greater glory of God and the benefit of man. At the turn of the 15th century even the Pope granted Privileges for post mortem examinations and by 1594 the rejuvenated science of anatomy had established its own kind of workshop: the anatomical theatre. It was based on principles evolved somewhere around 1500 by Alexander Benedictus, an anatomist then working in Padua. It was modelled on the arena of ancient times and as the picture on the left shows, the theatre indeed rises around the dead body like a miniature Coliseum. The lecturer and

his assistant can move without hindrance round the raised dissecting table. Closely serried tiers of galleries rise above it allowing a clear view from the wooden balustrades. Artificial lighting was provided. It was in this university that, fifty years before the inauguration of the amphitheatre, Andreas Vesalius laid the foundations of modern anatomy.

Above: In Vesalius' display of the tools of his profession there is something of the showman's pleasure in playing upon the spectator's nerves. Board B served as a base during the dissection of animals; ropes, threaded through holes (C) and rings (D, E) held the animal's body firmly in place. There are also knives (including wooden ones: K), scissors, scraping knives (left front), a saw and mallet, two little tubes (R) to inflate the lungs and other organs, awls (V) to drill through the bones and wire (S) to pin them together, pliers (Y) and pincers (X), various needles, hooks and long rods (M) to expose muscles, nerves, etc. To the young anatomist of the Renaissance such a collection of instruments was as important as the compass to men who set out on their voyages of discovery: and in the hands of a master like Vesalius it opened up an unknown world.

A Dance of Death from 1493

No more than fifty years separate the two woodcuts on the left and the right; but, judging by the anatomical knowledge of their creators, there is a wide gulf between them. The elbow and knee joints and the ankles of the dancing skeletons are pure fantasy, as are the bones in the foot, which are split right up to the heel, and the peculiar attachment to the bottom of the spine of the dancer in the centre. This is art without anatomical knowledge, the very opposite to that of the artist's contemporary, Leonardo da Vinci, who like a medical man made his observations from corpses. Moreover it lags behind even the scanty medieval knowledge of human bone structure. By comparison, one is struck by the novelty and spirit of discovery in Vesalius' skeleton. Even so, no one will deny the visionary power of the woodcut from Hartmann Schedel's World Chronicle: there is magnificent movement, almost bursting out of the frame, as the dead rise from lonely graves to take their places for a wild dance. From time immemorial popular belief has held that the realm of the dead was the storehouse of things gruesome and ominous.

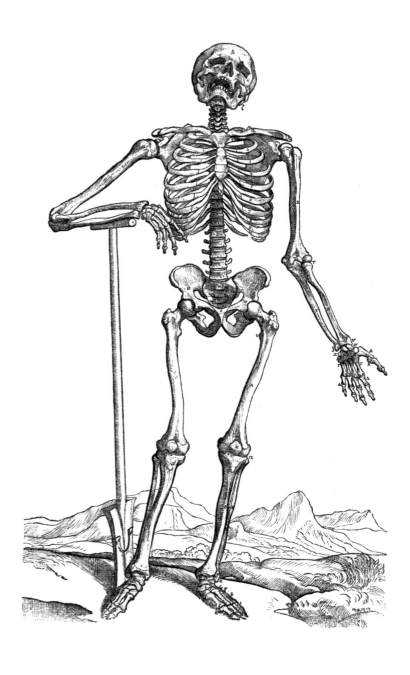

Vesalius' texts and illustrations, for the first time since the early efforts made in the ancient world, presented a picture of the human body which is still largely valid to this day. Vesalius, the son of a doctor, had read about and re-lived the greatness of the Alexandrian school. He had also witnessed the spiritual stagnation of Galen's slavish successors in Paris. There his teacher, Jacobus Sylvius, showed students the organs of a dog in order to explain the human body according to Galen. Like other students, the young man from Flanders took the law into his own hands and studied the organs of corpses which had been illegally procured from cemeteries. Many things were not as Galen had described them. It was not surprising that Vesalius moved on to Northern Italy. He graduated at Padua, where experts were given permission to carry out dissections, and was immediately appointed lecturer in surgery. Vesalius threw himself passionately into his work, and within five years *De humani corporis fabrica* (1543) appeared. It was like the taking of an inventory, of a kind never before attempted. The idea was to provide a thorough representation in accordance with nature, of the total system of bones, muscles, intestines, blood vessels and nerves of the body. A pupil of Titian's named Jan Stephan van Calcar was the artist who created, in the grand manner, the woodcuts for Vesalius' inspired work. A fierce dispute ensued over the new image of man. Vesalius's teacher Sylvius denounced him as a 'monster of ignorance who is poisoning Europe with his pestilential breath'. Meanwhile, the monster of ignorance had become personal physician to Charles V. Vesalius' work, which had appeared in a second, improved edition in 1555, became established. Its famous author died in a shipwreck in 1564.

All his knowledge is related to the living man. Even the skeleton shown above is standing in a striking position with a landscape as background. It looks like that of a peasant. Perhaps the forearm is too long and the collar bone too massive. Vesalius left much that had to be critically examined and discarded. Nevertheless, his *Fabrica,* which was intended to glorify the human body as God's work of art, remains an immortal achievement in the history of natural science.

AN ILLUSTRATION FOR A BOOK ON ANATOMY IS BEING MADE

In his *Osteographia* of 1733, William Cheselden (*see* p. 214) shows how the brilliant illustrators of his book set to work. The artist is seated behind a camera obscura. It consists of a long rectagonal wooden box, blackened on the inside. At the front, facing the object to be traced, it has a convex lens mounted in a board which covers the end of the camera. This frame can be moved to and fro until a sharp image of the object appears on a pane before the illustrator's eyes. Because of the convex lens the image is upside down—which is why the skeleton is hanging with its skull pointing downwards. The pane of glass facing the illustrator has a matt surface: on it he makes an exact drawing of the skeleton. (They distrusted freehand contours.) Later the drawing is transferred to paper or a copper plate. The author, on the right of the picture, is making notes for his future book.

Right: MAN'S MUSCLES, ACCORDING TO ALBINUS

In the seventeenth or eighteenth century all the anatomists who dealt with the human body tried to complete the picture sketched in by Vesalius. In Vesalius' time Padua played the most important role in the study of the structure of the human body. In the two subsequent centuries this role was taken over by the Dutch university of Leyden. Bernhard

Siegfried Albinus was regarded as the most outstanding anatomist by his contemporaries there. No one had ever produced such accurately measured human skeletons and muscular systems as Albinus' collaborator, the artist Jan Wandelaer, in his large illustrations, or drawn them with greater precision and labelled every detail. This copperplate engraving, the fourth in his series of pictures, shows man after the careful removal of three successive layers of muscles and of the intestines. Gradually the skeleton becomes visible. Only the deepest layers of muscles which move the head, the chest and the thighs are left. The cartilages below the knee-cap are correctly drawn. A number of the ligaments, which normally function hidden beneath the muscles, are now visible: they are tough sinewy cords which maintain the bones in their position. In the right hand, for example they are to be seen binding the finger-joints together.

And what is the rhinoceros doing in the picture? Is it just the fancy of an unusual illustrator who likes portraying striking contrasts? The unwieldy beast was included at the anatomist's behest. It was exhibited in 1747, shortly before the book of anatomical plates was completed, as a kind of wonder of the world, in that famous centre of science, the town of Leyden. And so (Albinus says) 'I deemed it right to include this monster because of its great rarity'.

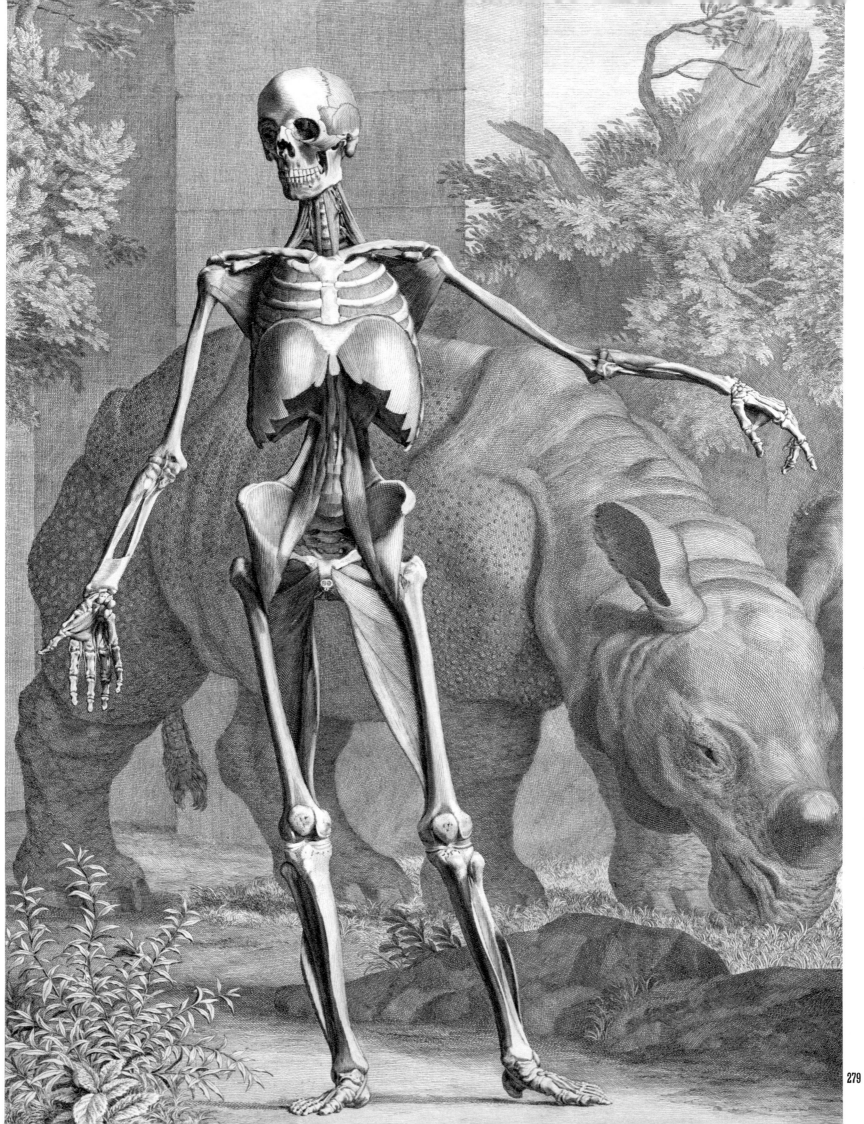

THE PHYSICIAN JOHANNES HARTLIEB PRESENTING HIS 'BOOK ABOUT THE HAND' TO THE DUCHESS ANNA OF BAVARIA, IN 1448

'The science of the hand, as seen by the symbolists, chirognomists and palmists, is the search for the truth about man.' This astonishing remark does not come from some crank or fortune-teller, but can be found in an extremely interesting book on the hand published in 1834 by the distinguished Scottish physician, Sir Charles Bell. Long before the anatomical structure of the hand had been studied, civilized peoples of the ancient world believed that something of man's inner nature was reflected in the hand just as it was in his face. The astrologists were quite dogmatic about it and gave each finger a name signifying a connection with a god or planet. By contrast, the chirognomists tried to find out whether a firm hand meant that its owner was a man of energy, a weak hand the opposite, and so on. The palmists mainly measured and interpreted the lines of the hand. Examples of this kind are contained in the illustrated book shown above which was copied and printed many times.

Here the personal physician to Duke Albrecht III of Bavaria is seen on his knees presenting it to his sovereign lady. It is one of the works which claim to increase knowledge of man through knowledge of the hand. Books like this have been written for centuries and are generally held in little esteem by the Church and universities; but every now and then we find among the worthless multitude of writings a highly sensitive study of the hand, such as that which the German physician Carl Gustav Carus produced in 1846, inspired by the French chirognomist Stanislas d'Arpentigny. *Right:* Carus, who was well aware of the difficult problems he had set himself, classified hands into four basic and several mixed types. Top row, starting from the left: the elementary hand is thick, hard and has a large palm; the thumb is often blunted, the hand of a robust Sancho Panza. The sensitive hand is of refined structure, with a delicate skin and narrow nails, the fingers on the whole are tapered:

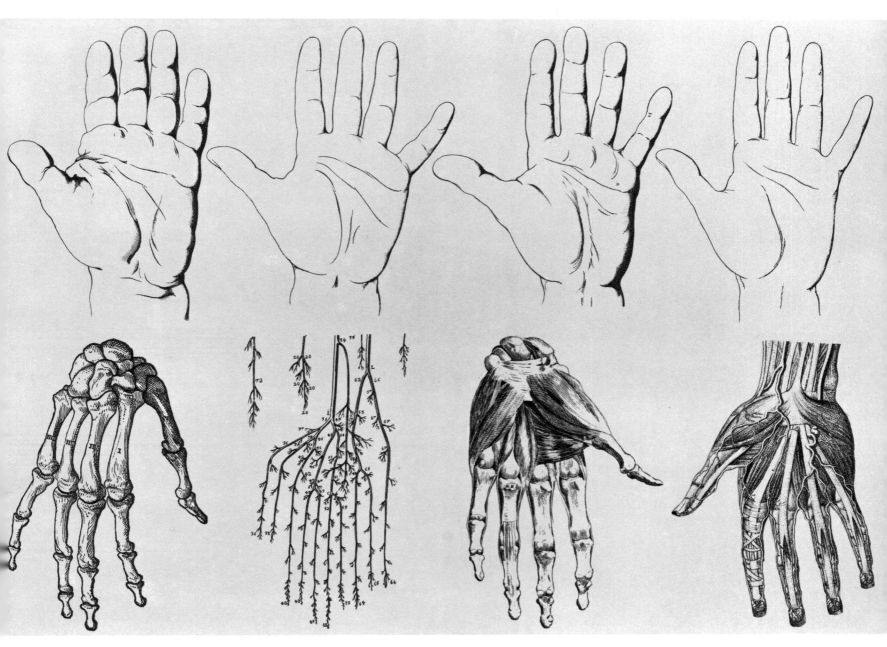

FROM THE HISTORY OF THE STUDY OF THE HAND

the signs of a Tasso character. The 'spatular hand' is a cross between this sensitive type and the knotty, dynamic hand of a virile senator or merchant. But Carus considers the fourth as the most beautiful and also the rarest form of hand: of medium size, the palm slightly longer than wide, with a tender, only lightly creased skin, finely-jointed and fairly long fingers—the spiritual hand.

The sequence of pictures in the row below sums up the anatomical discovery of the hand. On the left a masterpiece by Vesalius: a powerful representation of the eight wrist bones, of the bones of the palm and of the prominent finger-joints. The fame of the French anatomist Raymond Vieussens rests on his *Neurographia universalis,* published in 1685. There, extracted with his scalpel, we find the five pairs of nerves of the hand and their ramifications (second from left).

According to Charles Bell, more sensory and motor nerves lead to this highly developed prehensile organ than to any other part of the body. Most of the muscles which for example, control the finger movements of a pianist or a skilful typist are in the forearm. In his *Icones anatomicae* (1801–14), Leopoldo Caldani shows how they separate near the wrist. And the German anatomist Friedrich Tiedemann shows, in a picture appropriate to the subtlety of the subject, how the impulses of the muscles are propagated through the hand by a system of long tendons which are kept in position by ligaments, and how the arteries conduct the nourishing and purifying blood into it.

Many animals possess keener senses, faster legs and surer instincts than man. But two of his organs, the brain and the hand, make him superior to all other living creatures. The brain is the foundation of the miracle of thinking; through it the mind is mastering knowledge. The hand which can conjure shape from shapeless matter has made man master of the world of things.

'All the blood in the body is controlled by the heart ... The blood flows in a continuous circle and the flow never ends.' These two sentences from a *Book of Medicine,* said to have been written about 2650 BC by the Chinese Emperor Hwang-Tu, sum up the most important life-carrying process in the human body, more correctly than Galen had done. In the sixteenth and seventeenth centuries some Europeans finally solved the mystery of the flow of the blood. But they knew nothing of that ancient wisdom of Asia or of the Arab physician Ibn an-Nafîs who had described the lesser circulation which takes place between heart and lung as early as the thirteenth century. And so one of Vesalius's successors in Padua, Realdo Colombo, and the Spanish physician and martyred theologian, Miguel Serveto, rediscovered this pulmonary circulation independently of each other round about the year 1545. But the credit for proving conclusively the entire double circulation of the blood goes to the Englishman William Harvey, a pupil of Hieronymus Fabricius ab Aquapendente. In London Harvey became personal physician to the imaginative Lord Chancellor, Francis Bacon (*see* p. 98), and to Charles I. Both professionally and on his own responsibility Harvey untiringly carried on his research.

Right: Some knowledge about the structure of the heart had been available since Vesalius' time. It was known that the arteries leading away from the heart guided the blood through the body, apparently by a pulsating movement. It had been clear for some time that if an artery were cut the blood would flow from it at the rhythm of the heart-beat. From this Harvey concluded that it is the heart and nothing else which, by its vigorous contractions, sends the arterial blood on its long journey. He carried out some simple calculations which made history. Suppose the ventricle of the heart contains only two ounces (56.7 grammes) of blood. Then, if the pulse beats 72 times a minute, the left ventricle of the heart will press no less than $72 \times 60 \times 2$ ounces of blood into the aorta within one hour. This makes 8,640 ounces, i.e. three times the weight of a fairly heavy man. This enormous amount of blood obviously could not be flowing in a perpetually new stream from the liver into the vena cava, as had been assumed since Galen; nor could this quantity of blood seep away into the body. Where then did it come from? And where did it flow to? Harvey's experiments showed that it obviously flowed back through the veins towards the heart. If he tied off the upper arm as for

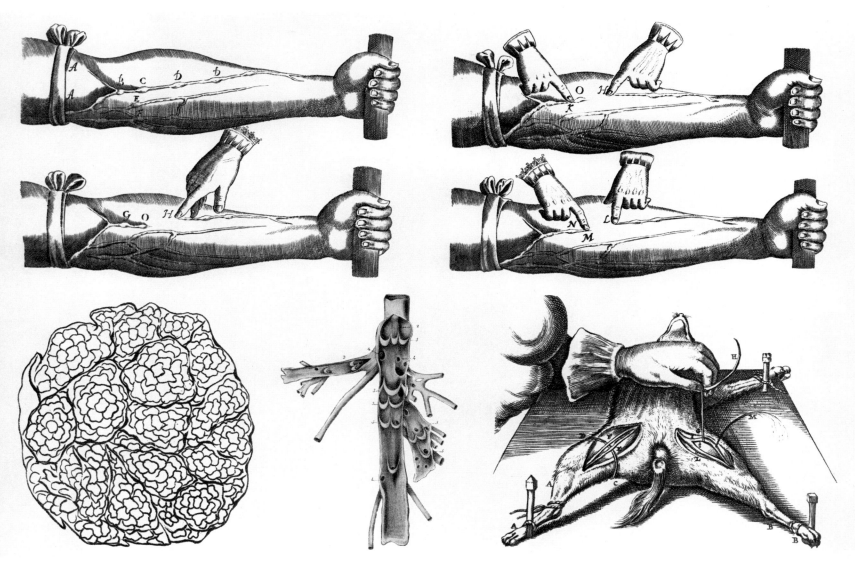

THE DISCOVERY OF THE CIRCULATION OF THE BLOOD

blood-letting (top left), the veins lying underneath the skin stood out; and the valves were brought into relief as little knots (CDD). And if (as in the picture of the arm, lower right) he pressed one vein from the wrist towards the body before tying up the arm, and then applied the ligature, without removing the finger from point L, the vein would fill up strongly from the hand, and not from the heart. If (picture to the left) he smoothed the vein with his finger below valve O while keeping it under pressure at H, no blood would flow from O because at that point valve O obviously barred its way towards the hand. (In 1834, the French scientist Cloquet produced a very good picture of the arrangement of these sail-shaped valves which force the blood in a one-way circulation (*see* central picture).) Clearly, the blood flowing through the veins back to the right auricle and ventricle was the same as that which had entered the arterial system through the aorta after completing its pulmonary circuit. 'And so we are bound to conclude that the blood ... is forced into a circular course and that it is in constant motion.' Harvey reached a similar conclusion in 1628 as the Chinese Emperor four thousand years earlier. Three years after Harvey's death, posthumous descriptions

were published in The Hague of experiments on animals which Jan de Wale had undertaken in order to put an end to the violent dispute over Harvey's views. The Dutch naturalist tied off the vein in the left thigh of a dog (bottom right, H, G). Parts near the heart emptied themselves; only a few drops of blood trickled out when the vein was cut at that point. But if the vein was punctured further away from the heart, it produced an unbroken stream of the blood which was flowing back towards the heart (M), and this lasted at least as long as arterial blood was able to continue flowing to this point along its long route from the heart. But if the whole thigh, including the arteries leading the blood to it, were tied off (CD), without however also tying off the veins (FE), the reverting blood in them naturally ran dry.

How did the blood find its way from the arteries into the veins? Harvey could give no information on this, but Malpighi, using a microscope, found the solution to this puzzle in the lungs of a frog (bottom left). He saw that the lung was penetrated by a fine web of capillaries, the minutest branches of the veins and arteries: this was where the blood entered the veins from the arteries as if through invisible apertures.

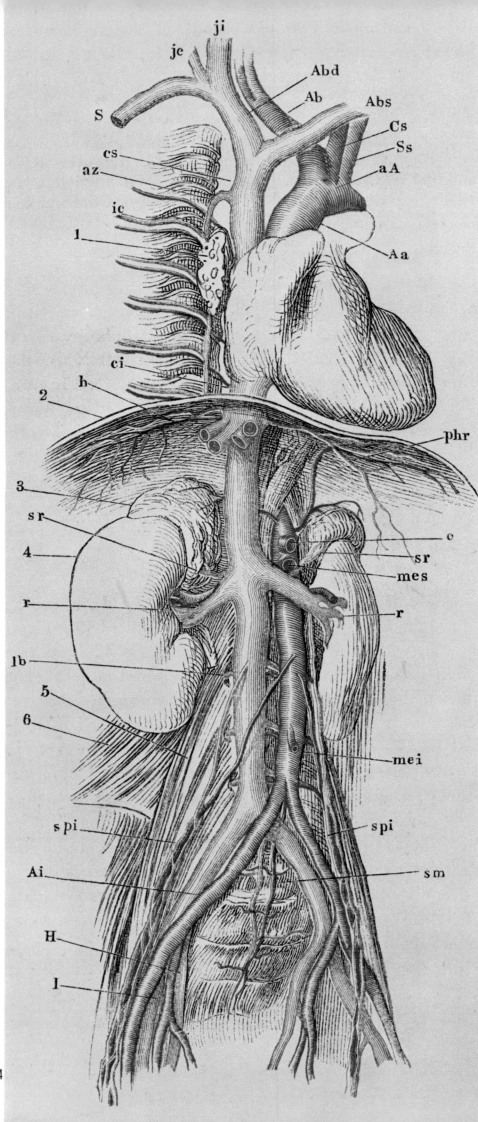

ji

jc

Abd

Ab

Abs

S

Cs

Ss

cs

aA

az

ic

Aa

1

ci

h

2

phr

3

o

sr

sr

4

mes

r

r

lb

5

6

mei

s pi

spi

Ai

sm

H

I

A GLANCE AT JAKOB HENLE'S BOOK OF ANATOMY

Miguel Serveto, Harvey, de Wale, Malpighi: these and other men established the laws of blood circulation, piece by piece, like a jigsaw puzzle. But the ceaseless flow of blood through the human body still posed innumerable questions. In the eighteenth century and later, chemical science realized that on its journey blood absorbed carbon dioxide and other substances secreted by tissues and cells while distributing oxygen and nutritive substances to the tissues. It was found that the blood was purified for a second time in the kidneys. The blood was seen to contain minute red corpuscles with haemoglobin in them which loosely combined with oxygen in the lungs; their number was estimated at 25 thousand million—which meant a tremendous increase in the capacity of the body's most vital carrying instrument. In the nineteenth century, when physiologists like Bernard, Ludwig and others investigated the chemical miracles in the blood and when the great new problems of cellular biology, comparative morphology and embryology attracted more and more scientists, anatomy seemed to have completed its historical task. But it assumed new importance with the growth of modern surgery, when the surgeon had to know precisely where to use his scalpel, what it would meet on its hazardous path and where a ligature might have to be applied. The picture on the left is taken from a famous work on this subject published in 1868—Jakob Henle's *Handbuch der systematischen Anatomie des Menschen.* It is full of new insight into the structure of tissues. The illustration gives a general view of the main arteries (red) and veins (blue), of the thoracic and the abdominal cavities in their anatomical setting: diaphragm (2), right root of the lung (1) (next to the heart), kidney (4), adrenal gland (3), and loin muscles (6).

Henle's textbook coincided with an age which was turning away from unproved romantic speculation and was searching for strictly causal, empirical explanations of nature. Henle used his microscope for systematic anatomical research. As Schwann had done, he soon concluded on purely logical grounds that infectious diseases were caused by micro-organisms, possibly by 'mobile animal-like beings or their eggs, or by germs of plants of a low order.' Robert Koch, who together with Pasteur pioneered research into these destructive micro-organisms, had been Henle's pupil in Göttingen. But another reason for the lasting effect of this book on anatomy was that it was a model of production from the visual point of view, and added to the reputation of the illustrators of science books. In this work, illustrations were no longer arranged in a special volume, separate from the text; they were interspersed among the text, if necessary repeated on several occasions, and so made reading much easier. The pictorial representations of anatomical subjects were modelled on Henle's own blackboard drawings, which ignored inessential points and provided memory aids by using the Latin initial letters for innumerable items. In 1882, a congratulatory address to the aged scientist said: 'You have brought artistic beauty of form even to the student's textbook.'

Right: AN 'ARTERYMAN' BY GODFRIED BIDLOO

This picture takes us back again to the days when England and Holland led the world in anatomy. In 1685, the Dutchman, Godfried Bidloo, published an *Anatomia humani corporis.* The huge plates were by the artist Gerard de Lairesse, who liked dramatic effects. The book was another example of the type of collaboration between scientist and artist which produced such magnificent works on anatomy as those by Vesalius or Albinus. But, valuable as his work is as a whole, Bidloo's plate gives anything but a reliable topography of the paths of the arteries, as can be seen from their ramifications above the heart. It was much more difficult to record the intestines, blood vessels and nerves than bones and muscles. This was eventually achieved only with the help of very advanced techniques. On Bidloo's picture some specimens of his microscopist's work on detailed structure can also be seen, neatly displayed on tiny slabs: fibres in the walls of blood vessels and in muscles (1, 3, 5); blood vessels in membranes (4), gland-like formations and such fibrils and round corpuscles as he thought he could recognize in the blood (16). There is also an example of research into the main anatomical question of the century—the circulation of the blood; figures 8 to 13 show valves of the veins.

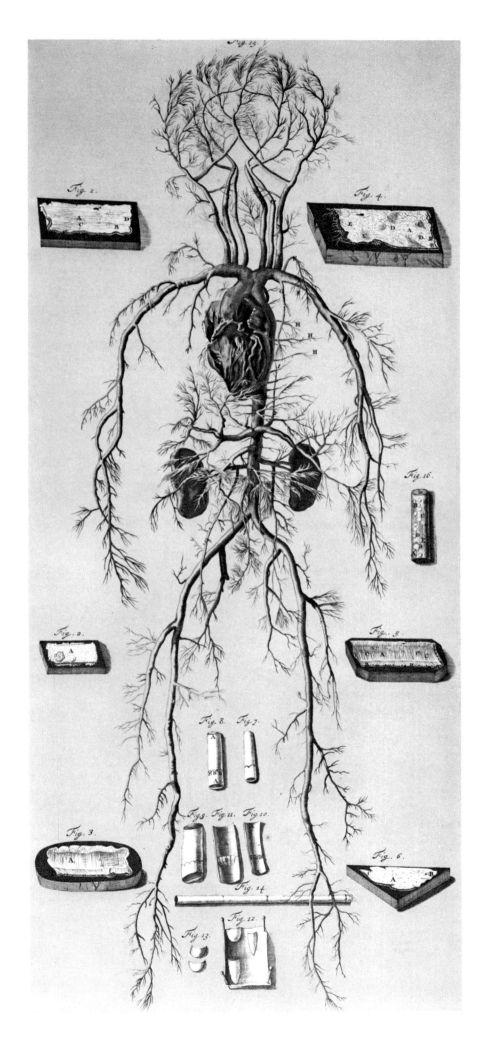

A SINISTER TOMB

Had there been no science of anatomy Friedrich Ruysch would have invented it, they said in Holland round about 1700. Ruysch delighted in producing anatomical preparations. Up and down the country he set up natural science museums, and, above all, he invented the most incredible methods of injection. They made the invisible visible and the perishable imperishable. His preparations of blood vessels, hearts and membranes showed nature's miraculous structures in their minutest detail. In the illustrations of his *Thesaurus anatomiae* (1701–14) he gives free rein to his penchant for the macabre and the bizarre (above). Two child- or foetus-like skeletons mourn upon a mound, weeping into handkerchiefs of membrane preparations. Dead, rigid branches of tubular blood vessels grow luxuriantly from the tomb which is strewn with human bones and stiff, veiny lobes of lungs. Bony arms and hands stick out as if people had been buried alive.

Right: THE ANATOMICAL THEATRE OF THE UNIVERSITY OF LEYDEN

Leyden was moving into the lead in the study of anatomy with the building, in 1594, of an anatomical theatre on the Italian model. It became the central feature of the university. But whereas Padua had a narrow anatomical theatre, Leyden built a spacious, bright and gently rising amphitheatre. As a rule, the front row was reserved for the aristocracy, scholars and distinguished visitors; behind them there was room for the students. People visiting Leyden were allowed access upon payment of an entry fee. The baroque century, which revelled in curiosities, made anatomy one of the attractions—a show-piece. When no dissections took place at the university, the anatomical theatre was used as a natural science museum. Hence the animal skeletons mounted on poles, and the human skin which the two visitors (front left) are examining with great interest. The artist, Johannes Woudanus, has put flags in the hands of a number of the human skeletons. All the inscriptions are reminders of death, addressed to an audience bursting with vigorous health. But death lurks even behind the allegorical figures of Man and Woman in the top corners of the picture. And one of the flags bears the sentence *Nose [nosce] te ipsum,* 'know thyself', as if it were the last word on anatomical wisdom. But surmounting all these reminders of the transitoriness of life is the proud picture of the aspiring town of Leyden and the emblem of its progressive university.

LVGDVNVM

Batavorvm.

SIGIL. ACA. LVGD. BAT.

ARCHIVM INSTRVMETO. RVM ANATOMICORVM.

MEMENTO MORI.

Mors Vltemum. Vita Breuis.

HOMO BVLLA.

Finis.

Iohannes Corneli Woudan Delineabat

The University of Leyden was at the peak of its fame in the first third of the eighteenth century. Anatomists like Bernhard Albinus and Bidloo, for whom the structure of the human body seemed to hold no more secrets, attracted medical men from all over the world; but when Boerhaave lectured, the largest hall would be packed with an entranced audience. His most famous pupil, Albrecht von Haller, tells us that, so important were the views of this professor of medicine, botany and chemistry, that frequently a book Boerhaave had praised in the morning would sell for double the price in the bookshops in the afternoon. In the picture (left) Boerhaave is purposely portrayed larger than life. He was the spokesman of the Age of Enlightenment. The task of the scholar was to collect and co-ordinate in an encyclopedic fashion the knowledge of his time. The most precious gift to the audience were glimpses into the rule of purposeful, all-powerful universal Reason, and the strong incentive to spread the light of rational thought and research. In Haller and Boerhaave this intellectual stimulus was combined with vigorous Christianity; but it led another student of Leyden, Julien Offroy de La Mettrie, to a philosophy of crass materialism.

Boerhaave wrote academic textbooks which enjoyed wide circulation. They laid stress on the practical application of knowledge; and they represented the human body as a wisely designed mechanism in which all organs were interdependent and formed a universe in microcosm which functioned in the same way as Newton's astronomic universe.

Leyden not only kept pace with the latest contemporary discoveries but also revived works of the past which had sunk into undeserved oblivion. For example, in 1744, Albinus brought out a new publication, together with his own commentary, of the anatomical illustrations which the Pope's personal physician, Bartolomeo Eustachio had left unpublished when he died in 1574. He was a contemporary of Vesalius, and his equal. Hyrtl called him a genius of anatomy. His illustrations drew attention to many facts which Vesalius had overlooked or omitted. Boerhaave's colleagues admired his knowledge of the larynx, the pulmonary vessels and especially his insight into the ways in which the blood reached the muscles (top right) and his illustrations of the sympathetic nervous system (below). He made a clear distinction between this and the other fibres which transmit impulses from the brain to the muscles, or yet others which carry sensations from the skin and the sense organs to the brain. The nerves of the sympathetic system, on the other hand, were arranged in a twin cord of their own, along the sides of the spinal column; they were connected at specific points to the spinal marrow and led in delicate ramifications to the lung, heart and intestines (*see* p. 292). The more advanced physiologists of the nineteenth century solved the mystery of this regulatory system, which operates almost independently of consciousness and among other things controls man's breathing and the heart beat.

Albrecht von Haller's catholic mind delighted in investigating physiological problems of such magnitude. He introduced concepts of the essence of organic, living matter into contemporary discussion. He found that, upon being stimulated muscular fibres had an inherent tendency to contract involuntarily and then to relax. He called this tendency irritability and saw in it a basic quality of living matter. At the same time he proved that tissues as such were not sensitive and that only the nerves were the recipients and conductors of pain and other impulses. He made comparative studies of the role of this second principle of life, sensibility, covering the entire range of living beings. When his work on physiology, *Elementa physiologiae* appeared in 1759–66 it replaced the books by his teacher Boerhaave all over the world.

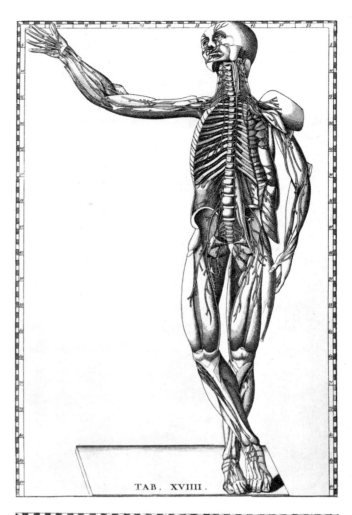

TAB. XVIIII.

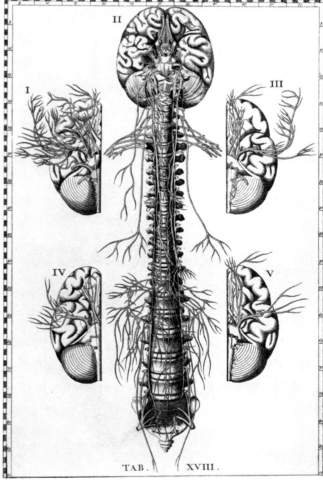

TAB. XVIII.

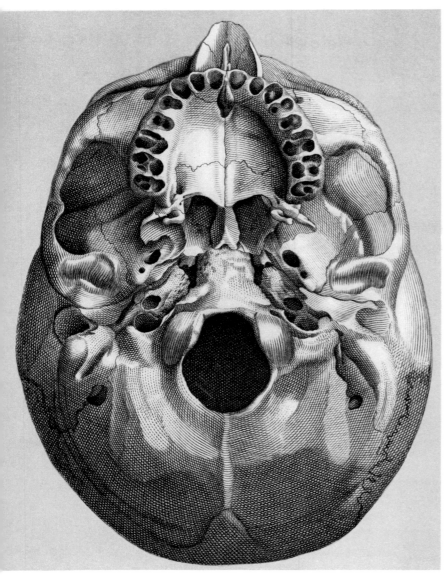

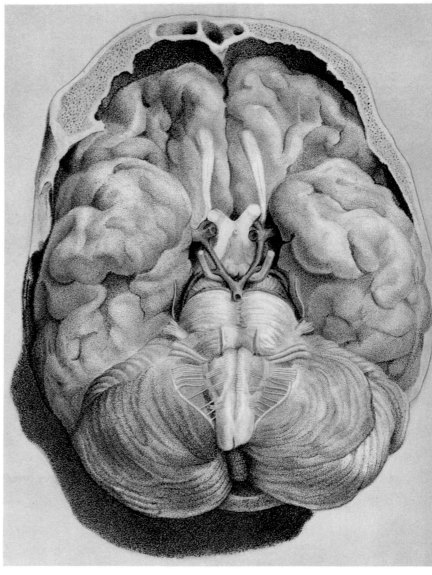

SKULL FROM BELOW (CALDANI, 1801)　　　　BRAIN FROM BELOW (SANTORINI, 1775)

'Ever since the beginning of scientific thought in medicine outstanding physicians of all civilized nations have been endeavouring to find the site where the sensitive soul fights its battles and the thinking mind shapes the world.' So wrote Paul Flechsig, who was conducting research into the human brain, in 1896. Hippocrates, whose sharp physician's eye had seen that brain injuries meant damage to a man's capacity to think, would never have looked for the seat of thought where Aristotle believed it to be: in the heart. For a short time in the Hellenistic period, when scientists in Alexandria were permitted to carry out dissections, Herophilus and Erasistratus made a decisive advance in the knowledge of the most sensitive of all organs—the brain. It is located in the bony shell of the skull, protected by membranes and cerebral fluid. Even then, they distinguished between the cerebellum, which lies lower down at the back of the head, and the brain proper (cerebrum) which includes all other parts; they also saw that the brain-like substance of the spinal marrow entered the brain from below through an opening now called the foramen magnum. Already Herophilus considered the convolutions of the cerebrum as the seat of man's power to think, and Erasistratus confirmed this by his comparisons: he argued that the brain of man,

who excelled all other living creatures in intelligence, had more convolutions and thus a larger surface than any other. It was clear already to Erasistratus that the brain, the spinal cord and the nerve system formed a single unit whose functions were of fundamental importance to man's life. In the nineteenth century, physiologists realized that the cerebellum was an organ which recorded within itself general conditions of the body as a whole, as for instance changes in its position. The picture opposite, the work of the German neuro-anatomist C.F. Burdach, shows its left half below the cerebrum. The horizontal white section is the cut surface of the band of nerves that connects the two halves of the cerebrum.

But the greatest interest was focussed on the cerebrum, in which physicians increasingly found the physical basis of man's capacity to think. Samuel Thomas Soemmerring, a physician friend of Goethe's who lectured at Kassel, Mainz, Frankfurt-on-Main and Munich, was passionately interested in the study of man. He followed Albinus, whom he took as his model, in carefully and precisely examining several hundred brains of human beings and animals and making drawings from accurate dissections. An illustration by the Italian anatomist Domenico Santorini (above right) shows

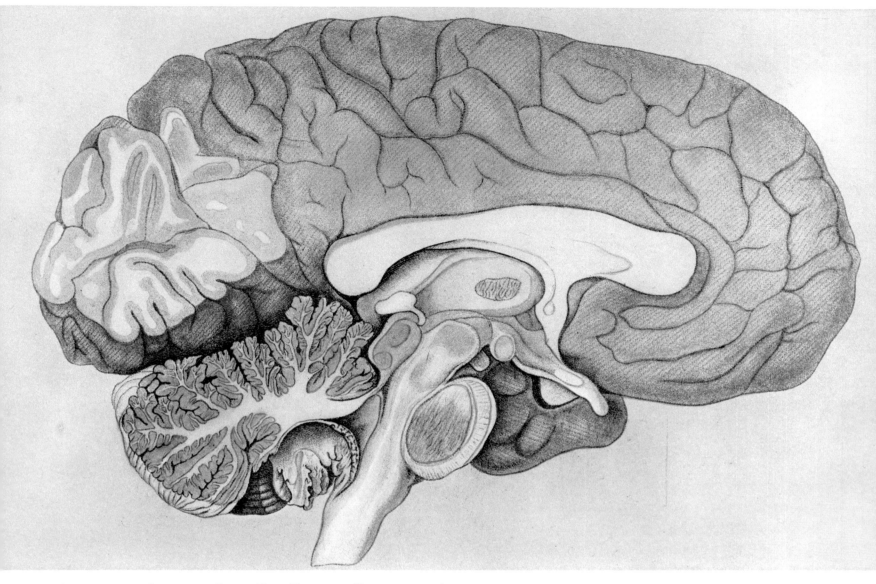

LONGITUDINAL SECTION OF BRAIN (CARL FRIEDRICH BURDACH, 1819)

the enigmatic landscape of the brain. Between the striated lobes of the cerebellum, the spinal cord is seen joining the hind part of the brain, or medulla, and this is continued under the pons (Latin for 'bridge'), which like a thick strap connects the two sides of the cerebellum. The bulk of the cerebral lobes fills the remainder of the cranial cavity. Soemmerring drew attention to the large number of sensory nerves ending in the cerebrum. The white X-shaped formation in the centre is the intersection of the optic nerves; above them are seen the long, club-shaped olfactory nerves, while the auditory nerves protrude horizontally on both sides just below the pons. We are looking into the region where all sensory messages come together close to the bulging chambers of memory. What was it that linked everything together at these points where the entire conscious Ego appeared to be concentrated? It was the cerebro-spinal fluid. Soemmerring believed this fluid to be the actual 'organ of the soul'.

Later scientists discovered, just below the crossing-point of the optical nerves, the pituitary gland, an organ about the size of a pea, whose hormones seem to be the controlling factor of other hormone-forming glands in the subtle regulatory system of the body.

In the nineteenth century, more information about brain diseases and injuries made clearer the functions of the cortex, the layer of grey matter on the surface of the cerebral hemispheres. If certain parts were destroyed, sight, hearing, memory, speech and other faculties were correspondingly put out of action. Because of these effects, anatomists such as Franz Joseph Gall, Paul Flechsig, and Walter R. Hess, and their successors to the present day, looked for the centres of man's vital functions in the cortex; there, they thought, stimuli became conscious sensations, judgments were formed and conscious voluntary impulses originated. Flechsig called for reverence for and restrained philosophical interpretation of these deeply mysterious regions where mind and body seem intertwined. Fifty years later the physiologist Alexis Carrel, a Nobel Prize winner, put his finger on one of the mysteries: 'Strangely enough, brain work does not seem to consume any energies, or it uses up so little that we cannot determine it by our present methods... Caesar's powerful will, Newton's mighty intellect, Beethoven's inspiration and Pasteur's scientific vision produced less change in the chemical reactions of their tissues than a few bacteria or a minor stimulation of the thyroid gland could have achieved in a flash.'

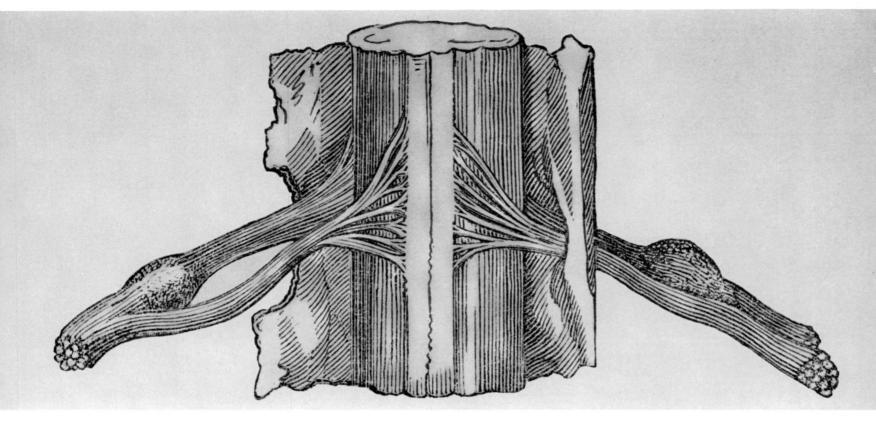

CHARLES BELL DISCOVERS THE 'SOUL OF THE SPINAL CORD'

Sir Charles Bell, an outstanding brain and nerve physiologist, will always be linked with the investigation of the spinal cord. In his native town of Edinburgh he gave brilliant lectures at his brother's private school of anatomy, but he was not admitted to the university because the anatomist Monro thought a second lecturer might endanger his monopoly. Edinburgh consequently lost this gifted scientist to London where he was in charge of William Hunter's famous school of anatomy for many years. Not until he was sixty-two was Bell called to Edinburgh University where opposition to his appointment had at last collapsed. Meanwhile, he had published astonishing discoveries based on experiments on animals, which radically altered existing concepts of the spinal cord. Magendie reached similar conclusions independently of Bell.

Above, much enlarged, is reproduced one of the thirty-one points in the spinal cord at which a bifurcated spinal nerve springs from either side of the cord. The so-called posterior root bulges into a ganglion, an accumulation of nerve cells, whereas the bodies of the cells of the anterior root lie in the grey matter of the spinal cord. The two roots unite their fibres in the mixed nerve, which soon divides again and leads into the body. Charles Bell succeeded in giving an explanation of what takes place at this point invisibly and at lightning speed. In the two roots we see the main functions of the central nervous system: through the posterior root messages from the highly sensitive sensory nerves travel to the spinal cord and through this to the brain, whereas the 'orders' from the brain are quickly conveyed through the anterior root to the muscles which are to be induced to move. These then are the distinct channels of the sensory and motor impulses. But as the cells of the motor nerves lie in the spinal cord, the 'detour' of messages via the brain can be avoided. A wave of sensory impulses passes along the posterior root into the spinal cord where it may also directly stimulate the motor nerve cells at the same level. The anterior root immediately passes on this impulse to a muscle, a simple reflex action without switching on the brain or will power, like the unconscious flicking away of a fly with the hand, the promptest reply of the body to a disturbing stimulus from outside. Bell reasoned that in the spinal cord was an automatic reflex organ, something like an accessory soul, as it were. He may have tried out the well-known experiment on his patients: if the sensory nerves in the tendon below the knee-cap are stimulated by a slight tap, the impulse races through the posterior root to the spinal cord. This wakes up the motor impulse which jerks the shin forward, a pure reflex movement in defence against the tap.

Bell's diagram on the right demonstrates the mechanism for the 'complete' path of impulses: the spinal cord (E) and the bifurcated nerves which pass to the body. Those at point 2 lead to the neck, those at 3 and 4 to the chest, those at 5 to the lumbar region and those at 6 to the sacrum. At the top, the two halves of the brain proper (A) and the cerebellum (B) are sketched. Near the point where they join there is the tri-partite trigeminal nerve which leads to the skin of the head and the face.

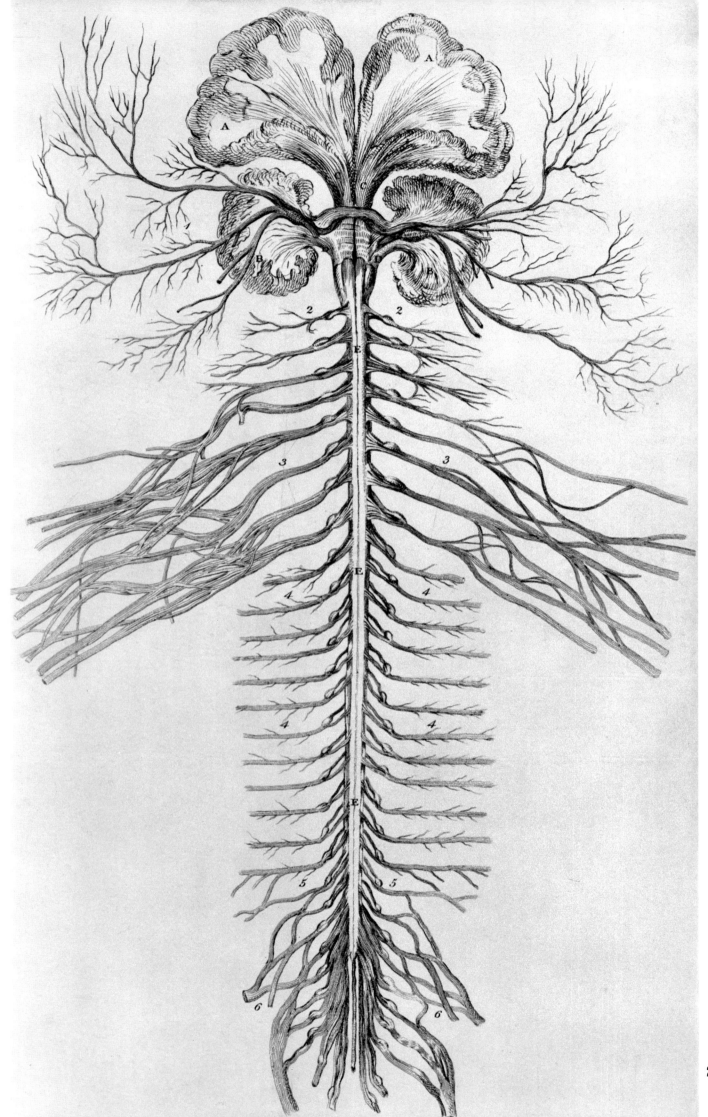

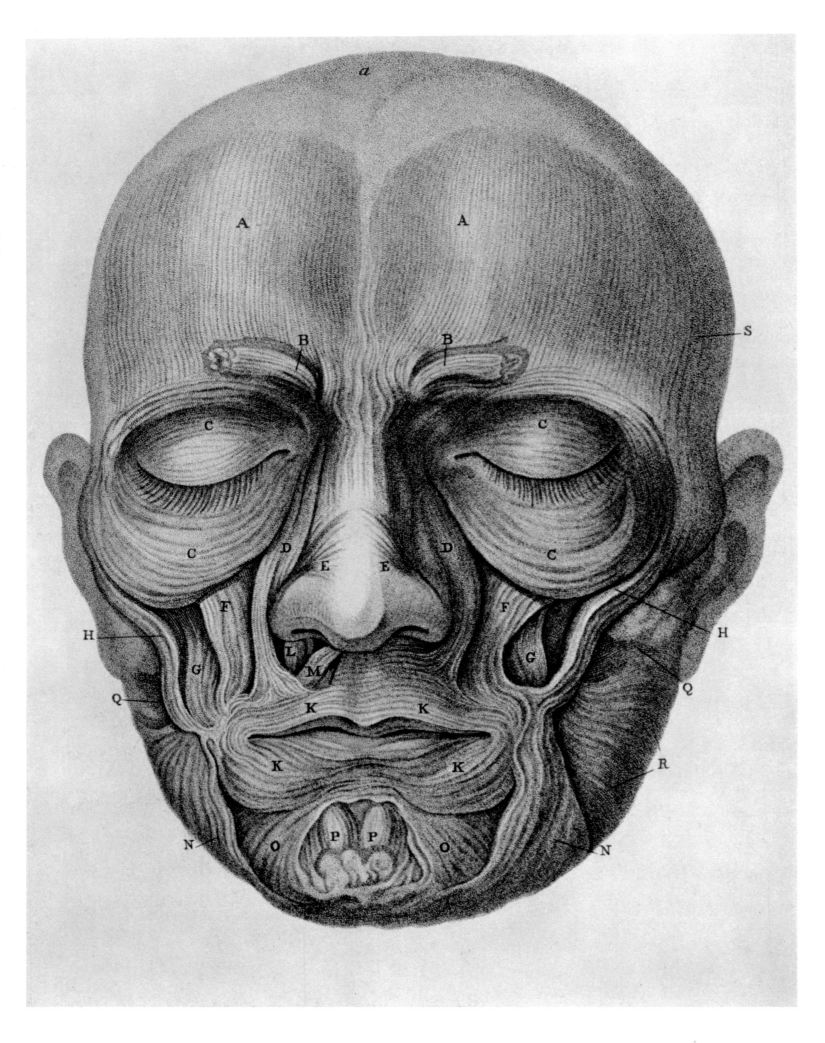

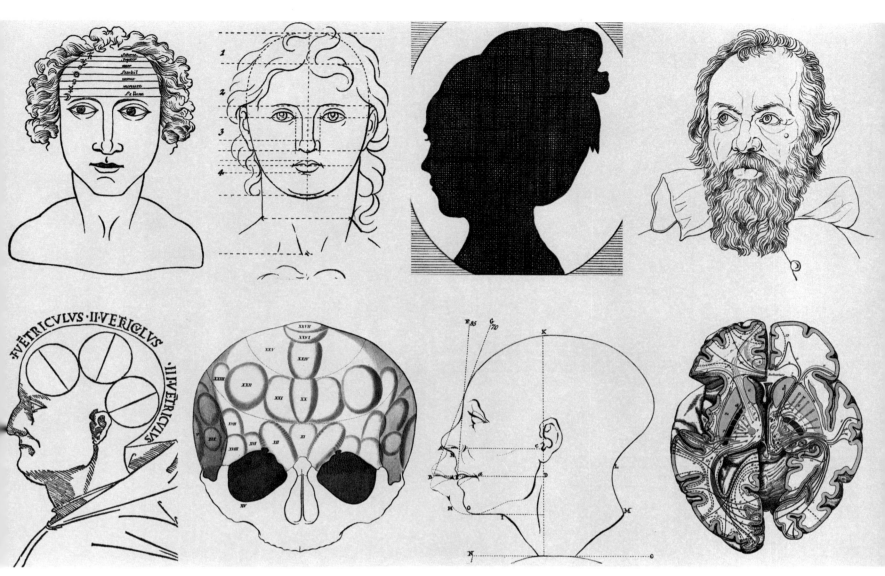

FROM THE STORY OF THE DISCOVERY OF THE HUMAN FACE

Throughout the ages the human face has aroused the interest of man's enquiring mind. For it is on the face that life leaves its traces, where the ebb and flow of the emotions is mirrored, and where some people even believed they could see the manifestation of some divine or diabolical powers. Astrologically, the planets were assumed to dominate the forehead, and magnanimity and nobleness were inferred if there was a wrinkle in the second zone from the top—the Jupiter-zone (top row, left); the search for some secret rules of proportion led to the working-out of a mathematics of beauty (second from left); physiognomists 'read' the human face and in the eighteenth century Johann Kaspar Lavater set the fashion for interpreting silhouettes. From Petrus Camper people learned how to use a system of lines to measure the facial angles (beneath silhouette) and to apply the rules which governed its changes in different races. Mention should also be made of the long line of those who sought to evolve an inner and outer topography of the human skull. There were, for example, the early Fathers of the Church who located man's higher intellectual activities in three ventricles of the brain, in accordance with the holy number Three: imagination and power of perception behind the forehead; memory at the back of the head (occiput), and

between them the powers of thought and reasoning (bottom row, left). In the eighteenth century Franz Joseph Gall propounded a theory of phrenology according to which the seat of the twenty-seven basic faculties could be located at specific points in the skull (second from left). Leading personalities of history, too, were scrutinized. In Galileo (top row, right) Gall detected the force which made men into philosophers or linguists, and he located this in sphere XIX, whereas he thought that Galileo's organ of orientation (XVII) was atrophied, as with all astronomers who think in terms of planetary distances. Finally, in 1896, Paul Flechsig published the first chart of areas of sensory perception and centres of association in the cortex, seen in two horizontal planes (bottom row, right).

Charles Bell studied the muscles of the face (opposite), and sought to account for the endless variety of facial expressions. A is the muscle which wrinkles or smoothes the forehead, C opens and shuts the eye and controls the skin around it, K does the same for the mouth while the complex arrangement of other muscles assists in control of the finer movements of the corners of the mouth and the lips. No less a man than Darwin gave enthusiastic praise to this journey of exploration behind the human face.

A Blind Man Regains His Sight

'It is the eye alone which really conveys the tremendous visual impact of the world to the mind, and the effect of this particular organ ... can be described as incalculable,' says the physician Carl Gustav Carus in his *System der Physiologie* (1849). Hence those acts by which the blind receive the gift of sight hold a high place in the hierarchy of healing, be it through the miracles of Saints or the skill of physicians. One of the Bible illustrators of the *Codex Egberti* of Trier chose a miraculous act of this kind as his theme. It is the healing of the man born blind at the pool of Siloam. With closed eyes, leaning on his staff, the blind man approaches Christ. According to the Bible, Christ makes a mixture from saliva and dust and places it on the dead eyes. 'And he said unto him: Go, wash in the pool of Siloam. He went his way therefore, and washed, and came seeing.' The picture gives a freer interpretation of the event. Christ, with a book and a halo containing a Cross, blesses the blind man with his right hand. Two Apostles accompany the man who by this miraculous deed can bestow the gift of sight. The pool of Siloam has here become a column-shaped well and water spouts into a basin from a peacock's beak.

Right: FROM THE STORY OF THE DISCOVERY OF THE EYE

'Iris' for the coloured layer round the pupil, 'cornea' for the bulge in front of it which protects it like the glass cover over the face of a watch, and 'retina' to denote the network at the back of the eye-ball, are all terms established since antiquity. Arab physicians in the Middle Ages had read Galen's description of glands spreading a fluid over the eye-ball; how it is lined by a network of delicate fibres (now called the retina), a soft layer full of blood vessels (choroid), a protecting layer (cornea) and a connective membrane; how it is moved by several muscles and how on the inside, between two 'humours', there is a vertical crystalline lens. Both Greek and Arab teachers of anatomy used to demonstrate the structure of the eye with the help of drawings of longitudinal sections; these may have contained traces of even older—Babylonian and Indian—knowledge, for in those epochs they already knew how to perform the operation for cataract.

The mathematician Alhazen's work on optics dating back to about the year AD 1000 is an attempt to understand the process of vision with the help of those earlier anatomical concepts. In his view, light falling on objects was reflected from countless points on their surface into the eye; the light rays penetrated the cornea and pupil to reach the lens which 'sensed' the pictures; Alhazen did not connect the retina with the 'sensing' lens, for he had shrewdly concluded that the picture of the outside world was bound to appear inverted on the retina, as in a camera obscura. But it was evident that the experience of seeing contradicted this—and so the

Arabs and all medieval writers continued to think that the act of seeing took place in the lens. Our picture (top right) which is also only approximately correct from the anatomical point of view, illustrates this concept. The lens is shown in the centre and not in the front of the eye-ball, the optic nerve *(Nervus opticus)* in line with the pupil and the lens. The space between iris and lens, which is filled with fluid *(Humor aqueus),* is too wide, and that between lens and retina *(Tunica reti similis),* filled by vitreous humour, is too narrow; the membranes are disproportionately thick (the *Tunica uvea* corresponds to the choroid membrane, which forms the iris at f). These main faults, however, persisted even in Vesalius' illustration, as our picture shows. The reason is that in 1572 this picture was simply transferred from Vesalius' *Fabrica* to the printed new edition of Witelo's *Optics* and thereby returned to its original medieval environment.

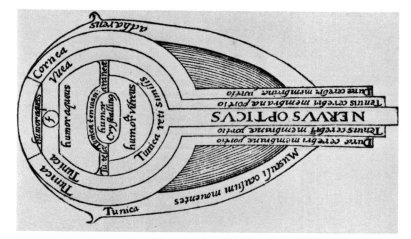

The world had to wait for Johannes Kepler to prove irrefutably that images of exterior objects really stand on their heads on the retina. To this day it remains a mystery why we do not feel anything of this inversion; indeed, we have the sensation of being at the centre of the entire field of vision. Haller's pupil, Johann Gottfried Zinn, of whom we are reminded by the name of the flower, zinnia, drew our second picture of the eye-ball resting in its bony eye-socket. He showed the arrangement of the muscles which turn the eye-ball in all directions, and explained how the arterial blood vessels supply the retina and where the optic nerve (t) enters. The tear glands (B) were lowered from the upper part of the eye socket. The fourth picture reveals the subtle hand of the investigator Soemmerring. It traces the paths of all the nerves which end in the eye's muscles and related tissues, the eyelids, the eye-ball and the tear glands. On the top right lies the optic nerve, and below it three other fine nerves which run from the mid-brain, and govern the muscles of the eye-ball and eyelid and the secretion of tears. The main question for eye research in the nineteenth century was: what exactly happens in the retina when we see? The Czech, Jan Purkinje, who was unceasingly carrying out experiments on his own eyes, discovered those 'entoptic' phenomena in which the eye sees what lies at its own base. Purkinje held a piece of black paper with a little round hole close to his eye, so that light could enter the pupil. Looking through the hole at an overcast sky and rapidly moving the paper to and fro, he suddenly realized he was seeing the blood vessels on his own retina (bottom right). Where the optic nerve enters the retina he noticed a blank round spot, the so-called blind spot; it was there that the arteries and veins entered the back of the eye. He found as a result of a similar experiment that the entry point of the optic nerve appeared as a bright patch (bottom left).

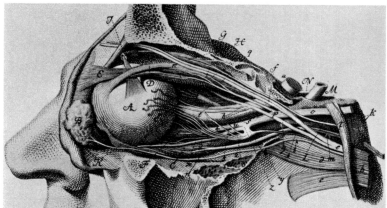

The microscope brought scientists closest to the answer to this major question. In 1856 Heinrich Müller managed to identify various layers in the complex structure of the retina. The third picture shows (on the right) the end of the retina bordering on the interior of the eye, the light penetrates from the right through a layer of ganglion cells and two layers of little grains to a series of long thin rods, between which there are somewhat broader cones—not visible in this early simple diagram. Here the light meets the real recipients of the light rays. Ten years after Müller's discovery Max Schultze found that the rods convey the sensation of light, and the cones that of colour, in the process which, according to Carus, 'conveys the tremendous visual impact of the world to the mind.'

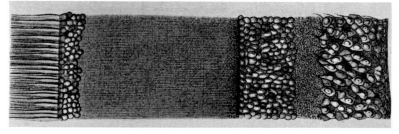

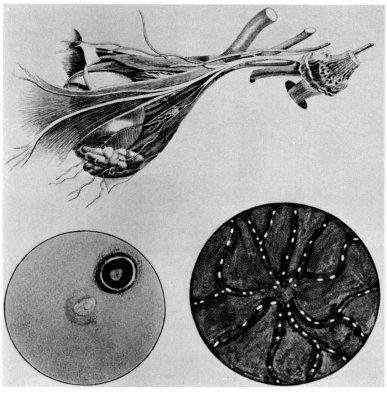

AN ALLEGORY OF THE EXPERIENCE OF HEARING (1618)

The English physician and theosophist Robert Fludd regarded the human ear as a mystical organ. He uses the picture of a tower to illustrate the process of hearing. Two open doors lead into the building like the auditory canals into the ears. Outside there is the sound of music: lute, human voice and Pan's pipes are joined and harmoniously linked by a series of arches. The circle of rays around the singer on the left points to the divine origin of music which is a gift of Apollo. According to Agrippa von Nettesheim, whose occult writings were minutely studied by Fludd, musical harmony created a profound sense of union. Man and beast were bound by its spell, so that they listened jointly; it widened man's mind, making him aware of his bond with the Earth and the Universe; for the Universe, Earth and the human mind were in the same secret divine harmony of which music was an echo. Sounds were vibrations of the air, circular or spiral-like motions which penetrated into the ear and mind like those filling the tower in the picture. In music the ear perceives the world harmony through the medium of sound. Through the ear man partakes of it. To Fludd the ear is a sacred organ. Two hundred years later the romantic German naturalist Lorenz Oken praised hearing in a similar vein as the innermost sensation which directly unites the human soul with the essence of the world. He said: 'Seeing places man in the world; hearing places the world in man.'

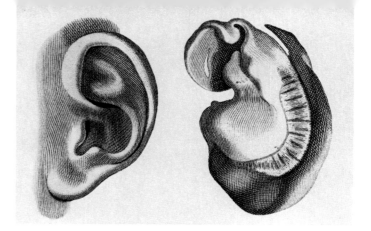

The eye and the ear seem to be outposts of the body, immersed in a sea of light and sound, and therefore easily accessible to the scientist. But the real eye and the real ear, those extremely subtle parts where external impulses are received by the nerve cells, lie deeply concealed. This is why the details of the delicate structure and functions of the ear were only revealed quite late. And so the fanciful concepts about the secret of hearing became more and more abundant. To the ancient Chinese the ears were the 'windows of the kidneys'; Plato assumed that the perception of sound was located in the liver which was regarded as the seat of the soul. Aristotle was cautious and confined his pronouncements almost entirely to the auricle and the external auditory meatus; he believed that hearing proper took place in a secluded internal cavity filled with air.

The meticulous anatomical illustrations of the physician Samuel Thomas Soemmerring always had an indefinable quality of reverence for the beauty of nature's forms. This also applies to the picture of the auricle (top left) which acts as a receptacle of sound and channels the noise towards the auditory canal. The picture next to it shows it without the skin and exposes the supporting cartilages. Below these, there is a picture from a book by Malpighi's pupil Antonio Maria Valsalva, who in 1705 introduced the terms 'outer', 'middle' and 'inner' ear. This illustration would be impossible without the fundamental discoveries made by Gabriele Falloppia in his *Observationes anatomicae* in 1651. He based his work on Vesalius, but forged further into the unknown with scalpel and chisel than did Vesalius or those other scholars who already knew of the little auditory bones—the hammer, the anvil and the stirrup. The outer ear ends with the external auditory canal in front of the taut ear drum or tympanic membrane (*b*); behind it lies the middle ear, which consists of a small, air-filled chamber with the vibrating bridge formed by the three little bones of the ear. The Eustachian tube (*e*) connects the cavity of the middle ear with that of the pharynx, the cavity behind the nose, the mouth and the larynx. This cleverly ensures that air pressure on either side of the ear drum is the same; one-sided pressure without counter-pressure might burst it. (This accounts for the piece of advice about opening one's mouth during a violent bang.) Falloppia called the secluded inner ear the labyrinth. According to Aristotle it was filled with air; but instead of air, Falloppia found a fluid. Immersed in it were, side by side, the most important parts of the ear: three semicircular canals (*1, 2, 3*), the organ of balance, as later investigations proved, and the snail-like windings of the cochlea (*5*). The auditory nerve, leading to the brain is shown at (*6*).

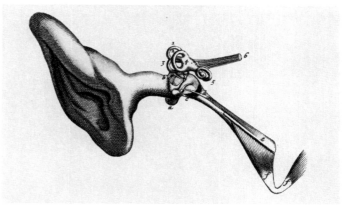

The Italian surgeon Antonio Scarpa continued his country's significant tradition in anatomy in 1789 by tracing, for the first time, the path of the nerves from the inner ear to the brain and by separating the membranous from the surrounding bony labyrinth. The next picture shows his skill as an illustrator: it is a view from the auditory nerve towards the labyrinth. The picture below that, by Soemmerring, again leads us back into the interior of the tympanic cavity set in the mass of the cranial bones.

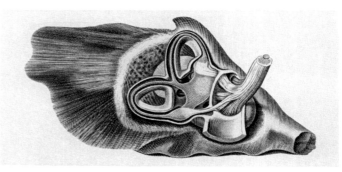

Even after so much precise anatomical work the great physiological question remained unanswered: in view of this delicate system of little cavities, bones, membranes, helical tubes and nerves, how could one explain the process of hearing? This is where the microscope and the concept of resonance provided further help. In 1683, Joseph Duverney, a scholar of the Jardin des Plantes circle, published a study of the propagation of sound waves: these made the ear drum and the auditory bones vibrate and were ultimately bound to be transmitted by the vibrating cochlea to the auditory nerve. Helmholtz evolved what is relatively the most credible theory so far: he thought the point where the vibrations reach the auditory nerve was in the so-called organ of Corti in the separating wall of the cochlea. Here, in the basilar membrane (bottom) many thousands of tiny hairs are situated at the ends of auditory nerve fibres, which act as resonators, pick up the vibrations and pass on the messages. The strange thing is that these fibre-ends vibrate in resonance in groups, like different tuning forks only at a certain sound each (at f, c, h², etc.), so that a confusion of vibrations is separated into its components.

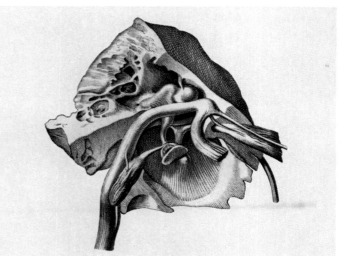

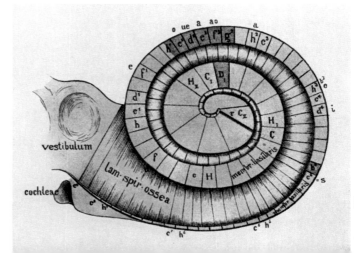

299

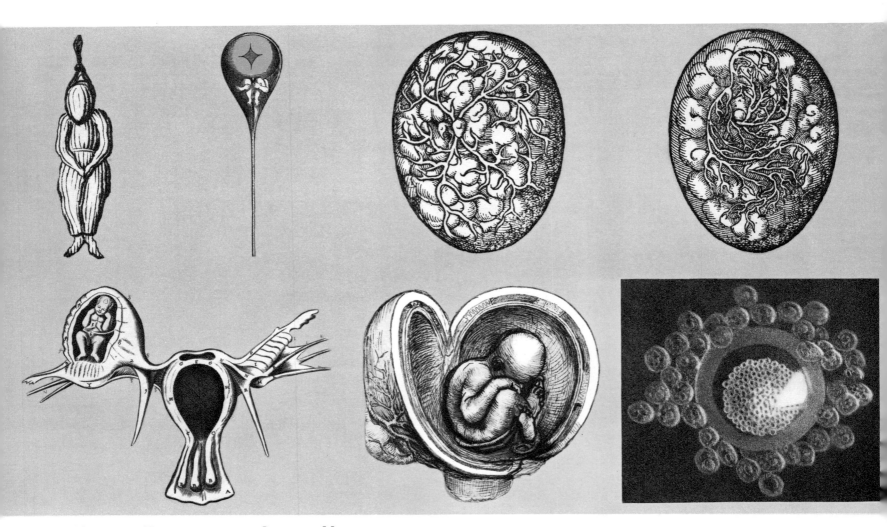

Aristotle had assumed that a new human being was created by a male principle imparting its formative strength to the nourishing menstrual blood. What other possibility was there, since the menstrual flow was no longer apparent with the onset of pregnancy? Even fifteen hundred years later, these two woodcuts (top right) from a book for midwives in 1554 testify to the continuing acceptance of Aristotle's ideas: in the left-hand one, we are shown how from a yolk-like substance the heart and four systems of blood vessels are beginning to take shape; in the other, the network of blood vessels already assumes the contours of a baby, the assumption apparently being that muscles and bones grow into it at a later stage. Top left, we find two figures from the days after Leeuwenhoek and his pupil Ham had informed the Royal Society in 1677 that they had discovered 'spermatozoa' in man. Before long, other microscopists thought they had seen minute homunculi in the spermatozoa. In 1694, for example, Nikolaus Hartsoeker quite seriously assumed in accordance with the theory of pre-formation then prevalent, that the human sperm was of minuscule adult form (second figure, top row). The first figure on the left caricatures this absurd belief. The artist was the Secretary of the Academy of Montpellier, F. de Plantades. The opposition to the believers in the male sperm as the true creator of the human being came from the Ovists, who swore that the producer was the egg and not the sperm. They received fresh support from the physician Regnier de Graaf who proclaimed in 1672 that he had found the first egg of mammals in the cow. This put an end to the fertilization theory of Aristotle. It turned out that he had discovered not the egg but the follicle (which is now named after him), a little sac which protects the egg in the ovary. De Graaf thought that the path of the follicle lay through the oviduct into the uterus. To prove this he published the picture of a case in Paris (bottom row, left) where an embryo had developed halfway along this route.

The 'battle of the sexes' came to an end when in 1759 Wolff (*see* p. 232) finally refuted the theory of preformation. Meanwhile Leonardo da Vinci's anatomical sketch books lay forgotten. They contained, among other things, sketches of the human embryo (bottom row, centre) which were far ahead of his time. The last figure which sums up the knowledge of the 1840s, is a diagram of the human egg with the ball-shaped yolk, surrounded by fluid containing albumin.

Right: HUMAN FOETUS IN THE FOURTH MONTH

This is how the Munich physician Pius Erdl drew the foetus, with great reverence, in 1845. The embryo is surrounded by the thin membrane—the amnion—which is filled with the so-called amniotic fluid; another membrane, the chorion, is turned upward in folds, and in between lies the whitish nutrient placenta. The embryo sleeping in the womb preparing for his life to come, already occasionally gives a gentle stir in his mother's body. The future human being is clearly discernible, his sex is recognizable, his chest and abdominal cavity, fingers and toes are formed, and his biography already spans four eventful months.

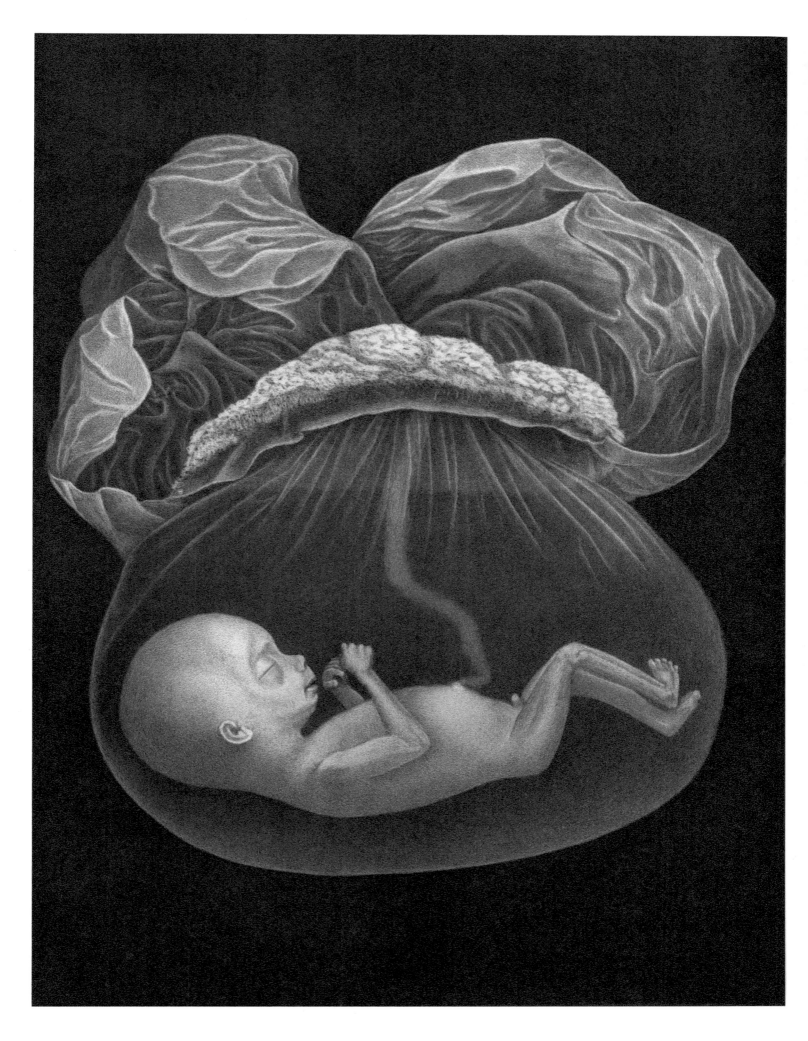

FREDERICK THE GREAT DURING THE NIGHT OF HIS DEATH

During the night of 16th to 17th August 1786, at 2.20 a.m., Frederick the Great died at the Château of Sans Souci, at the age of seventy-four. The end came eleven months after a stroke which had planted the seed of death in him. The heir to the throne, Frederick's nephew Frederick William, is called. He is bursting with self-confidence. His counsellor, Count Hertzberg, and the physician, Christian Gottlieb Selle, were present when the king 'exhaled his great soul without any convulsive movement'. For eleven months death had been lurking in the breathing and circulatory organs, their functions had been paralyzed by dropsy and his old body had been using up its last feeble powers of resistance. Only the strength of the mind and will of the stoic of Sans Souci were unbroken. They accounted for the miracle that from this room until the day before his death 'an entire kingdom was ruled by one man on his deathbed', as one of his friends, Lucchesini, put it. Servants are standing behind the armchair. One of them is raising a candlestick. Its light is falling on the pale, hollow-cheeked, bloodless face of the aged man. It bears the marks of the inexorable withering of the body's substance, which the science of death calls atrophy, the stage preceding death from old age.

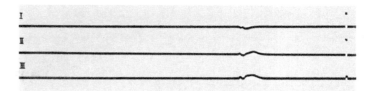

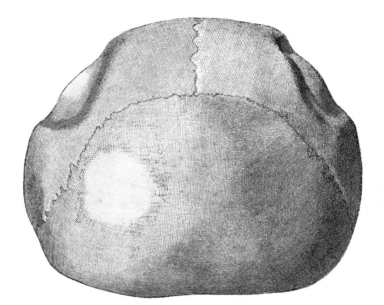

The whole body does not die all at once. A trace of life remains for some time in individual groups of cells, as for example in hair that continues to grow. The real death is the death of the heart. 'As long as it contracts within the breast, however feebly however laboriously, man is alive, but all is over, irrevocably, with the last beat of the heart,' said the physiologist Hermann Nothnagel. Modern electro-cardiograms can show this last and feeblest heartbeat (top right). The horizontal lines were registered after a seventy-four-year old man had stopped breathing; they deflect a little for the last time and then remain for ever straight.

Not all senile bodies are a prey to death in equal measure. Only very rarely can death be predicted with mathematical precision. Nevertheless, physiologists of the nineteenth century made some substantial contributions towards clarifying the mysteries of the preliminary stages of natural death. They looked for traces of death through their microscopes and found them in the cells. It was Rudolf Virchow who first systematically observed ailing and dying cells. And in his revolutionary work on the pathology of cells, *Cellularpathologie,* he wrote in 1858: 'The gradual atrophy of vital cells is the forerunner of death from old age.'

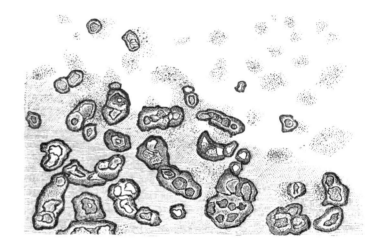

The bones get thinner and more brittle, the adipose tissue atrophies, the skin grows wrinkled, the spinal column curves. The second picture shows the top of an old man's skull. On the right and left shallow pits have formed in the parietal bones; the atrophy of the bones is far advanced. In the third picture Virchow shows, 300 times enlarged, how the preliminary stage of calcification begins at the end of an old man's thigh bone (femur). Calcium salts are deposited in the form of angular little grains in the thick, inert substance which surrounds the live cartilage cells, and in this way the cartilage loses its structure and elasticity.

Sinister evidence of atrophy appears in the internal organs. The picture at the bottom shows, magnified 200 times, a microscopic section through the urinary tubules in an old man's kidney. No sign of age is yet visible at (*a*); the opening (light area) for the unimpeded excretion of dissolved waste substances is clearly visible. At (*d*) atrophy has affected a so-called vascular knot or glomerulus, a very delicate arterial formation. At (*b*) another can still be seen in its normal condition capable of functioning. At such points death can be seen threatening the living tissue. For where the normal metabolism in the cell is disturbed, where nutrient substances, especially oxygen, can no longer be fed to the individual cell and the waste not be disposed of, life is endangered, as was the case with the Prussian King at the Château of Sans Souci after a stroke had marked him out for death (*see* p. 302). 'We die because the heart gives out as a result of changes in the muscular or nerve cells which control its functions' (A. Lipschütz).

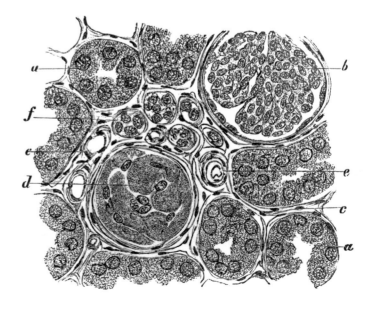

303

A MAN BREATHES HIS LAST

Gruesome Death has gripped a dying man's throat. What for a lifetime was one, is separated; an incorporeal substance departs from the material body. With the last breath the soul floats as if in mockery right through the skeleton of Death, away into a realm of immortal life. The mortal remains are lowered into the earth in a coffin.

The anonymous eighteenth-century picture bears a clumsy verse proclaiming that Death's triumph is also the gateway to Life, and the unknown author believes that a good Christian whose last hour has come should surrender his soul joyfully. The ordinary man and with him, on another level, the philosopher and theologian, carry on the great dialogue between man and reality where empirical science falls silent.

It is an age-old dialogue. It was carried on among primitive peoples no less than in the ancient civilizations of Asia and among the Greeks and the Christians. The views of Plato, who believed (as did, intrinsically, our 18th-century artist) that an imperishable soul disengages itself from a perishable body at death, were different from those of Epicurus, who could not accept the existence of anything indissoluble beyond the dissoluble organism. Whereas for La Mettrie, Diderot, Feuerbach, Haeckel and others immortality was nothing more than the perpetuation of valid concepts in the memory of posterity, other thinkers from Plato through Newton to Driesch and Planck believed that the soul lived on timelessly in a new kind of existence. Like Goethe and Kant, they found it possible to bring the idea of an existence that continued into eternity into accord with inward experience and with far-sighted interpretations of human life.

ASTRONOMY

From the very beginning man, observing the circling stars in the night sky, was confronted with an incomprehensibly great, unearthly phenomenon. Until well into the century of Galileo no astronomer had any doubt that his science lay intellectually on the boundary between time and infinity, in fact between this world and the next. The Greeks were the first to throw into prominence the three apparently timeless elements in astronomy, of which also their most important teachers, the Babylonians, were well aware. Astronomy, as they saw it, gazed into a heaven of divine creative powers. Plato in his *Timaeus* calls the universe an animated representation of eternity formed by a creative God to make eternity present. Right up to Copernicus and Kepler astronomy recognized the traces of these powers in the second timeless element, namely the immutable uniformity of the celestial processes. Spheres described circles, perfect bodies following perfect courses, as Aristotle taught. Ancient peoples told the time from this eternally regular world clock. About 2000 BC the Babylonian year had twelve months each of thirty days based on the original lunar months. As an additional unit the week was introduced. When today we call the days after sun, moon and five planetary gods we are still 'Chaldeans'. Mathematics alone of all the sciences 'is completely contained in the investigation of an eternally self-consistent world', as Ptolemy proudly proclaimed, thus indicating the third timeless element in astronomy. Both the harmony of the celestial bodies and the divine power was contained in a law of astronomy mathematically expressed, for the ancients as for the men of the Renaissance who constructed new systems of the universe. Copernicus praised astronomy as being 'the summit of all intellectual activity and the most dignified occupation of a free man'. A science so closely related to religion and philosophy was easily assimilated and developed by the Arabs in the eighth and ninth centuries and by the learned teacher of the late Middle Ages.

Astronomy was in a unique position in another respect: the object of its study was inaccessibly remote. The observer was separated from the moon, the sun, the planets and the fixed stars by an unbridgeable abyss, a situation occurring in no other science. The history of astronomy is the history of the attempts to bridge this abyss. The difficulty was overcome to an amazing degree by the superlative achievements of the human eye, the human mind and human skill in constructing apparatus to aid both. In the centuries preceding the invention of the telescope in 1609 we have the astronomy of the naked eye. They mark the powerful struggle of the critical spirit to determine the truth of the picture of the universe presented by the senses. It ended with the victory of the heliocentric system over the illusory geocentric system offered by the senses. A further historic achievement of the spirit of enquiry is Newton's doctrine of the forces which hold the stars of the universe on their courses. In the solar system, according to the gravitation theory, the movements of the planets originate from two elements, a spontaneous motion of the planet which would by the law of inertia carry it off course in a tangential direction, and a force of gravity operating from the dominant central star. It attracts the flying planet with a force proportional to the mass of the dominant body and in inverse ratio to the square of the distance (*see* p. 336). During the eighteenth century a few gifted mathematicians—Euler, Lagrange, Laplace and others—went further in this direction and summarized in a corpus of differential equations even the most complex mechanical phenomena in the solar system. Their aim was a system of celestial mechanics making it possible to calculate the state of the universe 'at any given point in the past or in the future' (Franz Becker).

These attempts to bridge the cosmic gulf by the mathematical spirit were followed by attempts by astronomers armed with telescopes. About 1610 saw the beginnings of a 'qualitative astronomy', a science of the perceptible individual properties of single stars, while Galileo and a handful of others were busy observing the sun, moon and planets through the newly invented telescopes. Their inaccessible remoteness already seemed partially overcome. In centuries the human eye caught up on knowledge withheld from it for thousands of years and eagerly discovered the mountains of the moon, Saturn's rings, solar prominences and hitherto unobserved planets. Gradually even the mightiest object, the hitherto neglected sphere of the fixed stars, entered the field of vision of the refractors and reflecting telescopes which became increasingly powerful every day. While a zealous champion of the quantitative, mathematical astronomy, Friedrich Wilhelm Bessel, still proclaimed in 1840 that the primary task of astronomy was 'to devise rules for the motion of every star', the prevailing mood of other astronomers was a frenzy of 'qualitative' discovery, for Kepler's ecstatic praise of the telescope was still ringing in their ears: 'Has not the man who holds thee in his right hand become a lord over God's creation?'

The Renaissance astronomer was still ignorant of the chemical substances present in the universe. The astronomer of today can identify at least sixty chemical elements in the solar atmosphere apart from hydrogen and helium. The cosmic abyss has been bridged by spectral analysis (*see* p. 117). Since the late nineteenth century, when the human eye was replaced by the more sensitive camera at the eye-piece of the large telescopes, it has been discovered that thousands of millions of stars can be counted in the resulting photographs. The twentieth century created a further technical miracle in the conquest of space. The radio telescope picks up electromagnetic vibrations from the universe and elucidates questions of distance, interstellar matter, and the Milky Way. More than ever some astronomers secretly cherish the hope of the greatest discovery —a living being similar to man inhabiting other worlds.

THE CONSTELLATIONS: DRAWN BY
FRANZ NIKLAUS KÖNIG (1826)

How was man to find his way about the glittering myriads of stars in the night sky? Which were the fixed points of reference to determine the movement of the planets and the moon? In later ages an imaginary grid was superimposed on the sky as it was on the earth (*see* p. 345), but the oldest marked positions in the great firmament were individual, conspicuous, fixed stars or groups of stars. The ancient Babylonians (and the Chinese and Egyptians each in their own way) started by dividing a vast realm of space along the celestial equator into twelve equal parts, called the signs of the zodiac. Greek and Roman mythology combined with the popular fancy of the time added yet more fictitious shapes to the starry skies.

This great subject has inspired many artists. In 1826 the Swiss painter, F.N. König in his *Astrognosie oder Anleitung zur Kenntnis der Sterne* used an unconventional method of drawing the immemorial figures round the outline of the constellations in the northern sky—white on black. At times he let his imagination run away with him. On the right, starting from the top, we see the signs of the zodiac proper: the Pisces (beneath the winged Pegasus), linked by a ribbon, Aries and Taurus, then Gemini and Cancer, Leo and Virgo in the shape of an angel. In his outline of other constellations he immortalizes the heroic legends of Greece. In one group, on the right of centre, the unhappy Argonaut Cepheus passes by behind the throne of Zeus, while below it, linked with the others by the Milky Way, we see Perseus who cut off Medusa's snake-crowned head with his sword. Behind Cepheus can be seen the snake-like water-dragon Cetos, with his dog's head, above him the Lyre and at the tail-end the Great Bear and the Little Bear; the body of the Great Bear clearly shows the familiar constellation of the Plough, and on the tail of the Little Bear we find the Pole Star, which is now man's chief guiding point in the night sky; the northern axis of the entire circular vault of the heavens seems to run through this star.

In the last five centuries before Christ, Greek astronomy inherited a wealth of knowledge which generations of Babylonian astronomers had gathered by observing the skies from the towers of their temples. They had produced mathematical tables which enabled them to predetermine the phases and even eclipses of the moon; the Greeks also took over the Babylonian calendar. No Babylonian astronomer would have doubted that the earth was the stationary centre of the universe and that the 'planets'—the sun, the moon and the five planets which are visible to the naked eye—were revolving in circles around this centre, and that at times some of them, inexplicably, turned back on their tracks. This theory agreed with appearances for thousands of years, and so it was accepted. Some of the greatest Greek astronomers, however, proved these assumptions to be wrong. About the year 345 BC Plato's disciple, Heracleides Ponticus, declared that what appeared to be the daily revolution of the fixed stars was in reality merely the rotation of the earth on its own axis. Aristarchus of Samos pursued this thought further and boldly challenged age-old concepts by placing the sun at the centre of the universe and arguing that the planets and the earth revolve around it. But the 'Greek Copernicus' did not secure acceptance for his idea of a heliocentric system. After the year 150 BC the main opposition to this concept rested on the authority of Hipparchus, an astronomer who had convincingly explained that the seasons were due to the sun moving in an eccentric circle around the earth and radiating varying amounts of warmth at different times of the year. When, in the second century AD, the astronomer and geographer Claudius Ptolemy of Alexandria co-ordinated the entire astronomical knowledge of antiquity, he supported Hipparchus' concepts. Ptolemy's handbook on astronomy, which the Arabs called the *Almagest,* was the authoritative work on the subject from the end of the Greek era to the close of the Middle Ages. So it happened that the earth remained, seemingly ordained by God, the centre of the planetary system and the universe, with the sun, moon and planets revolving around it. On the right is how Andreas Cellarius portrayed it in 1660.

Ptolemy propounded five theories which in the Middle Ages enjoyed, as the Laws of Astronomy, an authority as unassailable as the Laws of Moses:

1. The vault of heaven with its stars revolves like a globe. The pivot is at the pole of the celestial globe, because the nearby stars move in smaller, and the more distant stars in ever larger, orbits, as far as the celestial equator, which is at an angle to the equator of the earth. The twelve zodiacal constellations gird it like a broad band. (The shell of the celestial vault itself with the fixed stars is not shown in the picture.)

2. The earth, too, has the shape of a globe.

3. Its position is exactly at the centre of the firmament.

4. In view of the vast size of the firmament the earth is but a tiny point compared to the heavenly bodies.

5. The earth is stationary. All heavenly bodies gravitate towards the centre of the earth, which is also the centre of the universe. All obey a concentric pressure which also keeps the earth in position. If it moved, would not a cloud or any object thrown into the air immediately disappear westwards while the earth in its mighty revolution was racing towards the east?

Round this earth, describing their eternal circles, are, closest to it, the moon *(Sphaera lunae)* and the planets Mercury and Venus; next comes the sun, and farthest away Jupiter and Saturn. In the bottom left-hand corner of the picture we see these seven spheres surrounded harmoniously by four celestial spheres (VIII to XI) of the rest of the heavenly bodies right up to the empyrean, the sphere of light which is the abode of the blessed dead according to Christian theology. The celestial vault was dominated by the most perfect of all shapes—circle and globe—and could be measured by the most perfect of all sciences, mathematics. Ptolemy and his predecessors were aware of the fact that the planets moved at different speeds and, at certain points, in a loop-like orbit. Ptolemy solved the problem by assuming that they revolved in circles which had their centres on the circumference of an eccentric circle around the earth. This formulation did not hold its own for long against the challenge of criticism from sharper intellects and later mathematical reasoning. Attempts to explain the retrogressive movement of the planets became more and more spurious. One of these explanations is shown in the bottom right-hand corner. The astronomer Tycho Brahe believed that the sun and the moon *(Luna)* revolved around the earth *(Terra),* whereas the planets Venus, Mercury, Mars, Jupiter and Saturn revolved around the sun. It was a compromise at a time when Copernicus had already laid the foundations for a system which was to replace Ptolemy's concept.

NETARUM PLECTEN GRAPHIA.

ZODIACI

SPHÆRA SATVRNI

SPHÆRA IOVIS

SPHÆRA MARTIS

SPHÆRA SOLIS

SPHÆRA VENERIS

SPHÆRA MERCVRII

SPHÆRA LVNÆ

ÆQVINOCTIALIS

FIRMAMENTVM STEL: LARVM FIXARVM SEDES

Orbis Saturni
Via Iovis
Orbita Martis
Venus et Mercurius circa Solem
Terra
Luna

HYPOTHESIS BRAHEA.
in quâ centrum Lunæ et Fir-
mamenti est Terra, reliquorum
quinq; Planetarum Sol.

GEMENI

TAVRVS II

ARIES

PISCES

AQVARIVS

LEO

CER

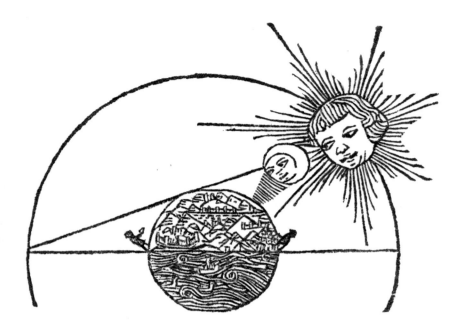

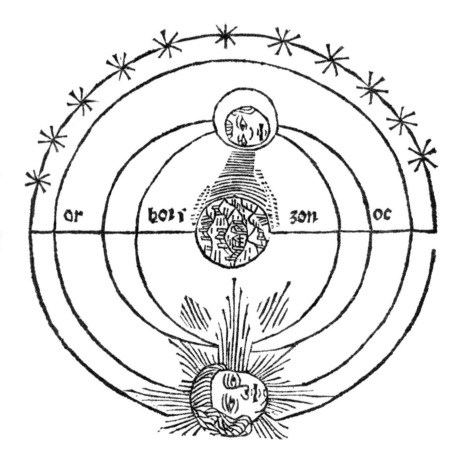

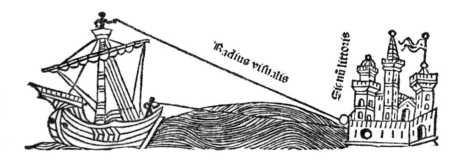

In the twelfth century Europe was beginning to build cathedrals whose slender spires, seemingly unencumbered by gravity, soared to the skies. It was at this time that Ptolemy's ideas of the Universe were widely disseminated and became the focal point of medieval astronomy. The clergy not only practised the art of fixing the right dates for the church festivals in a calendar calculated in accordance with established patterns; they also easily merged Ptolemy's spherical firmament, in which the sun and the planets performed their revolutions in harmony with each other, with the heavens of the Scriptures.

An English clergyman, John Holywood (Sacrobosco), adapted Ptolemy's *Almagest* in a booklet, *Sphaera mundi;* he took as his model the *Rudimenta astronomica* of Alfraganus, dating from the previous century, which in turn were also based on Ptolemy's theories. The *Sphaera mundi* became the basic textbook for astronomers at the zenith of the Middle Ages and in their later stages. It was eagerly copied and commented upon in many places, including the universities of Paris and Vienna. The *Sphaera mundi* contains the circular and globular theories of the universe, which are easily reconcilable with Christian concepts, and elementary astronomic traditions of antiquity. Among them was the explanation of the eclipse of the sun and the moon.

Top left, we see the moon in a straight line between the sun and the earth, as may be the case at certain times. Hence the moon darkens the light from the sun, 'without however stopping the sun from shining', as Sacrobosco adds reassuringly. The moon casts its shadow on part of the earth—and therefore not all the people on earth see the sun eclipsed.

The woodcut in the middle shows the earth at the centre of the universe, as if it had been there since the day of the Creation. This time the sun and the moon are in opposition to each other. In certain conditions the shadow of the earth which falls conically into space may strike the moon, that is, when it stands exactly in the sun's nadir; as the moon does not give off light of its own, the earth temporarily deprives the moon of the light it borrows from the sun.

The bottom picture proves that even the sea must conform with the most perfect of all shapes—the globe. The sailor on the crow's nest can see the distant strip of shore, but the man on deck cannot. The convex surface of the sea hides the beach from him although he can probably see the cluster of the town's high towers. Three hundred years later Copernicus elaborated this example poetically by saying: 'Conversely, if a light is tied to the top of the mast of the departing ship, those remaining ashore have the impression that it is gradually being lowered until it finally seems to sink and disappear.'

Right: THE CHRISTIAN FIRMAMENT

Throughout the ages, ancient civilized peoples imagined sacred powers ruling the skies. It was no mere whim that led priests to have their temples, or kings the ceilings of their tents, decorated with pictures of the constellations. The same religious motive was in the mind of Christian cartographers of the heavens when they sometimes replaced pagan heroes in the firmament by figures from the Old and New Testaments so that the stars should also glorify the deeds of archangels, evangelists and martyrs and such miracles as the crossing of the Red Sea when the waters divided (bottom right).

311

'The Bishop of Kulm has often urged me to publish this book, which I have kept hidden not nine but more than four times nine years, and to let it at last see the light of day. And not a few other distinguished and learned men have asked me to do the same. They all argued that the more absurd my theory of the motion of the earth would seem to most, the greater would be their admiration and gratitude when, as a result of the publication of my research, the apparent absurdity would vanish before the brilliant light of proof.'

These words are taken from the dedication to Pope Paul III which Nicolaus Copernicus placed at the head of his work on the revolutions of the celestial bodies, in 1543. They show a scientist in a typical situation: *Before* him uncertainty as to the probable reception the world would give to his revolutionary findings; *with* him only a few contemporaries who are convinced by his theory; but *in* him the 'brilliant light of proof', the slowly-matured, unimpeachable new truth. Canon Copernicus of Frauenburg in East Prussia was a versatile man educated in medicine, law and astronomy. For decades he had re-thought and re-calculated Ptolemy's inadequate, artificially supported concepts. In the end, he was spared the fate of Galileo: the first printed copy of his book arrived at his residence on 24th May 1543, the very day he died, aged seventy. His work aroused the opposition of theologians and academic followers of Ptolemy; but some also rejected it because Copernicus had to buttress his hypotheses by just such artificial means as Ptolemy, and because often they were not based on any new, precise calculations of the orbits of the stars. None the less, he was the creator of a new, and in its essentials correct, astronomical system of the universe. In the course of two centuries his system gradually became a central part of European knowledge, as for example in the form portrayed by Cellarius in this picture of the extensive golden realm of the sun in which the satellite planets revolve.

In 1510 Copernicus, in a first draft, had already intuitively erected the main supports of his edifice of the universe: 'The centre of the earth is not the centre of the universe, for there is not just one centre for all celestial orbits. All orbits encircle the sun, as if the sun were at the centre of all; hence the centre of the universe lies near the sun ... All movement that is visible in the heavens of fixed stars is not so *per se*, but as seen from the earth.' For the earth does not stand still as the heavens of fixed stars seem to; the earth moves, in triple fashion. First, it rotates once every twenty-four hours about its axis from west to east, and this is why the sun seems to rise in the east and set in the west; the celestial vault certainly does not revolve round the earth. Why should one not ascribe motion to the earth—which is part of the total—rather than to the universe which is the total? At the same time the earth, revolving on its own axis, joins the planets' progress round the sun, as it were in a round dance, and lastly even the poles of the earth are not entirely immovable in space. What is visible in the way of movement of the sun and the planets is largely a projection of the earth's own motions. The earth's movement is recognized as explaining the apparent movement of many celestial bodies; the deceptive behaviour of the fixed stars is exposed. And what people had until then seen in the heavens is revealed by Copernicus' inexorable logic as a cosmic illusion.

Nevertheless, in his heliocentric system, ruled by the sun as the centre of the universe, the timeless, sacred, basic shapes of Plato remain untouched: the mysticism of circle and globe inherited from antiquity and the Middle Ages lives on unimpaired in the new teaching. These two most perfect of all forms, manifestations of the divine Creator, dominate the entire universe: the planets—all of them spherical bodies—revolve in circular orbits. Mercury, near the sun, needs 88 days for one circuit, bright Venus 225, the earth twelve months, while it takes Mars 687 days, Jupiter twelve years and Saturn nearly thirty years. In our picture, drawn in the year 1660, Jupiter is attended by four of its satellites which Galileo had first seen through his telescope in 1610.

PLANISPHÆRIVM Sive VNIVERSI TO: EX HYPO: COPERNI PLANO

COPERNICANVM
Systema
TIVS CREATI
THESI
CANA IN
EXHIBITVM.

313

GALILEO INITIATES THE YOUNG JOHN MILTON INTO THE NEW ASTRONOMY

Copernicus, Tycho Brahe, Kepler and Galileo are the pioneers of the new, heliocentric astronomy. Galileo, the man who discovered the laws governing the speed of falling bodies, was also a great observer of the moon and the planets and one of the first astronomers to train a telescope on the night sky. In the Copernican theory he found the same incontestable truth as in the laws which he himself had discovered. After the trial by the Inquisition in 1633, which had compelled the seventy-year-old scientist outwardly to repudiate the Copernican theories, he went to live in a villa near Florence, under supervision of the Inquisition. A small circle of followers gathered round the indefatigable scholar. One day the young John Milton came to see him. The poet's visit to the astronomer has left its immortal mark in Milton's epic *Paradise Lost*. The Puritan's image of the world was based on the Bible and Ptolemy; nevertheless, he too was moved by the dispute between the new knowledge of astronomy and the traditional view—the great battle that had been raging ever since Copernicus. In Florence, Milton thus had the opportunity of observing the starry sky, the subject of the dispute, through a telescope under the guid-

ance of one of the experienced leaders in this dispute. He used one of the instruments with which Galileo had made epoch-making discoveries in his study of the planets. In Milton's epic the archangel Raphael propounds to Adam, the man, both the heliocentric and geocentric theories without deciding in favour of either; and both, the true and the false one, have retained something of their cosmic grandeur:

… What if the Sun / Be Center to the World, and other Starrs / By his attractive vertue and thir own / Incited, dance about him various rounds? / Their wandring course, now high, now low, then hid, / Progressive, retrograde, or standing still, / In six thou seest, and what if sev'nth to these / The Planet Earth, so stedfast though she seem, / Insensibly three different Motions move? / … But whether thus these things, or whether not, / Whether the Sun predominant in Heav'n / Rise from the East his flaming rode begin, / Or Shee from West her silent course advance / … And bears thee soft with the smooth Air along, / Sollicit not thy thoughts with matters hid, / Leave them to God above, Him serve and feare!

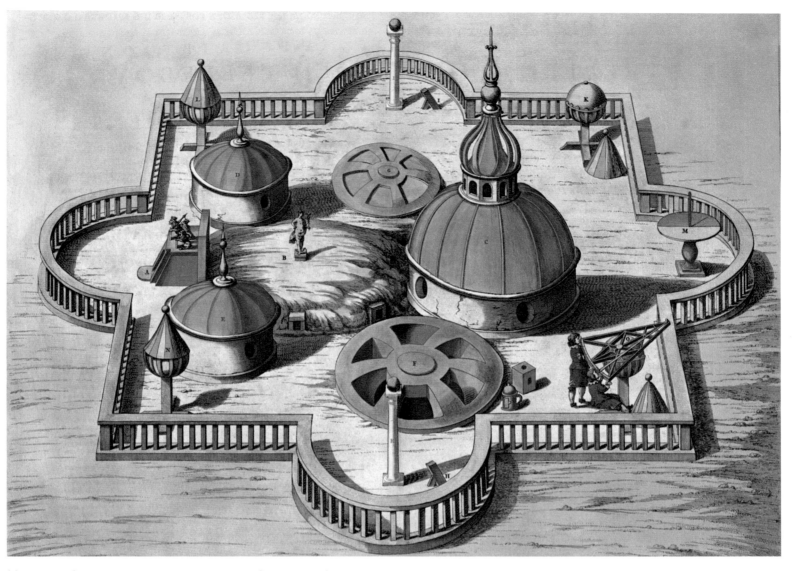

THE MOST SUMPTUOUS OBSERVATORY OF THE SIXTEENTH CENTURY

The Copernican system in many cases lacked exact, new and confirmed data on the position of the stars. In order to establish the concept of a heliocentric universe beyond doubt astronomers had to have more reliable observations. At the right moment in history the Danish astronomer Tycho Brahe, a wealthy man devoted to science, recognized his historic task: his role was to provide these missing observations as a foundation for astronomers of the future. The auspices were happy: his king gave him the island of Hven in the Danish Sound; Brahe thereupon set up an observatory containing the most precise measuring devices of the century, some of which he had designed himself, and for a matter of twenty years he lorded it over his island and over his assistants. In 1584 he built an underground observatory, Stjerneborg, next to the main observatory 'Uraniborg'; it was designed in such a way that no breath of air could enter and make the apparatus vibrate when Brahe was setting his instruments. The underground entrance is at A, on the left; three crowned lions guard the door. Below a straw and hay thatch there is a subterranean space for heating appliances. Several huge observation instru-

ments are protected beneath the three blue cupolas: a mighty quadrant (beneath D) to measure the height of the meridian of stars, armillary spheres to determine the equatorial (C) and ecliptical (E) co-ordinates. Smaller, rotary quadrants and sextants are in position beneath the domes F and G, which can be closed. Outside, two observers (front, right) are operating a sextant. The spherical support gives the sextant mobility. These supports can be protected from bad weather by conical covers. White columns (at the top and bottom of the picture) mark east and west. At M we see a round stone table, offering a firm base for smaller portable instruments. There is no sign of a telescope—astronomy from its inception until about 1600 was exclusively a science of the naked eye.

Brahe, who was too despotic a ruler, had to leave Hven and in the summer of 1599 he moved with all his instruments to Prague to become the Emperor's astronomer. Two years later he died. His collaborator in Prague was an astronomical genius: Johannes Kepler. He inherited Brahe's instruments and data from observations and completed the Copernican system.

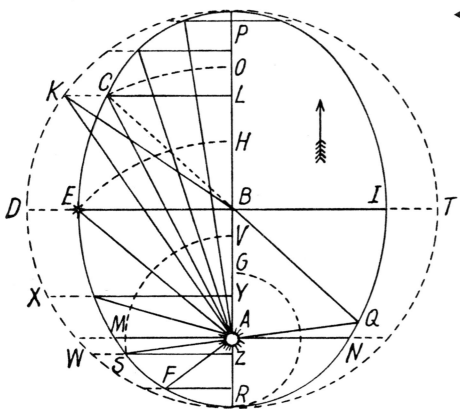

Right: The Harmony of the Planetary System, according to Kepler

Johannes Kepler, theologian, neo-Platonist, mathematician, adherent of Copernicus, astrologer, after 1600 Brahe's assistant in Prague, then court astronomer living in humiliating poverty, was the mystic among the founders of the new astronomy. Very early he realized that his life's great task should be to find the entelechy, the eternal laws—as manifestations of the Divine Spirit—of the planetary system.

Kepler's first comprehensive attempt at proving the harmony of the planetary system was a resounding failure. He had asked himself whether the various fluctuating distances between the orbits of the six planets were numerically related to each other. Kepler discovered that with the help of stereometric figures it was indeed possible to demonstrate that the system had a mysterious law governing it. The distances between the celestial spheres along which the six planets—Saturn, Jupiter, Mars, Earth, Venus and Mercury—were supposed to be circling the sun varied greatly, but they all obeyed one law: it was possible to fit one of the five so-called Platonic regular primordial bodies in a harmonious manner into each interval between two planetary orbits. The furthest of these spheres, that on which Saturn moved, precisely encompassed the figure of a cube. The picture on the right shows its lower half (which bears the symbol of its planet) with the built-in cubic structure. Into this cube it was possible to insert the sphere along which Jupiter journeyed (the second hemisphere, counting from the outside towards the middle); and between this and the third sphere, which carried orbiting Mars, a regular pyramid could be fitted harmoniously; continuing towards the centre, in the direction of the sun, a dodecahedron could be drawn around the earth's orbit and an icosahedron around

that of Venus. Finally Mercury's sphere was found to fit into the shape of an octahedron. That there were exactly six planets was explained by the fact that only five of these regular geometrical bodies were known.

As soon as Kepler, with the help of Tycho Brahe's positional measurements, calculated the orbit of Mars anew, the fine edifice of his earlier speculations collapsed, for the new observations would not fit the previous assumption of circular planetary orbits. First Kepler worked on the hypothesis of an egg-shaped planetary orbit, but this failed. Finally in 1609, he published all his findings in a new book on astronomy, *Neue Astronomie,* in which he expounded two new laws: Mars rotates in an almost circular elliptical orbit around the sun; the sun is in one focus (A). The radius vector drawn from the sun to Mars (M, E, C, etc.) covers in equal periods equal areas of the orbital plane. This was the mathematical explanation of the changing velocity of the planets: they move faster when they are nearer to the sun than when they are further away from it. A third law says that the squares of the periods of revolution of any two planets are in the same relation to each other as the cubes of their average distances from the sun. The teachings of Copernicus had been substantiated for all time to come. Kepler's last but one achievement—his book *Harmonices Mundi* of 1619—concludes with the humble yet proud retrospective statement of a scientist who has remained singularly true to himself and to the great idea of his life: 'I thank Thee, God and Creator, for having given me joy in what Thou hast created, and I rejoice in the works of Thy hands. Behold, I have now completed the task to which I was called. To the people who will read my writings I have manifested the glory of Thy works and as much of their boundless wealth as my limited reason has been able to grasp.'

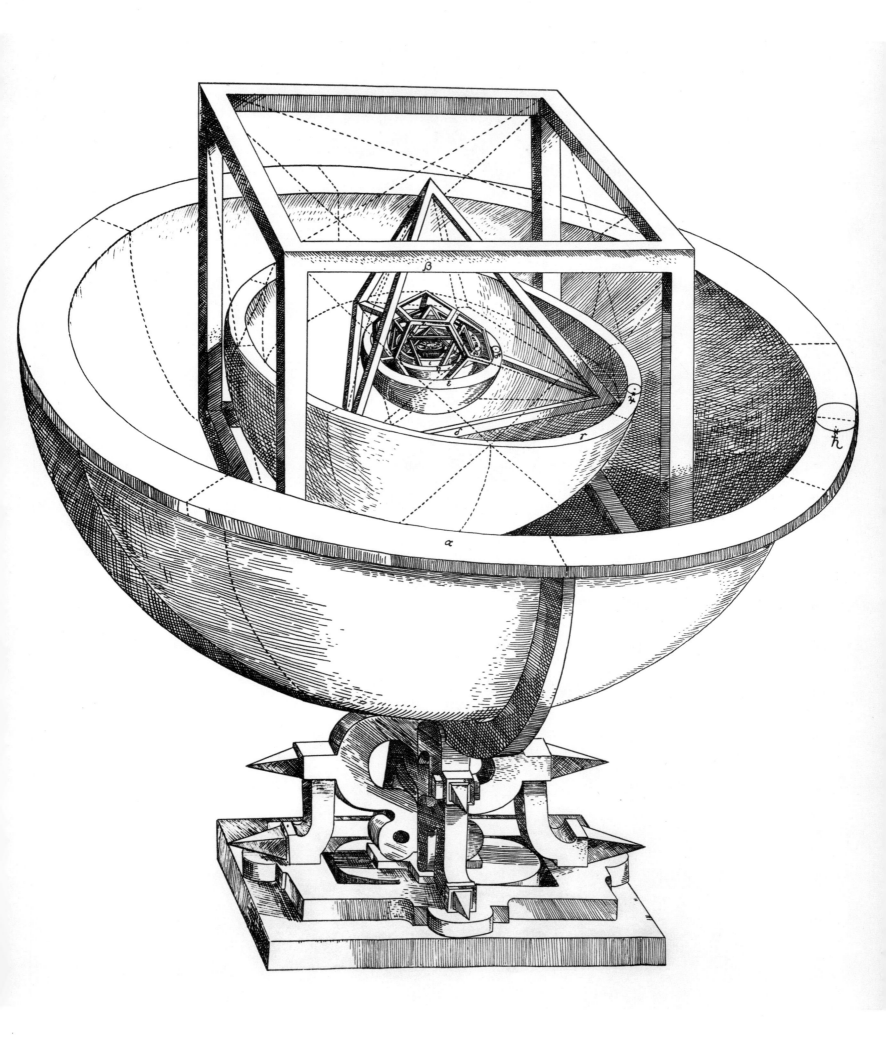

'I do not consider that view of Copernicus as true and never have considered it as true.' Galileo signed this recantation on 21st June 1633 before the Court of the Inquisition in Rome; and his signature sealed the Pyrrhic victory of the supreme ecclesiastical censorship over the most powerful supporter of the dangerous heliocentric heresy. This recantation is the very opposite of those brave words, 'Nevertheless, it (the earth) does move', which according to legend Galileo is said to have hurled at the Court of Inquisition after being sentenced.

This recantation was the unheroic end of a gallant struggle which the physicist and astronomer had waged for more than twenty years with a view to convincing the Church of Rome that Copernicus had 'led astronomy from darkness to light'. With his own eyes Galileo had, through his telescope, discovered four satellites of Jupiter and the changing phases of Venus; he had also observed the spots on the sun and the mountains on the moon. Modern science would not regard this as evidence of the earth's rotation, but these observations did destroy the basic concepts of Aristotle's followers which were closely allied to Christian dogma. For them it was certain that no planet could be accompanied by a satellite and that the celestial bodies were eternally unchanging, pure spheres.

Galileo the fighter was deeply convinced that faith and knowledge could never contradict each other. He knew that in the eyes of the orthodox believer the new astronomy subverted the truths of the Revelation and the Church. They held that the earth, as the centre of the universe, was sanctified by God becoming Man on Earth. According to the Psalms the sun rose at one end of the skies and moved round to the other end. It was heresy to upset this order of the universe. Between 1611 and 1630 Galileo journeyed four times from Florence to Rome to defend his case before the princes of the Church. When he made his fifth journey, at the end of 1632, he went to face the indictment of the Court of the Inquisition. In Rome, under Pope Urban VIII, Galileo's enemies had won the upper hand. His overbearing impetuosity had turned scientific opponents into personal enemies. In widely circulated letters Galileo had proclaimed the new teaching not as a hypothesis but as truth, despite an admonition from the Inquisition in 1616 which had forbidden him to do so. In his dialogue on the two world systems—*Dialogo sopra i due massimi sistemi del Mondo* (1632)—Galileo had compiled an ingenious survey of contemporary astronomical knowledge paying little heed to the requests of the Inquisition. Now sixty-nine years old, broken by ill-health and threatened with torture, Galileo was facing the assembled cardinals and other clergy at the monastery of Santa Maria sopra Minerva, and it was there that he had to listen to the sentence passed on him after he had saved his life and future work (*see* p. 83 ff.) by the recantation extorted from him. The painter Robert Fleury shows a man inwardly rebelling against the extorted recantation.

Galileo's trial has deeply stirred posterity. This trial was an example of a battle over some of the premises on which science and religion had to stand or fall in later ages. What was at stake was the right of the scientist to freedom of thought. The phrase, 'Nevertheless, it does move',—which was never spoken—typifies the free intellect's defiance of the might of authoritarian institutions, and it has never ceased to inspire men in similar situations. In the autumn of 1933, during the first year of the Nazi dictatorship, Max von Laue quoted it at a conference of German physicists and so challenged both Communism and National Socialism.

At the Santa Maria monastery another battle, too, was fought—between liberal ideas and narrow-minded ideas as to the relationship between faith and knowledge. Galileo was a scientist who saw no contradiction between the divine order of the world and the clearly proven facts of science. But his opponents lacked similar breadth of vision. They could offer nothing but the orthodox way of thinking which, as always and in all manifestations, suffered from its inability to distinguish between valid truth and merely ephemeral opinions among its own adherents. These men knew nothing of the creative tension between faith and knowledge. At Galileo's trial the loser was in reality the victor.

GALILEO BEFORE THE COURT OF THE HOLY OFFICE

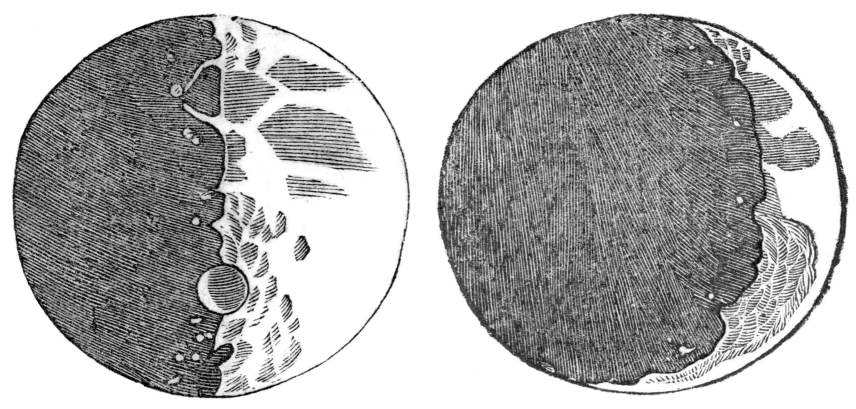

THE FIRST PICTURES OF THE MOON SEEN THROUGH A TELESCOPE (1610)

Left: NEVERTHELESS, IT DOES MOVE ...

Two hundred and nineteen years after Galileo had been forced by the Holy Office to abjure his belief that the earth rotated, the physicist Léon Foucault gave a demonstration at the Panthéon in Paris—the last and most conspicuous proof in a centuries-long chain of evidence that the earth does rotate. In the same year of 1852 Foucault's demonstration of the rotation of the earth was repeated before great crowds in other cities, and most impressively by C. Garthe, a school teacher in Cologne, who staged it in the city's lofty cathedral. He used a special, mobile suspension device: It consisted of a 34 lb. copper ball filled with lead suspended from a wire which was attached to a coping stone in the choir roof. The sphere, which had a steel tip, swung above a wooden frame fitted with an angle-measurement scale covering twenty degrees on either side of a central line.

When the huge pendulum was set moving with great care along this central line, it continued to swing very slowly in the same plane of oscillation for a long time because it was freely suspended. But the scale was firmly connected to the floor and so to the earth. After some time it was seen that the pendulum no longer swung along the central line; the plane of oscillation seemed slowly to shift because the earth had meanwhile swivelled below the pendulum which constantly maintained the same direction. The change of the plane of oscillation varies according to the place on earth where the experiment is carried out. Garthe tells us that the spectators in the cathedral watched the demonstration with 'intense interest'. Deeply stirred, they realized that the movement of the scale beneath the awe-inspiring swinging pendulum reflected the motion of an entire planet circling through the universe.

Above: The factual discovery of the moon, the closest of all celestial bodies, began in the year 1610 when the first scientists trained a telescope (probably a Dutch invention) on the skies and with one move brought the entire firmament nearer to the searching eye. Galileo, Kepler, Scheiner and Johannes Fabricius were the first to train instruments of barely ten-fold magnification on to the heavens; and as early as 1610 Galileo stated in his *Sidereus Nuncius* what he had seen: four satellites of Jupiter, 'nebulous stars' in the Milky Way, three Saturns, where the naked eye had only detected one, but most important the moon, which was now beginning to reveal its secrets. The scientist focused his home-made telescope on the new moon on the demarcation line (right) between the illuminated and the dark part of the moon's surface. It was a serrated line which meant that the moon could not be a smooth globe as most of the philosophers had assumed. There were mountains and valleys, including some like volcanoes whose shadows (left) indicated considerable heights. Galileo was not sure what the familiar large, dark spots meant, but some shining, round dots in the dark area recalled mountain peaks which the sunlight touches before it shines into the valleys.

Page 322: By the middle of the eighteenth century observers who were using improved telescopes had already amassed so much information that the astronomer Johann Tobias Mayer of Württemberg was able to publish a cartographical masterpiece: a moon map with a superimposed grid. Vast, dark plains—called seas—are clearly marked alongside bright, mountainous areas; they are pitted by many moon craters, the origin of which is not certain even now. The map also shows the mysterious, straight streaks of bright rays radiating from some craters and looking like rills filled with white, frozen magma.

JOHANN TOBIAS MAYER'S MOON MAP *(text on p. 321)*

Page 323: The map of the moon drawn by Julius Schmidt is one of the marvels of the history of astronomy. Here the moon's surface seems within reach, and is pictured against the void of space, as if seen from Jules Verne's spaceship. This map, measuring 6 feet across, is the work of a man fired by enthusiasm which inspired him to make observations of the moon at many observatories between 1839 and 1874. This sectional illustration shows the south of the moon on top and the east on the right, as seen through the astronomic telescope. The picture also makes visible the little 'volcanoes' within the rings surrounding the big craters, and the twin-crater Sirsal (16a) at the very bottom, behind which, stretching southwards, we see one of those long furrows which still puzzle the moon explorer.

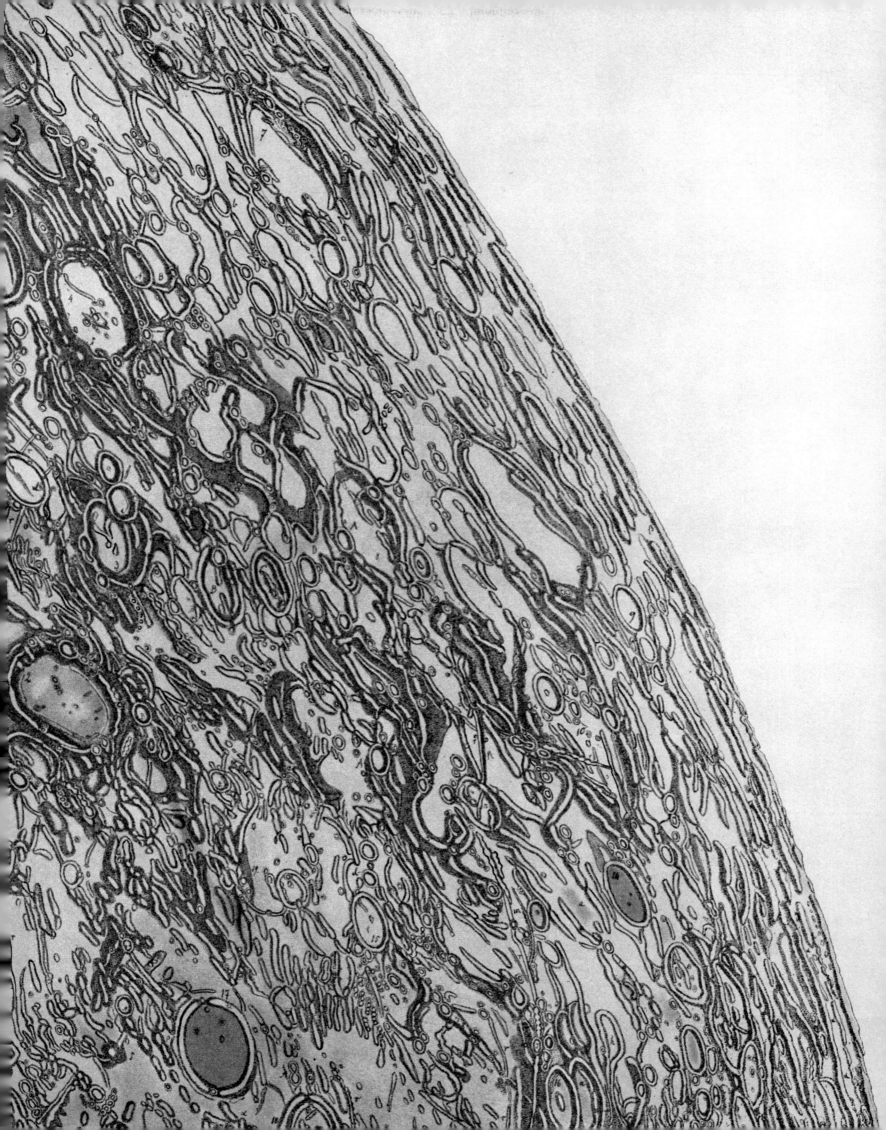

AN ASTRONOMER'S IMPRESSION OF A MOON LANDSCAPE

Long before Russian and American space rockets took photographs of the surface of the moon, scientifically-minded artists had in their imagination landed on the earth's satellite and had 'brought back' pictures of the moon's landscape. When that part of the moon which has been in pitch darkness is suddenly bathed in the dazzling light of the sun, the lunar night temperature of —80° C. climbs to a torrid lunar day temperature of 120° C. Above the chalky,

fissured cliffs surrounding a moon crater several miles wide is star-filled space and the globe of the earth. The deep darkness of space is due to the lack of atmosphere; it is this which diffuses the light and produces the sky-blue colour above our planet. Illuminated by the same sun as the moon, the earth displays its oceans and continents through the veil of the atmosphere. On the left, deep broad clefts furrow the flat floor of the moon crater; on the right, exactly below the earth, we see four depressions, little craters inside the big one, which seem to have been caused by meteoric bombardment. Behind the edge of the crater to the right there stretches a bleak plain; against its dark features we see the dazzling rocks of the moon, thick with dust. Nowadays it is believed to be basalt, because it reflects light so strongly. (Painting by Wilhelm Kranz, formerly in Berlin, destroyed during the second World War.)

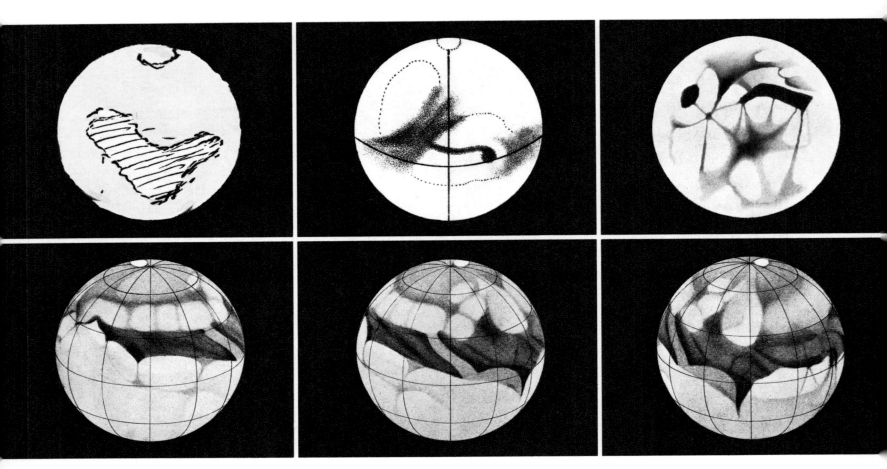

ASTRONOMERS BRING MARS CLOSER TO THE EARTH

Ancient peoples associated Mars with gods who brought death and evil (Asia) or war (Greece and Rome). Since the invention of the telescope the reddish-glowing planet has become a cosmic mystery which astronomers are just as anxious to solve as to fathom the secrets of the sun. Some high points of this dramatic endeavour of mind and eye are captured in our illustrations. Galileo's imperfect lenses did not yet enable him to distinguish details on the tiny disk of Mars. In 1638 Francesco Fontana, using an improved instrument, thought he could see a dark shadow on the planet; but it was not until Christiaan Huygens had perfected the lens and the art of observation that the first tenable scientific information was obtained. On 13th August 1675 he drew the dark patch which, since Schiaparelli, has borne the name of Gulf of Sidra on maps of Mars. Despite the blurs which frequently cause Mars to disappear from sight, Huygens must have succeeded in keeping his eye on this spot because he noticed that it wandered from right to left and reappeared after a certain interval—which meant that Mars was rotating on its own axis; Huygens estimated that it revolved like the earth once every twenty-four hours. He, too, was the first man to see the white south polar cap of the planet (first drawing). In September 1830, when the planet was close to the earth, the German astronomers W. Beer and J. Mädler made thirty-five drawings of the planet with a two-hundred-fold magnification (second picture). 'It usually took some time before the indeterminate mass which appeared at first sight resolved itself into recognizable parts.' This was their way of describing the difficulties that faced anyone trying to draw a picture of Mars. At an early stage observers supposed that many features of this changing face of the planet were blurred by its surrounding atmosphere. Beer and Mädler noticed that the polar cap fluctuated as if it consisted of melting snow or frost; this indicated to them that there might be seasons on Mars.

The third drawing was made by Giovanni Schiaparelli; it represents an observation made on 11th November 1881. On the right half of the picture there can be seen some ribbon-like darkish streaks, which used to break up on closer inspection; near these are straight lines, drawn somewhat coarsely, which Schiaparelli called *canali* (canals). They link two darkish areas. Sometimes (left half of picture) Schiaparelli saw that a whole series of canals merged into a small dark patch. He hazarded the proposition that the melting snow of the Martian cap flowed through a vast system of irrigation canals across the arid land mass of the planet. About 1900 the American Flagstaff observatory in Arizona under Percival Lowell became the headquarters of astronomers who believed that Mars was inhabited by a nation of technologists.

The brilliant observer Kasimir Graff, who was working with the large refractor at Hamburg Observatory in 1909, drew a series of pictures of Mars (see lower set of illustrations) which bear little trace of canals; but there is an eccentrically rotating south pole. From right to left are to be seen a variety of areas; the brighter ones have the 'colour of ripening corn' as the French Mars explorer Camille Flammarion put it; the darker ones are blue-grey like water or greenish like plants. The 'corn-colour' seems to indicate sandy deserts.

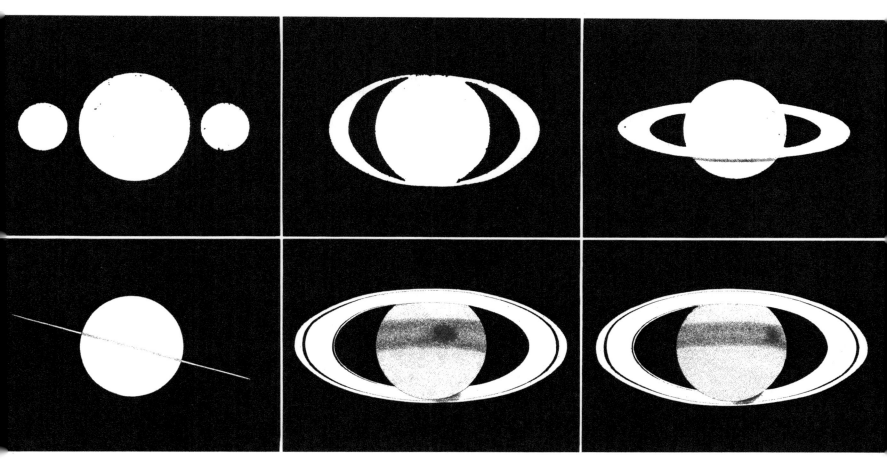

THE PUZZLE OF THE PLANET SATURN IS SOLVED

Before the invention of the telescope, Saturn was thought to be just one more spherical body following a circular path round the earth in accordance with the laws of the harmony governing the universe. From the moment in 1610 when Galileo observed Saturn with his telescope the planet began to play tricks of optical illusion on its observers. It was Huygens who half a century later put an end to them. To begin with, Galileo was convinced that close to Saturn he had seen two attendant planets (first figure, top). Two years later, they could no longer be found. 'Have they suddenly made off?' asked the discoverer. 'Has Saturn swallowed his own children? Or were the objects which I and many others have seen through the telescope really nothing but illusion and deception?' After a time the two presumed satellites reappeared in entirely different shape. The Italian Jesuit Giovanni Battista Riccioli saw Saturn looking like a cup with handles (second figure). Christiaan Huygens and his brother Konstantin attributed these peculiar transformations to the inadequacy of the telescopic lenses rather than to the imagination of astronomers or to the planet itself. 'As I was able to use only the ordinary five or six-foot-long telescopes I started to apply myself to the art of cutting lenses, and I do not regret having done so.' In 1656 Christiaan Huygens had solved the mystery of Saturn, but he kept the answer to himself until he could confirm it through further observations. In 1659 he made his great revelation in his *Systema Saturnium*: 'Saturn is girdled by a thin flat ring, nowhere touching, inclined to the ecliptic' (third figure). Huygens had even been able to observe the narrow shadow which the ring casts on the globe of the planet. For the first time

man was able to see the most beautiful silhouette in the entire starry firmament. The Dutchman had not only enriched astronomic knowledge but had also added another star to the great inheritance of nature's perfect forms, with which the picture of Saturn is now forever linked.

The lower set of pictures, dating back to the years between 1790 and 1792, shows Saturn considerably nearer to earth; this is how William Herschel had been able to see it through his reflecting telescopes. While Cassini had seen the dividing line between the two rings in the centre, Herschel placed it nearer the outer limit. When the earth was in the same plane as the rings, they would merge into an extremely thin line (bottom left). The last two pictures clearly show the globe's shadow on the ring, as seen by Herschel; this led him to the conclusion that the ring consisted of fairly solid and not of gaseous substances. Both the planet and its rings rotated. Herschel proved this by prolonged observation of little shining spots on the ring and large patches on Saturn during their nightly journeys. Laplace, Maxwell and other mathematicians worked out by calculation that the ring could not be a rigid mass. 'It is inconceivable that the ring system should consist of anything but a number of separate particles which circle the planet at varying velocities according to their distance.' This Maxwellian thesis was later confirmed.

Observations with the aid of spectral analysis and other modern methods provided new information about this unusual heavenly body, which, attended by nine satellites and a ring of meteorites revolves in its distant thirty-year orbit round the sun.

THE PARIS OBSERVATORY IN THE SEVENTEENTH CENTURY

The astronomers of the seventeenth century seemed intoxicated with the desire to penetrate deeper and deeper into unknown reaches of space; and with similar fervour the optical scientists rivalled one another in trying to produce lenses with greater and greater focal lengths. Telescopes seemed to grow in length year by year. Huygens had lenses of 125 and 135 foot focal length. The lenses the French physicist A. Auzout used are said to have attained 328 and 655 feet, and he dreamed of thousand-fold magnifications which would enable him to see animals on the moon. The focal lengths required soon began to exceed the practicable lengths of telescopes and the newly created observatories could no longer accommodate focal lengths or telescopes of such magnitude. In 1675 an observatory had been built at Greenwich, in 1700 one in Berlin, and the magnificent Paris observatory (shown above) began to rise among the rustic windmills between 1667 and 1672. Its first director, Giovanni Domenico Cassini, discovered four satellites of Saturn in 1675. As a rule, the lenses of his telescopes were housed in wooden tubes. One of them can be seen to the right of the building. It is attached to a perpendicular mast, and is movable, but it is liable to sway in the slightest breeze. The observation of the stars which is in progress in the centre of the picture is a major astronomical achievement. The enormous focal length of the lens in use here makes it impossible to house it in a tube. This is why they have brought up a former water tower from the pumping station at Marly. The structure is provided with balustrades to protect the assistants helping with the operation, and there is a device to carry the telescopic lens. It directs the rays from the star through the atmosphere to the holder of the eyepiece through which an astronomer is seen gazing at the skies. On the roof of the observatory there is a similar lens for the observation of Saturn. It was at the Paris observatory that its director Cassini discovered the narrow line dividing Saturn's ring into two parts.

The Sun

'Source of life, bright ocean of joy, God whom none other can equal, effluence of pure spirit, sister, all-seeing, almighty and holy.' These are some of the names given to the source of light in mankind's great hymn to the sun, from Ikhnaton and Francis of Assisi to Goethe and Hölderlin. They are confessions by people overwhelmed by its power and possessing a direct appreciation, sometimes without any scientific knowledge, of the significance of man's daily companionship with the sun.

Early scientific investigation of the sun was not accompanied by such majestic harmonies. Astronomy made its distinctive contribution to the age-old catalogue of the sun's marvels relatively late. It combines with earlier sunlore to bestow on the modern sun-worshipper aware of his rich inheritance a wealth of information about the daystar which no sun-priest ever possessed.

In the practical economy of ancient peoples the sun was a powerful aid in establishing the calendar and measuring the year and the seasons. To theoretical astronomy it was a mighty planet revolving with other planets round the centre of the universe, the earth, on a course which could be calculated. What was its size? Heraclitus of Ephesus, some five hundred years before Christ, thought it was exactly the size it appeared to the naked eye, that is, not more than a foot across. Two centuries later Aristarchus accorded it the central place in the universe and already calculated that its volume was three hundred times that of the earth. Then for more than fifteen hundred years it reverted at the behest of Ptolemy and others to a mere satellite of the earth occasionally causing alarm when in eclipse. Finally it was accorded its rightful place at the heart of the planetary system by Copernicus and his followers, in an intellectual revolution during which solar scientists were burned or arraigned before the courts, books were banned and doctrines proscribed. From now on the sun moved other worlds—a fixed star, no longer a planet. Even before Newton drew attention to the powerful interplay of the forces of gravitation in the solar system, the real era of solar science was inaugurated in 1610 by that first telescope which some historians like to think ushered in the golden age of astronomy. In their passionate urge for knowledge men even risked their eyesight. The first scientist to report observations of sunspots, Johannes Fabricius, began by staring into the sun's fiery heat without protecting his eyes. 'While I was observing an irregularity on its edge a dark spot could repeatedly be seen, small in diameter compared to the sun's disk. At first I had grave doubts of the accuracy of my observation, when for example clouds veiled the rising sun so that I supposed the drifting clouds produced the illusion of something resembling a spot on the sun. At last I felt certain it was not caused by clouds. Even so I did not wish to rely on the evidence of my own eyes. I called my father so that he could take part in the observation. We each trained our telescopes on to the sun's rays, starting at the circumference of the sun and gradually moving in towards its centre, until our eyes became accustomed to the sun's brilliance and enabled us to survey the whole of the sun's disk. Now we saw the spot more clearly... 48 hours later a remarkable spectacle was afforded us. We saw that spot proceed on a slanting course across the sun from east to west; as we watched intently, we noticed at the sun's rim another, smaller, spot, which a few days later followed the larger one, nearly reaching the centre of the sun's disk. Finally a further spot followed these, so that three were actually visible at the same time; the larger one, gradually travelling towards the other edge, then disappeared from sight, whilst the others began to follow suit. A few days later they too vanished. This worried me somewhat; I feared that I had taken leave of them for good. I expected it to take some days for the matter to be determined. Meanwhile the larger spot, which had been the first to disappear, began to show anew at the eastern rim. By the time it had, with its slow rate of progression, penetrated deeper into the sun's disk, the others were duly following.'

The way was now open for a 'qualitative' discovery of the sun. It was investigated thoroughly, despite the ninety-three million miles separating it from the earth. The sunspots proved that the sun revolved and that its revolution could be determined. Its mighty dimensions were calculated; Heraclitus' diameter of one foot became a globe that would contain 332,000 terrestrial globes. During eclipses the wild agitation of the sun's surface could be deduced from the erupting prominences. Shortly before this, the question as to which elements were found on other stars, had been answered with regard to the sun. Spectral analysis (*see* p. 117) revealed that it was composed mainly of hydrogen and helium, and considerations of atomic physics explained the mighty energies of a heavenly body in the interior of which the temperature rises to about fifteen million degrees and the gases solidify to the hardness of metals. A study of the earth's northern and southern lights revealed which corpuscular emissions the sun sent hurtling through space (*see* p. 126). Countless solar problems still await solution; even the sunspots discovered by Fabricius, Scheiner and Galileo with the earliest telescopes remain a mystery in the age of the giant reflecting telescope. We do not know for certain what is their cause.

Yet scientific discovery has very accurately borne out the mighty truth of those ancient hymns to the cosmic life-force: 'All life and all movements [for example, of air and clouds of vapour] on our earth are with few exceptions sustained by the sun's rays, which bring us light and warmth. Only under its influence does the vegetation acquire its bright raiment; the plants amass organic substance within their body, which serves as nutriment for the entire animal kingdom. Our ancestors were right in regarding the sun as the bestower of all life' (Helmholtz).

STONEHENGE

In this sepia-drawing by J.W.M. Turner, a mail coach is passing by a flock of sheep on its journey into the dawning day; not far from the coach Turner has made the tall ruins of Stonehenge rise up like a vision from their dark enclosure exactly where the morning sun will soon rise above the horizon. Thousands of years before, two concentric rows of stone blocks in a horse-shoe shape opened towards this point. These uprights of stone were joined by horizontal slabs, like columns by an architrave. Further out, facing east there is another stone, the Heel Stone, so situated that on 21st June, at solstice, the rays of the rising sun travel above it and fall exactly on the altar in the centre of the horse-shoe. Some people think these magnificent ruins in southern England were once a Celtic burial place, others believe they were a Temple of the Sun dating back to 1500 BC. Turner surrounds the ruined Temple of the Sun, where man worshipped the mightiest of all cosmic forces, with an atmosphere of awe; he seems indeed to suggest that behind these stones of Stonehenge ancient mysteries in honour of the sun were once celebrated.

THE SUN-GOD ATON BLESSES THE ROYAL FAMILY

History's greatest worshipper of the sun was the Egyptian Pharaoh, Ikhnaton, husband of Nefertiti. He raised to a state-religion the cult of the life-preserving sun, which embodied the one and only god Aton, and built a new city and temple in honour of the god-like sun at Amarna. He discarded the old world of deities, and when their priests resisted, he ordered the names of the ancient gods to be erased from the temples of Thebes and the priests' colleges to be closed. The disk of the sun alone was sanctioned as a religious symbol, and the name of the sun—that of the sun-god Aton—became the name of the King, for Ikhnaton means 'reflection of the disk of the sun'. In this low relief from Amarna it pours its rays down upon the Pharaoh Ikhnaton and his family. Delicious food, lotus and papyrus plant are heaped on three tables. In their hands the pharaoh and the queen are holding objects which have become obliterated by time. At the bottom, left, two young princesses

are playing. On the right, a third princess is handing a bowl to the queen mother. Aton is well-disposed towards the Pharaoh. The rays with blessing hands extend the loving protection of the sun to the whole family; and a god-like hand presents to the pharaoh and his queen the loop-like hieroglyphic symbol which signifies 'life', the gift of the sun since the beginning of time. The scene dates back to about 1400 BC.

'When thou risest on the eastern sky', runs Ikhnaton's Hymn to the Sun, 'thou fillest the entire land with thy beauty. / Thou art beautiful and great, and thou shinest high above all the land. / Thy rays embrace all lands to the limits of Creation. / Though thou art far away thy rays fall upon the earth and the faces of man are thy reflection. / All eyes see thee when thou hangest above the earth as Aton of the day. / Thou hast created their eyes so that they, too shall be able to see what thou hast created.'

THE SUN-GOD OF THE AZTECS

Moving on from the evidence of the sun-cult in Europe and Africa we see here the Aztec Calendar Stone which comes from a country where men built pyramids not to their kings but to their gods, including the sun-god. Hundreds of stone steps led up to the platforms of the pyramids. Towards the end of 1790 the circular stone disk pictured above was excavated from among the ruins of the great pyramid-temple of Mexico City. The disk measures thirteen feet across. In 1836, C. Nebel made a careful drawing of it. In the centre is the sun-god with whom everything on this symbolic sun disk is related. The symbols in the four rectangular frames round his head signify the four past suns, that is, the four ages of the earth ruled by these suns. At the end of each age the sun was destroyed: by a flood (the epoch of the water-sun, bottom right); by a collapse of the heavens, because a jaguar devoured the sun (jaguar-sun, top right); by fire in the heavens and volcanic eruptions

(fire and rain-sun, bottom left); and by whirlwinds (wind-sun, top left). The present (fifth) sun was born in the year indicated by its hieroglyph 'thirteen reed' between the tips of the serpents' tails at the top. Some day this age will end with an earthquake. In order to avert the evil prediction of this calendar of disasters, the sun had to be nourished each year by human blood—hence the human sacrifices of the Aztecs, hence the many wars from which prisoners would be brought back to be sacrificed, and hence the two serpents framing the disk; they were the disguise of the god of fire and the god of war, for the fire of the sun and war were closely connected in this gloomy religion. The Aztecs divided the year into eighteen months of twenty days each, adding five days to each year so as to make it conform to the rhythm of the sun. The signs of the twenty days make up the ring from which eight V-shaped symbols of sun rays radiate (lizard, adder, skull, stag, water, dog, etc.).

Immillione Refractoria composita.

CHRISTOPH SCHEINER OBSERVING THE SUN-SPOTS IN 1611

The few tiny black dots which can be seen on the circular illuminated screen of paper in the wooden frame above dramatically changed age-old concepts about the sun. Hitherto this dazzling disk of light in the skies had been regarded as the most immaculate of all heavenly bodies; it was impossible that this god-like, perfect star—heavenly giver of light held in sacred reverence by many peoples—should be stained. But the telescope disproved this assumption. Dark patches travelled across the face of the sun! As soon as the first weak telescopes reached the hands of astronomers they trained them on the sun. At first, they exposed their eyes to its fierce glare (*see* p. 329), but later they took various precautions. In the end, the sun itself was made to cast its picture—no longer immaculate—on a sheet of paper. The belief in the purity of sunlight, ordained by God Himself, was so ingrained that the Jesuit Father, Christoph Scheiner, one of the first to discover the sun-spots, initially thought they were small, dark planets travelling past the disk of the sun. For decades Scheiner had to defend himself against criticism from Galileo who claimed to have made discoveries on the subject before him. Galileo believed the spots to be clouds in the atmosphere of the sun. Actually, the findings of both men were anticipated by discoveries made with the 'quicker' telescopes of the Englishman Thomas Harriot and of Johannes Fabricius. Fabricius had already studied the sun indirectly, from its reflection in a camera obscura; but the method was perfected by Scheiner, whose observations, published in 1630, did not find their equal for a very long time. Here he is seen seated at a table; on the left, the rays of the sun pass through a telescope and cast the picture of the sun on to a paper screen. The movable wooden structure enables Scheiner's assistant to follow exactly the position of the sun, to prove day by day how the spots move. Scheiner found that the spots resembled hollows on the surface of the sun. They changed in shape and size and journeyed around the sun in a certain belt in the middle latitudes. The seemingly dark body of the sun appeared to be visible through the openings. In 1844 the German astronomer Heinrich Schwabe analysed statistics of groups of sun spots, listing the periods when there were no spots or a large number of them; the data were based on more than 4,500 days of observation. Schwabe's conclusion was that sun-spots occurred in a cycle of about ten years (later astronomers put the number at eleven). Shortly afterwards Wolf definitively proved that there was a connection between the magnetism of the earth and the sun-spots (*see* p. 126).

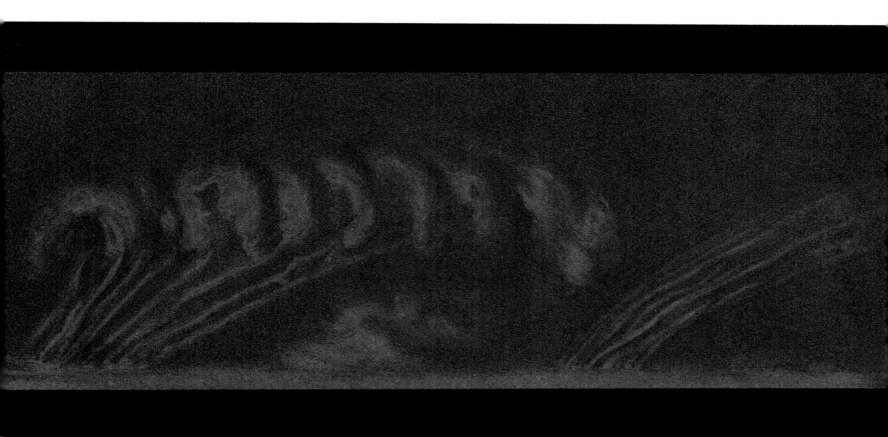

SOLAR PROMINENCES

On 8th July 1842 there was a total eclipse of the sun. Watching it through their telescopes a number of observers in Europe saw reddish flames and cloud-like protuberances at several points on the edge of the moon while it was obscuring the sun. These clouds of flame, they thought, must be enormous formations, as the earth would have fitted three or four times into them. Did they belong to the moon or the sun? Were they optical illusions? Or incandescent masses of gas which soared to tremendous heights? Or mountains bathed in red, reflected light?

Further eclipses of the sun had to be awaited. For thousands of years eclipses had terrified the majority of people, but to astronomic explorers of the sun they were feasts of new knowledge. Expeditions laden with instruments travelled round half the world for the sake of five minutes' observation of an eclipse, always hoping that overcast skies would not disappoint them. Within the first decade after 1842 a tentative explanation was offered: the prominences could not be mountains because they constantly changed their shape; they belonged to the sun, for the orbiting moon gradually cleared them on the western side whereas it obscured them in the east; the prominences were obviously tremendous masses of gas being expelled in fantastic shapes.

Steadily improved instruments furnished prodigious ideas as to the tremendous power of these phenomena which had originally seemed to be tiny protuberances on the edge of the moon. In 1872, the director of the observatory at the Collegium Romanum in Rome, P.A. Secchi, succeeded in producing pictures of prominences, one of which is shown in three-fold magnification in our picture above. Red, incandescent masses of gas erupt in long radiating tongues from the edge of the sun. High up they unroll in the shape of clouds, or break up into streaks which descend again in parabolic curves and, within half an hour dissolve at a certain depth into luminous nebulae. It is like the sun letting off fireworks that make all man-made efforts look hopelessly inadequate. More recent observations have led to the belief that some of the gases escape into the universe. The spectacle takes place against the light thin chromosphere, the sun's atmosphere proper, which extends about 5,000 miles into space. At the bottom we can see the extreme edge of the sun, the luminous photosphere. Modern scientists have calculated that the hot gases of the solar prominences are expelled at tremendous velocities up to average heights of between 12,000 and 25,000 miles. This gives an idea of the enormous energies in the interior of the sun.

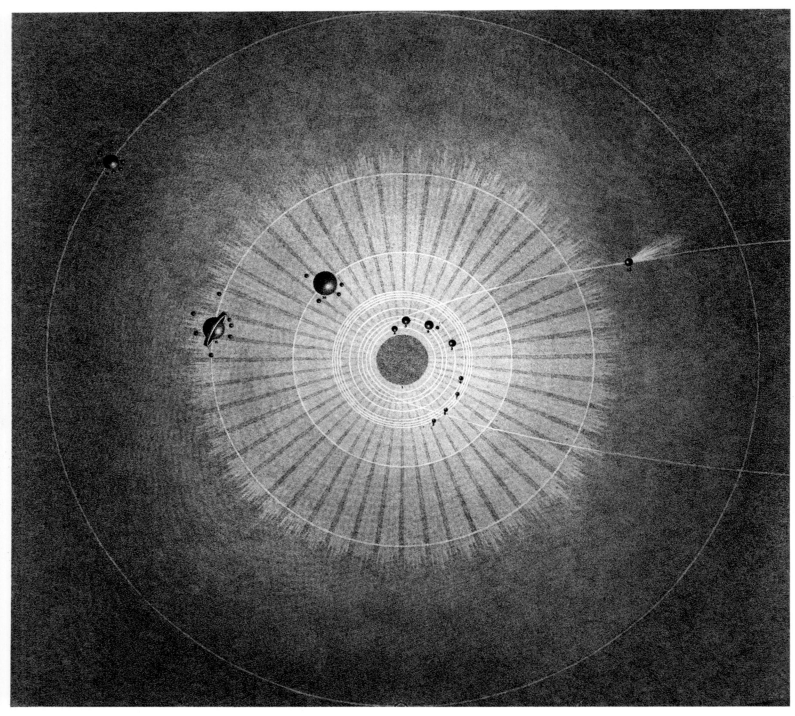

THE SOLAR SYSTEM AS SEEN BY NEWTON

This picture by Sigismond Visconti shows the sun, the planets, the satellites of the planets and the comets (most orbits simplified into circles) as they were known about the year 1810. Four tiny planets had been discovered: Vesta (6), Juno (7), Ceres (8) and Pallas (9). Uranus (12), Saturn (11) and Jupiter (10) are circling in the outermost orbits, while Mercury (2), Venus (3), earth (4) and Mars (5) are following the innermost ones. They all obey the universal law of gravitation as described by Euler: 'This force of gravity of each planet extends to great distances around it. In the same way as the moon revolves round the earth and the satellites rotate round Jupiter or Saturn, all the planets themselves circle round the sun; whence Newton drew the well-known conclusion that the sun, too, possesses gravity and that all bodies round the sun are being attracted towards the sun by a force which might be called the gravity of the sun.' This force, combined with a centrifugal tangential power, extends to a very great distance round the sun and far beyond the planets. The picture is in the possession of the Bibliothèque nationale in Paris.

A Meteor Shower about 1550

Meteorites are not volcanic discharges or red-hot particles of the earth's atmosphere, as people used to believe; nor are they usually as large as shown in this imaginary drawing from the sixteenth century. As a rule, they are either tiny fragments of inter-stellar matter, or 'dust' from the orbit of a disintegrated comet, as Schiaparelli already knew. Alexander von Humboldt summed up their importance in these words: 'They are parts of matter which come to our atmosphere from space and which remain on earth. A meteorite is the only thing not belonging to our planet which we can touch. Non-terrestrial things are usually known to us only through measurement, calculations and rational conclusions; and so we are amazed at being able to touch, weigh and break up something that comes from outer space. It provides a stimulus for our emotions and makes us reflect; this has its effect on our imagination, whereas the ordinary senses merely perceive a dying spark in the bright heavens and see in the black rock crashing down from the bursting cloud nothing but the coarse product of a wild natural force.'

The night sky presented another phenomenon besides meteorites: comets, which upset the great harmony of the stellar system ordained by God. They struck fear and terror into the hearts of men. Already Kepler had asserted that there were as many comets in space as fish in the sea. But only a few comets had appeared in such ominous fiery shape above the earth as to be chronicled like earthquakes and storm tides. They seemed to hurtle through the atmosphere very close to the earth, and the terror-struck people saw in them harbingers of epidemics and war or cosmic warnings from God—which 'incidentally did not make them mend their ways', as a chronicler from Zürich wrote with resignation in 1802. Even Seneca had urged that the comets' motions should be systematically observed throughout whole decades. He declared: 'Some day a man will be born who will be able to show the position of the comets' orbits, their size and their nature and the reasons why they move separately from other stars.' Early observations of this kind led to an important discovery which Peter Bienewitz, known as Apian, reported in his *Astronomicum Caesareum* in 1540, almost simultaneously with Girolamo Fracastoro. He said that the tails of the comets always point away from the sun (see below). Kepler and Newton assumed that this was because the luminous 'vapours' behind the head of the comet were carried along by the rays of the sun. Apian had noticed the so-called pressure of the solar radiation. Tycho Brahe later proved that the sinister comets were cosmic bodies and that they never entered regions on *this* side of the moon. In the seventeenth century, several huge comets obligingly came into the telescopes' field of view. Now it was realized that the comets, too, travelled through the skies along definite, mathematically predictable orbits. It was the country parson George Samuel Dörfel who discovered the parabolic orbit of the great comet of 1680. Newton, at about the same time, observed the hyperbolic and parabolic orbits of these tailed stars. Shortly afterwards, Edmund Halley rounded off these important conclusions by discovering the existence of reappearing comets which travelled in infinitely elongated elliptic orbits through celestial space. The comet which Apian had observed in 1531 reappeared in 1607 and was again seen by Halley in 1682. 'This is why I feel able to venture a prediction that it will come back in 1758', he wrote in 1705. Anxiously the astronomers watched the night sky as the time drew near. Halley's comet did appear, and he was the man whose coming Seneca had forecast.

Natural science has freed mankind of some of its greatest fears, the fear of lightning and of catastrophic epidemics, and it has liberated man of the age-old fear of the comet. Halley and Newton were no longer alive when David Herrliberger produced this copper-plate engraving of a night scene at Zurich in 1742. It shows some citizens of the peacefully sleeping town observing the comet in amazement but with little fear, except perhaps in the remotest corners of their hearts. The new scientific truth that the comets followed their fixed orbits as obediently as the planets and the sun was still fresh in their minds.

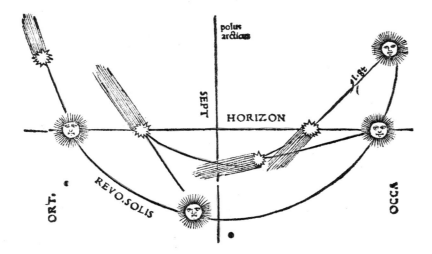

A Comet over an Administrative Building of the Monastery of Einsiedeln in Zurich on the Night before 10th March 1742

The Sphere of the Fixed Stars

Of all the inaccessibly remote objects studied by astronomy the fixed stars are the furthest away. While the early astronomers investigated the sun, moon and planets the sphere of the fixed stars was by no means neglected but proved impenetrable to the scientific thought of the day. It was divided into constellations; the Milky Way was described by the Roman poet Ovid as the route taken by the gods of Olympus to reach Zeus' palace, with the dwellings of the immortals on either side of it. Democritus was bold enough to realize that these legendary patterns were an accumulation of innumerable stars, but in any case astronomers from Aristotle to Copernicus and beyond regarded all the fixed stars as existing far behind the other celestial bodies.

Galileo was probably the first to perceive a hitherto unseen world of fixed stars behind what appeared to the naked eye: 'Beyond the stars of the sixth magnitude you can see through the telescope myriads of other stars invisible to the naked eye, and they are so numerous as to be barely credible', he relates. But some years before the first telescope was put into an astronomer's hands there was one man whose visionary intellect alone had enabled him to shatter the age-old crystalline spheres in which the fixed stars were thought to rest, and to provide for the first time a glimpse of what was to become astronomy's main concern. He was Giordano Bruno, a Dominican who fled the monastery at the age of twenty-eight and, a restless nomad, proclaimed his pantheistic, Copernican philosophy of enthusiasm in Geneva, Paris, London, Wittenberg and Prague. His astronomy of the fixed stars is prefaced by a passionate song of praise. For the first time, a picture of boundless space and the limitless quantity of stars—a picture which philosophers such as Nicolaus Cusanus had hinted at—powerfully unfolds itself.

'There are countless suns and countless earths all rotating round their suns in exactly the same way as the seven planets of our system. We see only the suns because they are the largest bodies and are luminous, but their planets remain invisible to us because they are smaller and non-luminous.

The countless worlds in the universe are no worse and no less inhabited than our earth. For it is utterly unreasonable to suppose that those teeming worlds which are as magnificent as our own, perhaps more so, and which enjoy the fructifying rays of a sun just as we do, should be uninhabited and should not bear similar or even more perfect inhabitants than our earth. The unnumbered worlds in the universe are all similar in form and rank and subject to the same forces and the same laws.

Impart to us the knowledge of the universality of terrestrial laws throughout all worlds and of the similarity of all substances in the cosmos! Destroy the theories that the earth is the centre of the universe! Crush the supernatural powers said to animate the world, along with the so-called crystalline spheres! Open the door through which we can look out into the limitless, unified firmament composed of similar elements and show us that the other worlds float in an

DONATI'S COMET ON 29TH SEPTEMBER 1858

On 2nd June 1858 the Italian astronomer Giovanni Battista Donati discovered a small, diffuse nebula in the sky. When this nebula approached the sun in August, it showed traces of a tail; and in the two following months one of the most spectacular comets of all time traversed the night sky. Its tail stretched across an entire quarter of the heavens. Then it disappeared southwards, and finally only the head of the comet was visible as a haze. George Phillips Bond, the son of the founder of the Harvard College observatory in Cambridge, Massachusetts, spent those nights at his telescope using this opportunity to make a thorough study of the comet's structure. He attached to his description the drawing shown in an enlarged version on the left. We can discern the luminous, starlike head of the comet, a shape with a diameter varying between 6 and 60 miles, and in front of it a curved hazy shell of light, the coma. Here certain substances, apparently gases, are expelled from the glowing nucleus of the comet; and as the comet races through space they curve back into its tail which is most strongly developed on the side which is touched by the sun's rays. Its Italian discoverer was able to examine spectra of comets at about the same time as the Englishman, William Huggins, in 1865. They showed that comets carried carbon compounds, that is, terrestrial substances, on journeys through the solar system which lasted decades or even centuries.

ethereal ocean like our own! Make it plain to us that the motions of all the worlds proceed from inner forces and teach us in the light of such attitudes to go forward with surer tread in the investigation and discovery of nature! Take comfort, the time will come when all men will see as I do.'

Giordano Bruno was seized by the Inquisition in Venice and burned alive as a heretic in Rome on 17th February 1600, to the joy of the Aristotelian scholastic philosophers. What he had proclaimed ran contrary not only to orthodox Christian teaching, but also to the Aristotelian doctrines of the unity of the world, and whatever was not found in Aristotle could not be true.

The time foreseen by Bruno did arrive, as always happens with those who oppose the narrow view of orthodoxy with a broader outlook. It was slow in coming and was more critical in spirit than the visionary Dominican. It was heralded by the great maps of the sphere of fixed stars with which Flamsteed, Johannes Bayer and others attempted to chart the inaccessible. It was also heralded by the philosophical conversations of the late seventeenth century when the problem of the plurality of worlds, the structure of the universe, the habitability of the stars became the fashionable topic of the salons. Among its earliest achievements were the cosmogonic theories of Kant and Laplace (*see* p. 11), based on Newton. For a long time the centre of the sphere of the fixed stars was sought in a central sun, then in Sirius; Lambert sought to place it in the nebula of Orion, Mädler sought it in the Pleiades group. William Herschel declared it had always been the ultimate aim of his researches to discover the structure of the heavens, and he did in fact at the end of the eighteenth century lay the foundations of an understanding of the Milky Way with the aid of his reflecting telescopes. He could already distinguish nebulae from star clusters. He opened the way for those gigantic observatories, centres for spectral investigation and radiotelescopes from which emerged the modern picture of the universe. In 1801 Piazzi and others discovered that asteroids also revolved in the planetary system, ranking according to size between comets and a very small planet. Gaseous nebulae were also investigated and it was established that there are floating in space strongly agitated clouds of interstellar dust, diffuse matter of the universe which might one day solidify to nebulae which would in their turn form fresh stars by the law of gravity. Now as always the astronomy of the fixed stars is concerned with inaccessibly remote, gigantic objects, the inbridgeable gulf is bridged, and Giordano Bruno's dream is realized: 'Open the door through which we may look out into the limitless, unified firmament.'

A STELLAR PATHWAY AMONG THE NIGHT CLOUDS

The one-time sailor, Thomas Wright, author of *An Original Theory and new Hypothesis of the Universe* (1750) shows us a sector of the system of fixed stars between clouds parting like a curtain in front of a sacred shrine: it includes stars clearly grouped into three categories according to their luminosity.

PROSPECTUS INTRA CAMERAM STELLATAM.

THE ROYAL OBSERVATORY AT GREENWICH AT THE TIME OF FLAMSTEED

The view of the Thames through the door leading to the balcony explains why this observatory was created: a shipping nation engaged in world-wide commerce needed maps which gave the precise position of the stars and other data. England's sailors needed such maps as these as aids to navigation. Compared with the Paris observatory (*see* p. 328) the equipment of the Royal Observatory at Greenwich was very modest; the position of the stars was mainly determined by a quadrant (left) and a sextant; a number of large clocks and two telescopes were also available, one of them of a 10-foot focus and a screw thread to adjust the height (right). Nevertheless, its first director, John Flamsteed, using a number of additional instruments, was able to do work of fundamental importance. It was time for some stock-taking of the number of fixed stars. In 1677 Halley, who was then working on the island of St Helena, had taken great pains to determine 341 stellar positions in the uncharted southern skies. In 1763 Nicolas de Lacaille listed a total of 10,000 positions. But Flamsteed's *Historia coelestis britannica* had already been published in 1725. In it he had marked all stars down to the seventh magnitude which were visible over Northern Europe. Long before that, Ptolemy had produced a catalogue of 1,026 stars, based on Hipparchus, and drafted instructions for drawing up celestial charts; and in the eighteenth century Flamsteed carried on the practice of compiling star catalogues.

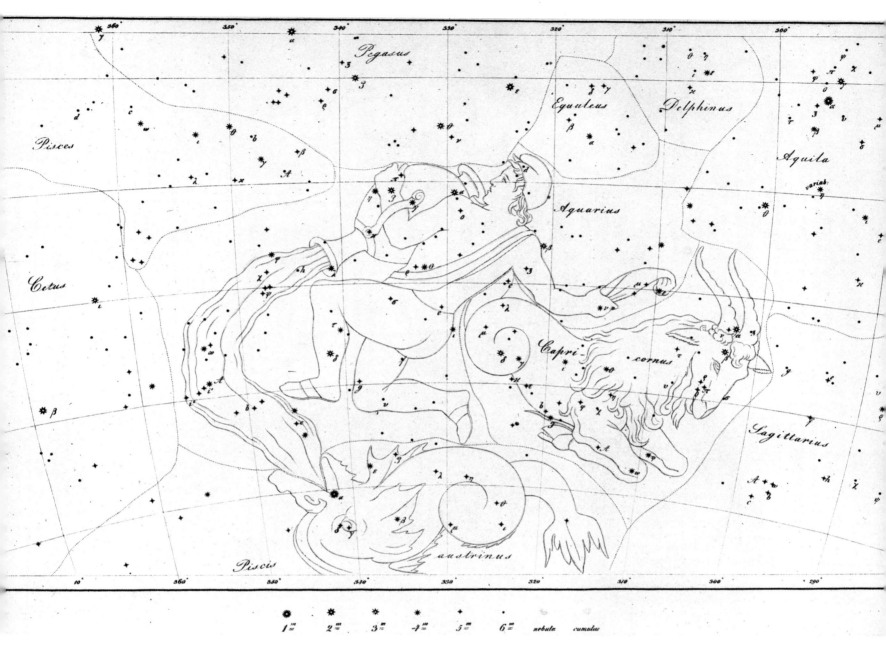

A Page from the 'Neue Uranometrie' by Friedrich Argelander (1843)

In the nineteenth century a professor of astronomy in Bonn, Friedrich Argelander, continued the series of invaluable stellar charts which had become an essential means of orientation. He relied more on the eye than on the still imperfect photometer. He entered in his grid the stars of the Central European firmament, cataloguing them according to their degree of brightness. They were classified up to those of the sixth magnitude, which were still just visible to him. Argelander accepted Flamsteed's stellar positions in the constellations; one of the Pisces, Aquarius and Capricorn can be discerned; and from Johannes Bayer's *Uranometria*, published in 1603, Argelander reverently took over the Greek letters, adding his own Latin ones for new stars.

Between 1852 and 1859 he and his collaborators carried out the so-called *Bonner Durchmusterung* of the northern sky, a scrutiny which catalogued the position of nearly 458,000 stars. The stellar system seemed to become immeasurable as the years went by.

Argelander, with many other pioneers, joined in the quest for the much sought-after objects of the new astronomy of the fixed stars: he inserted in his chart nebulae—the faint, cloud-like patches of light in the heavens—and star clusters (cumuli), but especially the mysterious 'variable stars' (top right, 'variab.'). So his chart was among the first to include those stars which emit enormous energies and intense lightly, usually at regular or irregular intervals.

THE PLURALITY OF THE WORLDS ACCORDING TO LEONHARD EULER

Left: THE WRITER FONTENELLE INITIATES THE MARQUISE DE G. INTO THE NEW TEACHINGS OF ASTRONOMY

A summer evening in the garden of a French château. There is disagreement among the philosophers about the stars in the night sky. Some still adhere to Ptolemy's closed system which regards the earth as the centre of the universe. Descartes has cautiously decided in favour of Copernicus; he accepts the sun as the central star, and explains the satellites' rotation round the planets and that of the planets round the sun by what he assumes to be vortices which stir up the moist matter filling the universe. A short time before, there had been the discoveries of Saturn's ring by Huygens and of this planet's four satellites by Cassini—all of which supported the Copernican theory. Are there 'men' on the satellites and planets? Is there more than one earth, and are there perhaps other solar systems beyond the known one? Everybody was asking such questions. In the following century Voltaire's Zadig took up the theme by declaring:

'The Supreme Being has created thousands of worlds, and not one resembles the other.' Voltaire's enlightened view of the 'modern' cosmos spread amongst intellectuals of Europe. Fontenelle was a forerunner of this enlightenment. His conversations with the Marquise de G., in which he drew a highly optimistic picture of habitable planets and satellites, appeared in twenty-eight constantly revised editions; translations in English, Italian and Russian followed. 'Can one be a man of honour yet take no note of astronomy?' J.-F. Bernard reproached those who persisted in ignorance. *Above:* Leonhard Euler from Basle, too, applied his high mathematical gifts to the motions of celestial bodies. In particular, he investigated the forces which accounted for their interactions; they were the most difficult to determine mathematically. His picture gives a schematic outline of the new concept of the cosmos but does so much more clearly than Fontenelle: the solar system is but one of many in the heavens; yet all of them obey the same tremendous forces of gravitation, just as the comets do in their orbits.

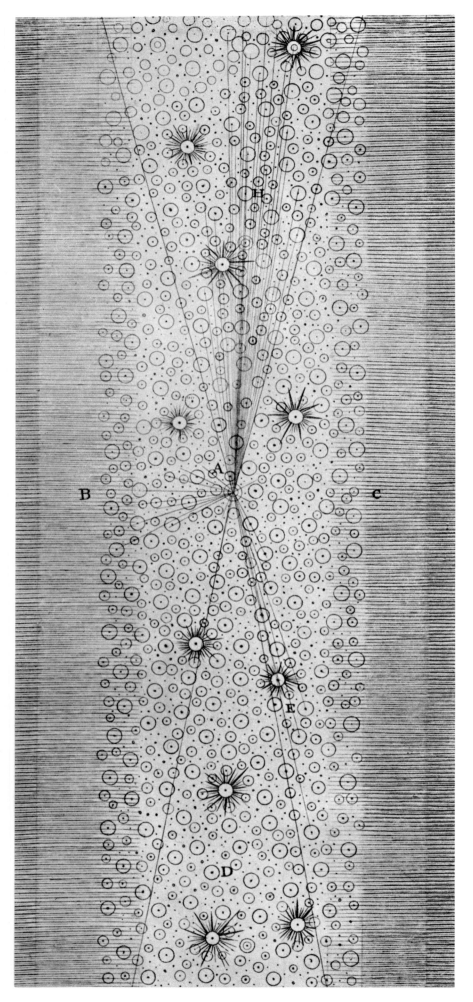

In the middle of the eighteenth century, Thomas Wright began to enquire into the nature of the Milky Way. He had spent many nights at sea observing this belt of stars; and with his own eyes he had seen it stretch far out into space, right round the earth. When better days came to this once poor sailor in England he made telescopic observations to supplement what he had seen during his voyages. In 1750, still striving to put his views into the right words, Wright published his *Original Theory or new Hypothesis of the Universe*. He used as his maxim for this work the words of the early Romantic poet Edward Young: '*One* sun by day, by night ten thousand shine, / And light us deep into the Deity.' The belt of starlight girding the heavens could only be a vast host of stars, circling with the earth in a kind of irregular cosmic disk round a focal point. Seen from A (left, in the centre) they seem to vary in magnitude and to be closely packed despite the enormous distances separating them. Undoubtedly the sun and the planets moved in the midst of this system of bright, distant bodies whose rays of light impinged upon the observer's eye. In 1761 a one-time tailor's apprentice from Alsace, Heinrich Lambert, later to become a Member of the Prussian Academy, revived this idea about the creation of the universe in his *Kosmogonische Briefe*: 'I am undecided whether or not the visible Milky Way is but one of countless others all of which form an entire system. Perhaps the light from these infinitely distant galaxies is so faint that we cannot see it.'

Wright's work (*see* p. 11) supplied Immanuel Kant with ideas for his theory of the origin of the world, but it was not until the end of the century that William Herschel placed researches into the Milky Way and the fixed stars on a firm scientific basis. With his new, powerful reflecting telescopes he carried out methodical 'gaugings' of the heavens, counting and comparing the stars in hundreds of celestial regions and estimating their total at thirty millions—an enormous number for Herschel's days. By 1802 he had located 2,313 nebulae and 197 star clusters. The frontiers of the universe receded ever further before this devoted star-gazer, who reckoned that the most distant galaxies were about two million light-years away. To him the Milky Way was undoubtedly a vast accumulation of suns, intermingled with nebulae and spread within an immensely wide but fairly thin 'layer'. Our Sun and its satellites were moving about near the centre and seemed somewhat lost. By way of explaining the Milky Way, Herschel published this diagram (opposite) in 1784. An observer standing on earth at point S amidst this huge, stratified assembly of stars stretching from *a* to *b,* will see the stars in greater or lesser density depending on the direction in which he is looking. In any case they will appear to be projected against the celestial sphere like a luminous belt of stars (ACBD), whereas the stars which are far away from the stratified Milky Way will seem to be scattered across the remainder of the heavens (MNVW). But if a second, smaller layer of stars (*pq*) divides off from the first, perhaps not far from point S, it will appear to the eye as a narrower, luminous belt of stars (PRRP) against the celestial sphere. This second layer will seem to be peeling off at first, then to be returning to the first stratum—in short, forming one of the branches of the Milky Way. In this manner Herschel sought to teach his contemporaries gradually to find their bearings in the increasingly complex structure of the universe.

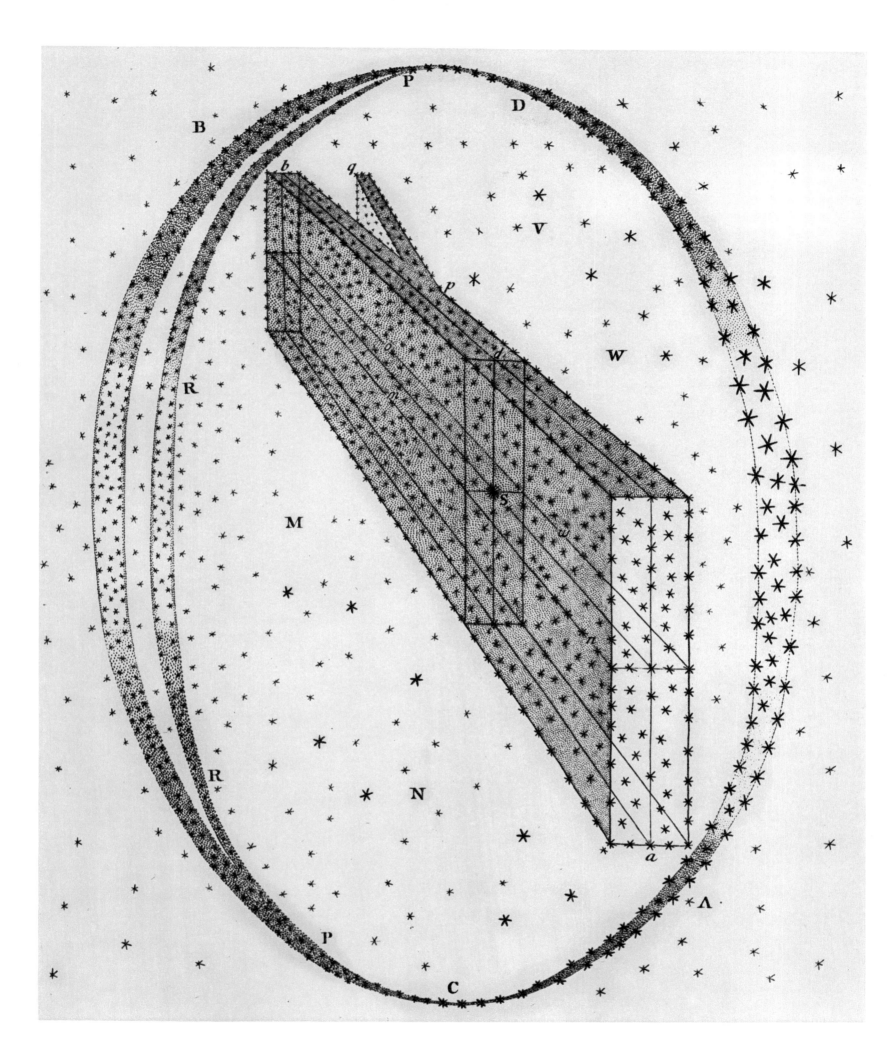

JOHN F. HERSCHEL'S REFLECTING TELESCOPE MOUNTED AT THE FOOT OF TABLE MOUNTAIN (1834)

Left: THE UNITED STATES BEGINS TO TAKE PART IN STELLAR RESEARCH

In the late nineteenth century, observatories of prodigious size began to be erected under the clear skies of the mountains of California. Their construction was financed by vast funds, and American astronomers using astonishing instruments probed deeper into the inaccessible remoteness of the fixed stars than any of their predecessors. The observatories of Mount Wilson and later of Mount Palomar became centres of research. Another one (left) was the Lick observatory on Mount Hamilton in California; a foundation by the millionaire James Lick provided the necessary money. Beneath the giant dome, we see one of the world's largest refractors. At the same research centre, with the help of the Crossley telescope, three of Jupiter's satellites were discovered, the velocities of certain star clusters determined, and photographs revealed hitherto unseen irregular nebulae. Edwin P. Hubble, 'the astronomical Columbus of America', who was the director of the Palomar observatory, carried on William Herschel's work. He set everyone the great task of discovering the 'shape of our universe'.

Above: In 1834 William Herschel's son took the highly efficient twenty-foot reflecting telescope, built by his famous father, to Cape Town. He set it up near the mountains in the orchard of a country house. He made pencil drawings of numerous double-stars, nebulae and star clusters in the southern hemisphere with almost miraculous precision.

THE ORION NEBULA, DRAWN IN 1834 BY JOHN F. HERSCHEL

In the winter months the bright constellation of Orion appears in the northern sky above the southern horizon. At other times it can be seen south of the equator. Herschel observed it from an ideal vantage point: 'This was situated on the last, gently inclined slope of Table Mountain, on its eastern side, protected from dust by oak trees and pine woods and partly sheltered against the wind; it was distant enough from the mountain and the clouds which disturb the view as they mass around its summit, yet near enough to the sides of the mountain to be protected against the strong south-east winds during the cloudless months.' It was here that this drawing of the Orion nebula was made—an amazing achievement of eye and hand. Herschel began by entering the larger stars as black dots of varying size, all the time taking precise measurements. Square inch by square inch he then proceeded to make a pencil drawing of the nebula around these points of orientation. Sometimes he used detailed sketches as a basis and the telescope had to trail the wandering star. Many weeks of hard work were needed to produce the picture with all the subtle and flickering shapes and shadings of the nebula which his eyes could perceive. In addition, he gave a description of more than 2,000 double-stars and of about the same number of nebulae and stellar clusters, many of which had never been described before. He also observed the satellites of Saturn, the sun spots and Halley's Comet which reappeared in 1835.

Three decades later Angelo Secchi published a treatise on the structure of the universe, according to which these nebulae were the places in the cosmos at which new stars could originate through condensation. 'Not so long ago it was thought that the heavens were filled only with solid stellar bodies of defined limits. Now we have discovered huge masses of gas which may be destined for the formation of other bodies—they may already be condensed but the light has not yet brought us news of this transformation! How many other secrets can there be in infinite space which we cannot fathom? Ten years ago, who would have dreamed of the marvels which the spectroscope has revealed to us?'

The Orion nebula is still one of the main objects of interest in astronomy. Spectral analysis shows the existence of glowing clouds of hydrogen in the nebula; this gas fills enormous spaces between the individual stars of the Orion constellation. In this dynamic formation dark dust and gas clouds are moving in front of the stars. Something similar can also be seen below the centre of Herschel's drawing. The irregular nebula, reproduced in a width of approximately 12½ inches, is in reality now thought to be so huge that a ray of light travelling at 190,000 miles per second, would take 150 years to cover it from end to end. Its distance from the earth is 1,500 light-years.

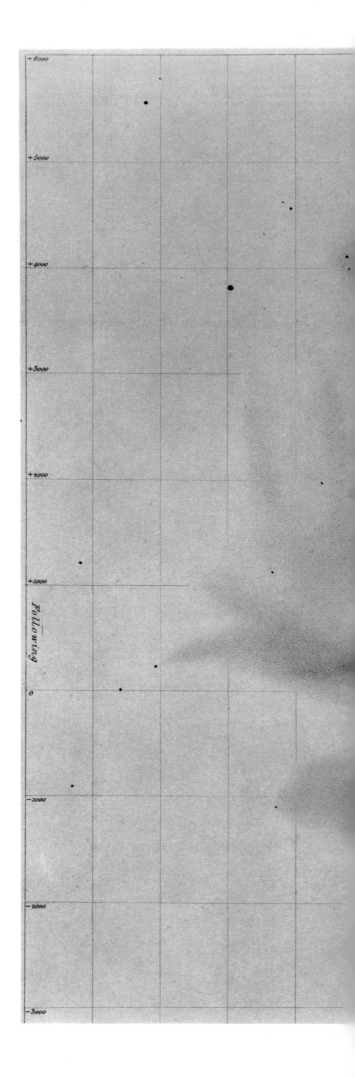

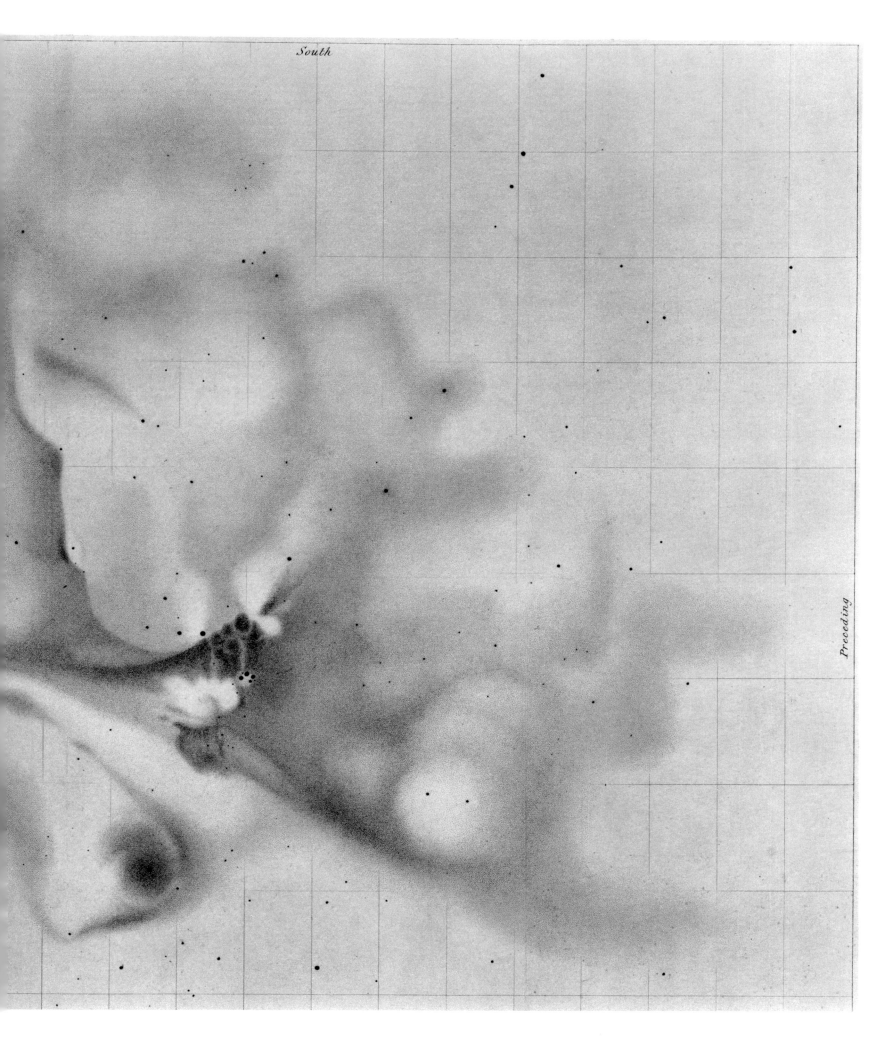

HOLY NIGHT

'When the night sky is clear, when there is scarcely a breath of air and rain has fallen, then upon seeing the infinite vastness of the heavens crowded with the countless banners and standards of the Heavenly Host and viewing it at once with eyes of our body and our spirit, it is then that we behold the invisible Sabaoth, adorned by his radiant diamond-studded mantle.' These lines are by Otto von Guericke, the natural scientist who solved the problem of the vacuum, constructed the first electrical machine and, as a politician, guided the destinies of Magdeburg through the distress of the Thirty Years' War. In those who have looked at the starry heavens 'both with the eyes of the body and the spirit', the celestial sphere has time and again raised thoughts and words to another dimension where the infinite could be seen through the finite, where the eternal appeared behind the temporal and where man grew ready for all-embracing liberating understanding of life. This is how the philosopher (and astronomer) Immanuel Kant expressed it:

'Two things fill the mind with ever-increasing wonder and awe, the more often and the more intensely the thinking mind is drawn to them: the starry heavens above me and the moral law within me.' The painter Adam Elsheimer from Frankfurt-on-Main, too, has portrayed the time when the Saviour was born to the world under the aspect of Eternity by calling upon the moon and the stars and by laying out the shimmering ribbon above the Holy Family on their flight to Egypt.

No great astronomer has remained unaffected by the power of his subject which, more than any other, appeals through the great things in nature to that which is great in man. In antiquity, the epitaph of Ptolemy read: 'I am mortal, I know, and only an ephemeral creature. But in my spirit I orbit with the wandering stars round the pole. No longer does my foot touch the earth. At the side of Zeus himself I partake of the heavenly food whose strength keeps the gods immortal.'

THE NATURAL SCIENCES

Natural history is pre-eminently a science which says: 'This exists.' Chlorophyll and gall-insects, the tubercle bacillus and infra-red rays, queen bees and quicklime, helium gas in the sun and electricity in the earth's atmosphere, all exist. They are eight discoveries from an immeasurable store of knowledge compiled by science.

This science has also entered a domain beyond the world of perception, the domain where may be found the causes of the processes animating nature: the laws determining the path of light rays or the connection between elements or the forces of heredity.

Many scientists went further behind the laws in a search for primary causes, for the ultimate rationale of nature, her true meaning. Here natural science is following in the footsteps of the ancient Greeks. With the Greeks we first encounter in its purest form this questing of the philosophic mind for ultimate causes. Is not eternal mutability the innermost essence of nature? men asked with Heracleitus. Is there no constant, permanent essence? asked the Pythagoreans. According to Empedocles, the four elements formed the permanently active principles in natural phenomena; according to Democritus, it was the atom. Thus the Greeks raised basic questions which remained part of the dialogue of mankind with nature for ages.

The creators of natural science in modern times and many others reproached the Greeks with drawing general conclusions too soon from too scanty observations. What is cold? Aristotle once asked, and gave the definition: 'It is the property uniting both similar and dissimilar.' 'Even a pile of silver and gold coins?' was Boyle's scornful retort, which thus reduced to absurdity the premature attempt to circumscribe the freezing process—the answer of the empirical to the speculative mind.

The following pictures can merely indicate extremely rapidly one or two stages along the road of those who after antiquity enquired into nature's first causes.

The Christian Middle Ages saw nature as part of creation's great plan of salvation. Actual observation of nature was unimportant; experiments like those made by Peregrinus with magnets are rare exceptions. During scholastic times Albertus Magnus summoned the aid of the greatest authority on natural science, namely Aristotle, adopting from his writings much that supported the Christian doctrine of nature. This regarded nature as a fifth gospel which revealed the divine wisdom. Plants, animals and stones were useful to man and bore testimony to a gracious providence. Nature was a starting point, not mainly for realistic investigations but for edifying mediations and in this way belief and knowledge were fused in a very intimate relationship with nature. An example of this is the story of the hare *(right)* taken from the *Physiologus,* the most popular medieval bestiary. Not until the end of the Middle Ages did a new, enquiring, empirical, experimental spirit gradually emerge. It was no longer satisfied with the information contained in the scriptures or in the works of antiquity alone. Copernicus, Galileo, Boyle, Gilbert and many others represent this attitude of mind.

When this more liberal outlook in the natural sciences hardened, again the reason was its own limited dogmas. They fill that vast graveyard of theories which contains the phlogiston hypothesis, the Neptunian theory, the doctrine of magnetic effluvia, of pre-formation, of world ether and so on. They have often attracted the world's scorn—and that of its greatest dramatist: 'There are more things in heaven and earth, Horatio, than are dreamt of in your philosophy.' 'Hamlet is no doubt right to say this', commented the sardonic Göttingen physicist Georg Christoph Lichtenberg, 'but there are also, on the other hand, things in philosophy of which there is no trace either in heaven or earth.'

Two contrary creative interpretations of nature stand out from the mass of hypotheses of recent centuries. They are somewhat loosely designated by the terms mechanism and vitalism. According to the mechanistic outlook the events in inanimate and animate nature occur as they do in machines; they are mathematically determinable and may all be explained without the necessity of assuming in them a force independent of the material world. Such a world, which could be interpreted mechanistically from the stars to the atoms, from the skeleton to human metabolism, could in fact be incorporated into a religious conception of creation, as it was by Newton and others. But the mechanistic view is most compatible either with agnosticism or thorough-going materialism, as in the case of some French philosophers, many physiologists of the late nineteenth century or the fathers of the theory of evolution. Other scientists found this interpretation of reality too narrow. In their view the unifying inner force directing and animating the entire organism, this accumulation of cells, was a life force intimately connected with it but of a non-material origin. It was impossible to imagine machines which 'arise spontaneously, are self-regulating, self-repairing, self-constructing and self-propagating' (Woltereck). Nature is pervaded by forces of a spiritual nature; this is the 'assumption' basic to the world view of Paracelsus, German natural philosophy, Goethe and many others right down to recent times.

'The mechanistic and the vitalist view should be scrapped along with all other hard and fast systems', claimed the biologist Alexis Carrel in 1935. That is not the voice of nihilism, but that of profound reverence for a material and non-material nature which has resumed her cloak of mystery in atomic physics as in the differentiated modern biology and medicine. Contradictions prove to be compatible, and supposed truths are shown to be partial truths by this new, complex, liberal mode of thought.

THE HARE

(From the medieval *Physiologus*. See text on the left.)
The hare is a good runner. When chased he flees into rocky, rising terrain. And then both hounds and hunter tire and no longer have the strength to catch him. But when the hare turns downwards on to steep slopes he cannot run so well because his front legs are too short; and the dog seizes him in a flash.
It is the same with man, when he is pursued by hostile powers, including the huntsman—the Devil. Seek the rocks and the heights of which David says: 'I will lift up mine eyes unto the hills from whence cometh my help.' For when the Evil One sees man running downwards caring only for worldly things then he seeks even more eagerly to ensnare him. But when he sees man running in accordance with God's will and seeking the true rock, Jesus Christ our Lord, then he turns back.

EMPEDOCLES LOOKING OUT INTO THE UNIVERSE ▶

In the fifth century BC Empedocles of Acragas in Sicily was the first philosopher to proclaim that there were four elements, and to interpret life in nature as a constant mixing and separating of the 'principles' of water, earth, fire and air. But this picture does not show Empedocles as history knows him. He is simply the prototype of a man who, obeying the thirst for knowledge and his inner voice, is looking out into the unknown, the unseen and the as yet unthought-of—into the infinite field of the sciences. (Painting by Luca Signorelli in Orvieto Cathedral.)

The building where Raphael has placed this imaginary assembly of noble Greek teachers with their audience and disciples appears to be a temple. Looking through a wide, open hall with two wings we see the buttresses and arched vaults of a rotunda. Its dome is not visible, but the wide expanse and soaring height of the building symbolize the prevailing spirit. The timeless powers to whose service it is dedicated are present in the shape of two deities: on the left, at the top we see a tall statue of Apollo, embodying the idea of beauty, and on the right, one of Athene, personifying wisdom. Pope Julius II, both a humanist and a great fighter for the faith, commissioned the twenty-five-year-old Raphael in 1508 to embellish some of the Vatican halls with frescoes, one of which was to pay homage to the thinkers of Greece, the first men in whose minds the restless inquiry into the ultimate origins and purposes of the world had so powerfully stirred. These were the minds which, combined with Christianity, had shaped the spirit of Europe. It was a combination which was much in evidence during the reign of this Pope, for he magnanimously overlooked the discrepancies which had so often divided Christianity and classical antiquity in the Middle Ages.

In the centre, Plato and Aristotle are seen passing between two rows of listeners. Plato, a Moses-like figure, carries his own book, *Timaios,* in his left hand. He is pointing upwards to the invisible divine realm of pure forms and ideas whose imperfect imitations are the things on earth. Only mathematics and geometry can grasp eternal values in their formulae and shapes and can indicate something of the divine, ideal design of the world. The seed of Pythagoras has ripened in the mind of his disciple Plato and has propagated itself through Ptolemy, Copernicus and Kepler. The founder of the Platonic Academy is flanked here by Aristotle, his hand not stretched upward but pointing straight ahead into the vastness of this world which Plato does not hold in such high esteem. For (as this gesture implies) thinking should not be linked to ideas but to what is real and visible, and from this it should proceed to concepts which explain nature and show the order in it. Aristotle has passed on such concepts to posterity in his theory of elements, his idea of a geocentric world, and his classification of the animals.

Among the group to the right of Apollo's feet, in his simple gown stands Socrates, Plato's teacher, the master of philosophical conversation, of creative, stimulating inquiry. He is seen enumerating various arguments on his fingers; among his listeners is the warrior Alcibiades. Just beneath him a bearded man (Pythagoras) is copying parts of the Pythagorean theories of numbers and harmony from a picture into a book. Aristotle's teachings are in the same vein; he says that the entire heavens are harmony and 'number', and the same applies to things. Later the alchemists' mystic ideas of numbers were to be based upon this theory (*see* p. 19) and it provided also a stimulant to Pansophic thought. In the group in the right foreground Archimedes or Euclid is using a pair of compasses to measure a geometrical drawing on a black board on the floor—one of those immortal instructional diagrams which have come down to our schoolbooks from the Greek scholars. The four men in the corner on the right are deeply engaged in conversation. The one with his back turned towards us is wearing an indented crown and is holding a globe in his hand. So is his partner with the strangely trimmed beard. Their topic is the earth, and the men discussing it are Ptolemy and the oriental Zoroaster, a preacher of astrological wisdom. Unceremoniously sprawled on the broad steps is the quick-witted provocative Diogenes of Sinope who coined the dictum that it is godlike to need nothing.

Everywhere we see men absorbed in thought, conversation, writing or reading, congregated around the great Greek teachers, representing, as it were, posterity which enthusiastically imbibed their philosophical truths as did Raphael and his Papal master. These teachings continued to influence also the history of science either by arousing opposition among more realistic generations or by revealing to them the depths of the real world.

'THE ACADEMY AT ATHENS'

ALBERTUS MAGNUS

Right: Joseph Needham says of the much-travelled and well-read Dominican, Albert Count von Bollstaedt, that he was beatified by both Church and Science. The Church had revered him because throughout his life he honoured God in His hierarchic Creation and devotedly did his duty as teacher, bishop and father superior of an ecclesiastical order; and natural science honoured him because as early as the thirteenth century he put forward the demand that sensory perception should be ranked higher than speculation. He described plants and animals in their natural surroundings from the viewpoint of the biologist. He was a pioneer in the work of incorporating the ideas of his model, Aristotle, into the system of Christian philosophy, in which he also managed to find room for many a fanciful theory of astrology and alchemy.

THE MEDIEVAL IMAGE OF THE WORLD

Left: Wherever nature is incorporated in the theological *summae* of St Thomas Aquinas or in such encyclopaedic works as the *Buch der Natur* (1350) by the Regensburg canon, Konrad von Megenberg, it seems to be part of a hierarchy embracing everything from the highest to the most lowly, created by God. This is also reflected in the picture of the Creation by an unknown Flemish artist, probably painted about 1570. Fixed stars and planets appear high above the clouds; sun and moon are moving across the skies—and all of them are circling the earth fixed in their invisible celestial spheres. Nature on earth, however, is divided into three realms, each of which is further sub-divided into smaller hierarchies. Minerals are piled high into mountains or grow as crystals in the interior of the earth; plants are classified, in accordance with ancient patterns, into trees, shrubs and the manifold species of herbs; in the animal kingdom the classes are determined by the creatures' habitats; they are divided into land animals down to the snake, and into birds and fishes. The great hierarchy is continued into the transcendental world, with the angels in the sight of God and those who, on the left in the cloud, plunge down into the metaphysical realm of the Evil One. But everything is part of the Creation; God himself is seen standing in the centre of the picture. The earth is the place where man can attain the salvation which the first man and woman forfeited (this story is told in a number of scenes in this picture). The medicinal plants, stones and animals all point to a divine design in the world, as do those fabulous creatures which were a constant feature of medieval stories.

From the late Middle Ages until the seventeenth century European thought includes mystical trends which could well have been based on the main principle of Hermes Trismegistos: 'The things beneath are like unto those above, the things above are like unto those beneath, and thus is the miracle of one single thing enacted.' In this world of ideas, which we might sum up, as did W. E. Peuckert, under the name of 'Pansophism', all is intertwined: ancient secret teachings and Christian thought, gnosis and popular belief, astrology and alchemy. Some important men drew their mystical wisdom of the earth and the heavens from this source: Paracelsus and Jakob Böhme, Pico della Mirandola, the French alchemist Nicolas Flamel, the English theosopher Robert Fludd, and many others.

In 1618 the copperplate engraver Matthäus Merian the Elder produced a philosophical picture for instructional purposes (opposite). Nature appears as a place full of allusions to mysterious interrelations. At the bottom are four globes representing the four elements of which the substance of the world is made: on the left, beneath the wings of Phoenix there is fire and air; on the right, below the eagle's pinions, water and earth. In the centre, we see the trees of the magical garden of alchemy. Seven big trees bear the signs of the planets, which coincide with those of the seven metals allied to cosmic powers (see p. 26). In front, on the left, we see the sign of sulphur, and on the right that of mercury—those 'principles' inherent in all metals. They break forth from the earth as a flame or a spring. Both, purified and unified in the highest chemical achievement of man on earth, yield the miraculous philosopher's stone. This unity seems to be portrayed in the one-headed lion which has two bodies. The water of life is pouring from its jaws as if from a healing spring. The man in the star-studded coat, the master of alchemy, is holding axes in his hands; they are symbols of the art of analytical chemistry. To the right and left of this symbol of chemical combination are man and woman, equally destined to be united in a higher entity and equally linked to the forces of the world: the man is assigned to the sun and the lion, the woman (who is carrying grapes as a symbol of fertility) is sister to the moon and night, and to the 'hermetic' river at her feet which symbolizes the elixir of life. As in Greek mythology, the Milky Way springs from her breast. On her right is Actaeon with his star-studded antlers—for accidentally seeing Artemis bathing he was changed into a stag as a punishment.

This terrestrial world borders on a transcendental one above, whose starry sky reaches down to earth. Both are linked by a system of circles. Some bear thrice-varied ciphers from alchemistic philosophy arranged round the sign of mercury; this symbol is framed by triangular signs which combined signify 'Universe'. In the lower semicircle we see five animals: raven, swan, dragon, pelican and phoenix—indicating the phases of the alchemistic process. Above this and emitting powerful rays of light is the supreme governing Christian Trinity of Father, Son and Holy Ghost, surrounded by choirs of angels. But terrestrial man and woman are fettered to the universe: human beings belong both to time and to eternity.

Phœnix

'MAN AND WOMAN CONTEMPLATING THE MOON'

Left: REASON REVEALS THE TRUTH

The *Encyclopédie* (1751–80), the main work of the French Enlightenment, has as its frontispiece a picture of an apotheosis of Reason. She is wearing a regal crown; she makes man free and raises him to the status of final judge of Truth as unveiled by Reason. Beneath the crowned one we see a whole cascade of her allies: Theology, deposed from the summit and carrying the Bible in her left hand (to the right of her, Philosophy with the flame of the Spirit, the Science of History at her back); Physics, closely allied to Geometry; Astronomy wearing a wreath of stars; then Optics, Botany and Chemistry, and at the bottom the beneficiaries of enlightened knowledge, the practical professions. On the left, the allegorical figures of the Fine Arts, Music and the various kinds of Poetry lead the eye to Fantasy, offering garlands of flowers.

In natural science this enlightened, autonomous spirit was inclined, as was Descartes, to regard the universe as a great mechanism and living creatures as little machines, parts of a completely intelligible and quantitatively measurable nature. God's place was at the fringe of the Creation, and for men like Laplace He had finally become a superfluous hypothesis; this attitude was shared by the late nineteenth century physiologists and exponents of the theory of evolution. The 'Enthronement of Reason' is as old as science; but history from Plato to Kepler, from Faraday to Planck, relates the most varied alliances between the power of thought and those of the emotions, faith and doubt.

Above: Around the year 1800 a romantic natural philosophy was born in Germany which was a protest against the mechanistic view of nature of the rationalists. Its chief protagonists were F.W. Schelling and L. Oken. This philosophy immediately comes to life in Caspar David Friedrich's

GOETHE, DICTATING TO HIS SECRETARY JOHN (1831)

picture dating back to about 1820. A man and a woman, barely visible against the night trees, stand listening to the silence of the universe, poised, as it were, at the extreme edge between earth and cosmos. The moon rises, enveloping the earth in its gentle, wan light. Man and nature, spirit and world are one, because both are manifestations of the primeval cause of existence, of the 'soul of the universe'. The picture seems to illustrate F.W. Schelling's dictum: 'That in us which recognizes is the same as that which is being recognized.' Philosophers of this kind were looking for forces which manifested the mysterious interrelationship between everything. They assumed spiritual and not material powers to be the prime movers of the world. They form a chain of thinkers stretching from Plato and Plotinus through iatrochemistry and Pansophism to the biologists Johannes Müller in the nineteenth and Hans Driesch and others in the twentieth centuries (*see* p. 356).

Above: The name of the German poet Goethe appears time and time again in countless international writings on natural science, especially in the twentieth century. Is he quoted so often because all his life he carried out research into nature? This is hardly a valid argument, since the quotations are not usually concerned with his studies on the metamorphosis of plants, the morphology of vertebrae or the science of colours. As a rule, fundamental observations of this kind are cited: 'He who denies that nature is a divine organ denies all revelation.' 'Perhaps man as such is nothing but an attempt to achieve a higher aim.' 'It is not the senses that prove wrong but judgement.' 'It is incredible how much dead and deadening matter there is in science.' The sage of Weimar has grown into the role of a mentor who warns us against narrow-minded human attitudes towards science, reminds us of the grand aspects of life and asks that nature as a whole be reverently integrated with man's existence.

ALEXANDER VON HUMBOLDT IN HIS STUDY IN BERLIN (1845)

In 1856 the American writer Bayard Taylor visited the aged 'monarch of science' at his home in Oranienburg Street in Berlin. His account recalls the scene depicted eleven years earlier by the painter Eduard von Hildebrandt in his water-colour, which shows a small, old man, radiant with know-ledge and wisdom, seated in his study surrounded by the symbols of the great master-work of his career: a compre-hensive account of the whole earth and the cosmos 'from the nebulae to the moss on granite rocks'. During the years from 1799 to 1804, Humboldt and the botanist Bonpland had made a world-famous journey of exploration through the region of the rivers Orinoco and Amazon, and through Mexico; and in Paris Humboldt spent decades working on a description of those countries, scarcely omitting a single aspect. In 1829 he journeyed to Siberia, gathering further material; and when he was prevented from undertaking any more long journeys the earth itself seemed to come to its

explorer—whole crates full of mineral samples, books and maps, which were sent to him from all parts of the world. The over-ambitious attempt at a description of the entire world in his *Kosmos* did not go beyond five volumes (1845–62). The rising flood of specialized knowledge in the new century was beyond the powers of Humboldt who endeavoured to carry out the tasks which Goethe had set himself: to make man as a whole being deeply aware, with all the powers of his senses, spirit and heart, that he belonged to the world as a whole. 'I shook the hand (related the reverent visitor) which had touched Forster's, Schiller's, Napoleon's, Jeffer-son's, Goethe's, Cuvier's, Laplace's, Beethoven's—in short the hands of all those great men whom Europe has produced in three quarters of a century. I looked into the eyes that had seen the cataracts of Atures, the forests on the Cassi-quiare, the Chimborazo, the Amazon, the steppes of the Tartars and the Caspian Sea.'

ANIMAL FAMILY TREE (ACCORDING TO A. HEINTZ AND L. STOERMER, 1939). WALL PAINTING IN THE PALEONTOLOGICAL MUSEUM IN OSLO

1. Sporozoa. 2. Flagellata. 3. Ciliates. 4. Amoeba (a naked rhizopod). 5. Difflugia (an armoured rhizopod). 6. Foraminifera. 7. Heliozoa. 8. Radiolaria. 9. Flagellata. 10. Volvox (colony of algae). 11. Porifera (sponges in general). 12. Calcispongia or calcareous sponges. 13. Silicispongia or siliceous sponges. 14. Receptaculites. 15. Archaeocyathus. 16. Hydrozoans. 17. Graptolites. 18. Scyphozoa (Aurelia) or jellyfishes. 19. Tabulata. 20. Octocorallia. 21. Tetracorallia. 22. Hexacorallia (stony corals; 19–22: different kinds of corals). 23. Ctenophores or comb-jellies. 24. Turbellaria. 25. Cestodes (tape-worms). 26. Nematodes (threadworms or roundworms). 27. Hirudinea (leeches). 28. Polychaeta (Nereis) (regworm). 29. Oligochaeta (earthworm). 30. Rotifers. 31. Trilobites. 32. Hemiaspidae (primitive Xiphosura). 33. Gigantostraca (marine scorpions). 34. Xiphosura (kingcrabs). 35. Scorpionida (scorpions). 36. Aranea (spiders). 37. Acarina (mites). 38. Branchiopoda (Phyllopods). 39. Copepods. 40. Ostracods. 41. Cirripedes (barnacles). 42. Leptostraca. 43. Syncarida. 44. Decapod crustaceans (lobster). 45. Amphipoda. 46. Isopoda (woodlouse). 47. Onychophora—primitive. 48. Onychophora. 49. Chilopoda (centipede). 50. Apterygota (silverfish). 51. Palaeodictyoptera (primitive winged insects). 52. Protoblattoidea (primitive cockroaches). 53. Orthoptera (grasshopper). 54. Anoplura (lice). 55. Lepidoptera (butterflies). 56. Coleoptera (carabid beetle). 57. Hymenoptera (wasp). 58. Aphaniptera (flea). 59. Diptera (bluebottle). 60. Loricata (primitive molluscs). 61. Lamellibranchiata (cockle). 62. Pteropoda (strombites). 63. Opisthobranchiata. 64. Prosobranchiata. 65. Pulmonata. 66. Orthoceras. 67. Pearly Nautilus. 68. Ammonites. 69. Dibranchiata (cuttlefish). 70. Brachiopoda Inarticulata. 71. Brachiopoda Articulata. 72. Articula. 73. Bryozoans. 74. Carpoidea (extinct echinoderms). 75. Cystoidea (extinct echinoderms). 76. Crinoidea (sea-lily). 77. Asteroidea (starfish). 78. Echinoidea (sea-urchin). 79. Holothurioidea (sea-cucumber). 80. Helminthomorpha. 81. Chaetognatha (arrowworms). 82. Tunicata (sea-squirt). 83. Acraniata (lancelet). 84. Ostracodermi. 85. Cyclostomata (lampreys and hagfish). 86. Placodermi. 87. Selachii (sharks and rays). 88. Palaeoniscidea (primitive ganoids). 89. Chondrostei (sturgeon). 90. Holostei (garpike). 91. Teleostei (bony fish, mackerel). 92. Crossopterygii. 93. Dipnoi (lungfish). 94. Stegocephali (armour-plated amphibians). 95. Urodela (salamander and newts). 96. Anura (tree-frog). 97. Chelonia (tortoise). 98. Ichthyosauria. 99. Crocodilia (crocodile). 100. Lacertilia (lizard). 101. Ophidia (snakes, cobra). 102. Dinosauria. 103. Pterosauria (pterodactylus). 104. Theromorpha. 105. Aves (birds—seagull). 106. Monotremata (platypus). 107. Marsupialia (kangaroo). 108. Chiroptera (bat). 109. Rodentia (rodents, squirrel). 110. Ungulata (hoofed animals, gazelle). 111. Carnivora (beasts of prey, jaguar). 112. Cetacea (whale). 113. Prosimia (bushbaby). 114. Simia (apes, chimpanzee). 115. Homo sapiens (man). A. Primitive cell. B. Morula. C. Blastula. D. Gastrula. E. Cnidaria. F. Porifera (sponge). H. Protostomia. J. Deuterostomia. K. Tentaculata. Numbers in circles refer to extinct animals.

An inexhaustible variety of plants and animals inhabit the earth, and it is beyond the most brilliant intelligence to comprehend this plethora of living things. Biologists have portrayed the totality of living creatures in the form of a family tree ever since they learned to view the multitude of species, genera, families, orders, classes and races as the outcome of an immensely long history of nature (*see* p. 243). But family trees, too, evolve. Since Haeckel's early sketches and as knowledge advanced, they have become more differentiated and less dogmatic. This is shown by the candid question marks in our folding picture, which is an attempt to offer a pictorial survey of the most important groups of extant and extinct animals.

A wavy line separates water from land and air. The animals inhabiting the water, the element in which organic life first appeared on this earth, are far more numerous than those on land. The area above the water is dominated largely by insects, spiders and mammals, amphibious animals and reptiles. Whales and ichthyosauri (98, 112) have returned to their primary element—water. A network of connecting lines covers the picture—old evidence of an orderly, systematic mind combining with evolutionary thinking. Everything that lives, lizard and butterfly, amoeba and bat, spider and sea-urchin, fish and man, is brought together by affinity of shape and history, is linked with the whole, and forms within the whole, a number of main branches of the animal kingdom. We note the echinodermata (74–79), the crustaceans (38–46), the unicellular beings (1–8) and so on. It is especially within such categories that life, with its tremendous urge to create, has produced an infinite variety of forms which are all adapted to their surroundings. People have asked whether living creatures do not constitute a whole series of family trees, independent of each other. But there are good reasons to believe that not only the animal kingdom but also the realm of plants springs from a common root. It is not easy to portray the world of the original organisms from which all others are said to have evolved. That world lies far behind the oldest fossils and the divisions of the animal world into its major groups. This is why the age-old, archaic individual ontogenesis has been shown as the representative of original organisms in the illustration. It presents the stages of development of all multicellular beings from the first division of the egg-cell onwards (*see* p. 236ff.). At the bottom, centre, we see a reconstruction of the original cell with nucleus and plasma; branching off to the right is the world of those organisms which consist of a single cell but one that is already capable of specific actions. To this group belong certain flagellates (9), which contain chlorophyll. Beyond the green colony of algae volvox (10) they point to the emerging realm of plants. Some modern scientists are inclined to go further back from the original cell to the viruses and to inorganic substances; they are prepared to consider the origin of amino acids under the impact of electrical discharges from the earth's original atmosphere, and interpret them as the first components of life in accordance with the theory of the American scientist, Stanley Miller. But the original cell of all multicellular creatures evolves through division via forms B and C into gastrula D,

as Haeckel, O. Hertwig, F.M. Balfour and others have taught. It is from this stage that the two branches of the cnidaria (E) and the fungi (F) are derived, which even in adult stage do not proceed beyond this primitive multicellular gastrula phase. Two, more highly developed basic forms (G, I) which are post-gastrula, can be assumed to be the two basic structures which appear in the two main series of all higher multicellular animals (H, J).

The comprehensive theory of evolution is a triumph of the art of comparison. It recognized evolution, survival through transformation, as the great guiding principle of everything organic. The earlier concept was different: the assumption was that all species, since the beginning of time, were immutable units of life. But new species have evolved from the old, many have perished forever, and the history of the development of man is part of this history of nature. After bitter disputes in the nineteenth century, this view has prevailed. It is supported by many things; by fossils, by certain repetitions of earlier phylogenetic conditions in the embryo (*see* p. 259), and by the metamorphoses of species which man has achieved in breeding animals and plants; by the phenomenon of mutation, which introduces an element of intermittence into evolution (*see* p. 195 ff.), and by the comparative anatomy of homologous organs (*see* p. 215). But still in dispute are the motive forces that account for the evolution of higher species. Is there only a natural selection among the different varieties struggling for survival? Or was Lamarck right in assuming that those organs on which increased functional demands are made develop further, whereas others which are not used, as for example the eyes of cave-dwelling animals, atrophy, and that such modifications are inherited? Is the wealth of varied forms an accident and without purpose, or are organisms subject to laws of their own which predetermine the direction of their evolution? Is it not a fact that the ability of living beings to determine their forms autonomously is generally underrated?

In the days of Darwin and Haeckel the theory of evolution encountered violent opposition from Christian theologians. In those days the choice of alternatives seemed for ever clearcut: on the one hand, theology had become too rigidly dogmatic to examine seriously the sound evidence of natural science and to compare scientific truth with the truth of religion; on the other hand, some protagonists of the theory of evolution—the tolerant agnostic Darwin was not among them—forcibly fitted man, his entire spiritual sphere included, into a purely mechanistic scheme of nature and evolution. Karl Marx triumphantly proclaimed that evolution dealt the death-blow to the theory of the Creation. But in the twentieth century both sides have grown more willing to re-think and to widen their horizons. Some theologians found a deeper truth in the concept of a Creator who paradoxically endowed the world with power to develop itself in the mysterious plan of His Creation. Teilhard de Chardin puts it this way: 'God does not so much "create" things; rather does he "make them create themselves".' And many a natural scientist has learnt to distrust rash, paltry, pseudo-philosophical views in the work of some of his own fellow-scientists. It is noteworthy that both believer *and* scientist went the furthest when they did not reach a conclusion.

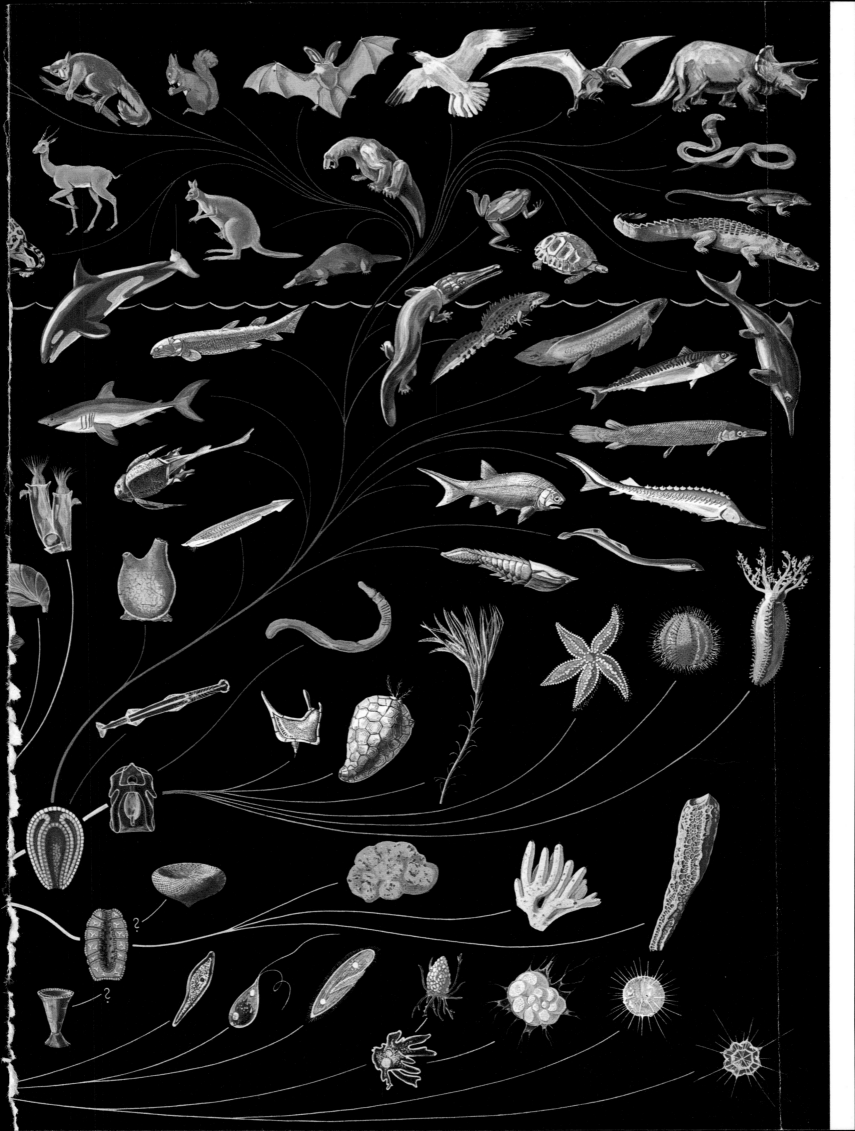

The questions about nature which Cuvier, Darwin, Haeckel posed, in an effort to unravel the history of its creatures date from late in the history of research. Others had been asked much earlier, in the initial stages of the encounter of man with plant and animal, with the substances of the earth and the stars of the heavens and with such reflections as: Where does nature bring benefit, where disaster to man? The long journey into the depths of nature began only with those who thought beyond both magic and practical experience and started to observe nature for its own sake—first recording, then comparing, classifying, investigating causes, recognizing connections and finally providing proofs through experiments and deducing various laws of nature. It was from nature that man learned the art of seeing and he learned too to distrust the evidence of his senses; for centuries nature served to train him and refine his brain power until he dared 'to re-think Creation once again'. He accomplished miracles of inventiveness in his experiments; and many scientists were ready to proclaim their findings, even though they had to risk their lives in doing so.

During these centuries of struggle for the spiritual conquest of nature, man surpassed himself time and again, and so mankind has come into one of its most glorious heritages. Science has brought us the gift of new dimensions of the real world; the microscope has revealed the minutest, invisible formations of life and the telescope has opened up to us a new firmament. Science has made all nature transparent and has given us insight into its motive forces. The history of this spiritual conquest is full of magnificent achievements. Newton's laws of gravitation and Kepler's discovery of the planetary orbits are equal to Beethoven's symphonies; and spectral analysis or the explanation of the great cycle of breathing between plant and animal are just as momentous as the building of the Parthenon.

The discovery of nature is recorded not only in the words of the explorers, it is also kept before us through the illustrations accompanying the history of this research, and the pictures make it much clearer to our senses than words could ever do. Often the illustrations merely state facts; but they also convey what is only clumsily phrased or not consciously put into words at all: emotions, or the irrational approach by man who observes and reflects upon nature. What would we know of some of nature's noblest aspects but for the illustrator's art? Think of the living, colourful beauty of its forms, the magnitude of terrestrial and cosmic landscapes, the elegance of a chain of experiments! The best pictures from the history of the natural sciences have

miraculously removed all barriers of time and space. The research of the scientist lives again before our eyes here and now (even where a painter reproduces a major event of the history of research in retrospect), and nature explored, with all its substances, plants, animals and stars, remains for ever alive and present.

In this volume we have assembled a selection from a wealth of pictorial material. The esthetic and documentary value of the pictures in this symposium and the calibre of the individual scientists' achievements must compensate for the omissions from the immense historical material which limitations of space make inevitable. Nor can our selection be expected to take into account subtle disputes about priorities in each individual case. On the other hand, the reader will often find many landscapes which are not illustrations from scientific books, like a grey, cloudy sky, a waving field of corn, or a waterfall in the mountains. Experiment and observation with microscope and telescope have produced a fragmented portrait of nature, no matter how many marvels they reveal. It is the task of these non-scientific pictures occasionally to lead the observer back to the unbroken abundance and harmony of nature. Both the scientist and the layman are liable to become lost in a one-sided science, 'where one learns more and more about less and less', as a wise saying goes. Natural science without nature has some justification. But a complete relationship between the fully integrated man and nature requires him to be ready to receive nature as a whole with his senses, mind and soul. This attitude alone makes man deeply aware that the earth is his home—and to create this spiritual experience is the ultimate purpose of natural science.

Right: Even contemporary observers of nature might benefit from occasional meditation on pictures of ancient Chinese landscapes before resuming work with the microscope, the herbarium or the test tube. What these pictures convey (the one reproduced here is by Ma Yüan-kung of the Ming period) is not scientific knowledge but the feeling of man's deep and awesome proximity to nature. Those in the West who have degraded nature to a mere object of unscrupulous exploitation have allowed this feeling to perish to their own detriment; in the East it has survived unscathed much longer. In Ma Yüan-kung's painting, trees, mountains and water appear to be mysteriously animated beings, and man is given his intended place in nature, just as nature is allotted its place in his inner world, because one without the other would not be a whole and because both reside in the same Tao, the same depth of being. This is how the Taoist Chuang-tzu puts it: 'I recognize the joy of the fish in my own joy as I stroll along the river.'

ACKNOWLEDGMENTS

The two lists that follow, one giving the names and dates of the scientists, the other the sources of the illustrations, are primarily for the reader's benefit; but they will also serve as a small token of gratitude to those to whom the author is most indebted—since this book owes its existence in the first place to the wealth of the scientists' achievements and of the illustrators' art.

In assembling and coordinating his material the author has drawn upon a wide range of mainly historico-scientific literature. From among these sources, it is only possible to select a few names for special mention. For Chemistry: J. Cueilleron, H. E. Fierz-David, F. Ferchl / A. Süssenguth, E. J. Holmyard, F. Lieben, J. Read. For Physics: A. Daumas, E. J. Dijksterhuis, G. Gamow, E. Gerland/F. Traumüller, P. Guaydier, E. Hoppe, M. von Laue, A. G. M. van Melsen, V. Ronchi. For Biology: F. S. Bodenheimer, R. Burckhardt, M. Caullery, K. von Frisch, F. W. Jessen, G. Koller, H. Linder, M. Möbius, J. Needham, G. Petit/ J. Théodoridès, A. Portmann. For the chapter on Man: K. E. Rothschuh, Ch. Singer, G. Venzmer. For Astronomy: G. Abetti, F. Becker, H. C. King, E. Zinner. For Natural Philosophy: B. Bavink, H. Dingler. For Bibliography and Iconography: G. Sarton and C. Nissen.

The libraries and collections where the author was given facilities to garner information are named in the Sources of Illustrations. He wishes in particular to acknowledge the unfailing help and cooperation he received from the heads and staff of the following: Zentralbibliothek Zurich (Prof. L. Forrer and Dr P. Scherrer), Library of the Eidgenössische Technische Hochschule, Zurich (Dr J.-P. Sydler and Mr A. Jaeggli), Medizinhistorisches Institut, Zurich (Prof. E. H. Ackerknecht), Universitätsbibliothek Basel (Dr Ch. Vischer), Department of Prints and Engravings of the Paris National Library (M. J. Adhémar) and Manuscript Collection (M. J. Porcher), Muséum national d'histoire naturelle, Paris (M. Y. Laissus), Senckenbergische Bibliothek, Frankfurt a. M., British Museum, Natural History Museum and Science Museum, London. For the planning and layout of the book the author had the benefit of the advice of Heinrich Kümpel, Zurich, who also designed the fly-leaf. The key on page 368 was drawn by Mr Kurt Hauri, Zurich. On the production side the author was well served by the staff of Imago and Regina in Zurich, to whom the book's technical quality is principally due.

SOURCES OF ILLUSTRATIONS

The numerals set against the entries provide the page numbers in this book on which the relevant pictures are to be found. Where no location is given, the works referred to are in the Zentralbibliothek, Zurich. ETH stands for the library of the Eidgenössische Technische Hochschule (Federal Institute of Technology) in Zurich.

Anonymous: Creation of a Homunculus. Page from the Schweizerisches pharmaziehistorisches Museum, Basel. 36

– Charlemagne and the *Carlina acaulis*. Codex Monacensis, icon. 26, Bayerische Staatsbibliothek, Manuscripts, Munich. 150

– A human Being breathes out his Soul. Page from the Medizinhistorisches Institut of Zurich University. 304

– Flemish Master: Creation of the World. Musée de Strasbourg. 360

Aesop: Life and Fables. Incunabula, Basel, late 15th cent. 208

Agassiz, Louis: Recherches sur les poissons fossiles. Neuchâtel 1833–43. 220

Agricola, Georg: Bermannus sive de re metallica. Basel 1530. 16

Albertus Magnus: Illustrissimi... Alberti Magni... opus Philosophie naturalis... Venice 1496. 295

– His portrait, painted by Thomas of Modena, Treviso, 1352. Photo Alinari, Florence. 361

Albinus, B. S.: Tabulae sceleti et musculorum corp. humani. Leiden 1747. 279

Alhazen: Optices Thesaurus libri VII; item Vitellonis libri X. Basel 1572. ETH. 104, 107, 297

Angoulême, Maître de Charles d': Les secrets de l'histoire naturelle. c. 1480–1500. Bibliothèque Nationale, Manuscrits, Paris. 151, 209

Apian, Petrus: Astronomicum Caesareum. Ingolstadt 1540. 338

Archimedes. Mosaic from Franz Winter: Der Tod des Archimedes. 82. Winckelmann-Programm der Archäolog. Gesellsch. W. de Gruyter, Berlin 1924. 76

– Opera, ed. by Torelli. Oxford 1792. 77

– from Walter Ryff: Bawkunst. Basel 1582. 78

Argelander, Friedrich: Neue Uranometrie. Berlin 1843. ETH. 345

Aubriet, Claude: The Swallow-Tail Butterfly and its Metamorphoses. Vélins, Muséum national d'histoire naturelle, Paris. 224

Aubuisson de Voisins, Jean F. d': Traité de géognosie. Paris 1828–35². 12

Audebert, J. B.: Histoire naturelle des singes et des makis. Paris 1797. 256

Baer, Karl Ernst von: De ovi mammalium et hominis genesi. Leipzig 1827. Universitätsbibliothek, Basel. 235

Bartholinus, Thomas: Anatomia... reformata. The Hague 1660. 283

Becher, Johann Joachim: Opuscula chymica... Nuremberg 1719. 35

Beebe, William: A Monograph of the Pheasants, III. H. F. & G. Witherby Ltd., London 1922. 266

Beer, Wilhelm: s. Mädler

Bell, Charles: The Hand, London 1833. British Museum. 215

– An Exposition of the Natural System of the Nerves. London 1824. British Museum. 292/293

– Anatomy and Philosophy of Expression. London 1844. British Museum. 294

Belon, Pierre: De aquatilibus libri duo. Paris 1553. Muséum national d'histoire naturelle, Paris. 210

– Histoire de la nature des oiseaux. Paris 1555. Muséum national d'histoire naturelle, Paris. 213

Bergman, Torbern: Opuscula physica et chemica, I. Uppsala 1779. 41

Beringer, Adam: Lithographia Wirceburgensis. Würzburg 1726. 246

Bernard, Claude. Painting by Léon Augustin Lhermitte. Sorbonne, Paris. 239

Bible, The: Old Testament: Woodcut by Johann Teufel. Wittenberg 1572. Bibelmuseum, Basel. 9

– Woodcut by Jost Ammann. Frankfurt a. M. 1564. Dept. of Prints and Engravings of the Kunstmuseum, Basel. 205

Bidloo, Godfried: Anatomia humani corporis. Amsterdam 1685. 285

Biedermann, Johann Jakob: Cascade de Pissevache. Oil painting, 1815. Kunstmuseum, Winterthur. 51

Bloch, Marcus Elieser: Naturgeschichte der ausländischen Fische. Berlin 1785–1795. 221

Bock, Christoph Wilhelm: Frederick the Great on his Deathbed (c. 1797). Germanisches Nationalmuseum, Nuremberg. 302

Boerhaave, Hermann: Sermo academicus. Leiden 1715. 288

Bond, George Phillip: Donati's Comet. In: Annals of the Observatory of Harvard University, III, 1858. British Museum. 340

Bonnet, Charles: Traité d'insectologie. Paris 1745. 223

– Recherches sur l'usage des feuilles dans les plantes. 1754. 176

Borelli, Giovanni Alfonso: De motu animalium. Leiden 1680. 80

Bourdon, Sébastien: Roman Lime-kiln. Oil painting, c. 1650. Alte Pinakothek, Munich. 46

Boyle, Robert: The Works of the Hon. Robert Boyle, III. London 1744. Science Museum Library, London. 90/91

Brahe, Tycho: Stjerneborg, in: Jan Blaeu's Grand atlas ou cosmographie blaviane, I. Amsterdam 1667. Bibl. publique et universitaire, Geneva. 215

Brown, Ford Madox: Dalton collecting Marsh-fire Gas. By kind permission of the Town Hall Committee of the Manchester Corporation, Manchester. 69

Brunfels, Otto: Herbarum vivae icones. Strassburg 1530. 153

Buch der Heiligen Dreifaltigkeit, Das, *c.* 1430–1440. Library of Germanisches Nationalmuseum, Nuremberg. 27

Buffon, Georges L.: Histoire naturelle. New ed. Paris 1769–1772. ETH. 10

Burdach, Karl Friedrich: Vom Baue und Leben des Gehirns. Leipzig 1819. 291

Burian, Zdenek: Marshy Wood of the Carboniferous Period. Painting, 1950. Senckenberg-Museum, Frankfurt a.M. 186/187

Caldani, Leop.: Icones anatomicae. Venice 1801–1810. 281, 290

Camper, Petrus: Verhandeling over het natuurlijk verschilder wezenstrekken in menschen van onderscheiden landaart... Utrecht 1791. 295

– Kleinere Schriften... I. Leipzig 1784. 228

Cardano, Geronimo: Metoposcopia. Paris 1658. 295 (Fig. 1 top)

Carus, Carl Gustav: Über Grund und Bedeutung der verschiedenen Formen der Hand in verschiedenen Personen. Stuttgart 1846. Universitätsbibliothek, Basel. 248 (top row)

Cassini, Jacques: Tables astronomiques du soleil, de la lune, des planètes. Paris 1740. ETH. 328

Cellarius, Andreas: Harmonia macrocosmica. Amsterdam 1661. 308/309, 311–313

Champollion, Jean Francois: Monuments de l'Egypte et de la Nubie, IV. Paris 1835. Universitätsbibliothek, Basel. 269

Cheselden, William: Osteographia, or the Anatomy of the Bones. London 1733. British Museum. 214, 278

Chladni, E.: Entdeckungen über die Theorie des Klanges. Leipzig 1785. 142

Chun, Karl: Wissenschaftliche Ergebnisse der deutschen Tiefsee-Expedition 1898/99, X, 4. Jena 1902 ff. ETH. 261

Cloquet, Jules: Anatomie de l'homme. Paris 1821-1831. 283

Codex Egberti (*c.* 980). Stadtbibliothek Trier. 296

Commission scientifique du Nord en Scandinavie 1838–40, Voyages de la (ed. Paul Gaimard, Paris s.a.). 126

Cook, James: 133 plates and 51 maps of his travels. Copper engravings by I.S. Klauber and others, Dutch edition, s.l. (1800). 161

Crookes, William: Model of the Periodic System of the Elements. British Crown Copyright. Science Museum, London. 72 (bottom)

– Strahlende Materie, oder der vierte Aggregatzustand. Leipzig 1879. 143

Curtis, William: Flora Londinensis. London 1771 ff. Victoria and Albert Museum, London. 166

Cuvier, Georges: Recherches sur les ossements fossiles. Paris 1812 ff. 247 (top), 248

– Cuvier lecturing in the Jardin des Plantes. Lithograph. Muséum national d'histoire naturelle, Paris. 250

– The new Palaeontological Gallery in the Jardin des Plantes. Illustration, Paris, 21 March 1885. 248/249

Dalton, John: Ein neues System des chemischen Teils der Naturwissenschaft. Berlin 1812–1813. 70

Dante: La Divina Commedia. Illustration by Gustave Doré. Milan 1869[2]. Prints Coll. of the ETH. 103, 127

Darwin, Charles: Mount Sarmiento, Tierra del Fuego (1834). Watercolour by Conrad Martens in the possession of Commander John Smyth, OBE, RN, London (detail). 254

– Darwin's study. The Century Magazine. New York 1883. British Museum, London. 255

– Portrait as an old man (1881). From Francis Darwin: The Life and Letters of Charles Darwin. John Murray, Ltd, London 1887. 258

Desaguliers, John Theophilus: De Natuurkunde uit Ondervindingen opgemacht. Amsterdam 1751. 81

Description de l'Egypte, IV. Paris 1822[2]. 147

Descartes: s. s'Gravesande

Dioscurides: Materia medica. Manuscript of the 9th cent. Bibliothèque Nationale, Manuscrits, Paris. 148

– Dedication page in the Anicia Juliana-Codex of the Materia medica (*c.* AD 512). Österreichische Nationalbibliothek, Vienna. 149

Dohmen, Wilhelm: s. Pflüger

Du Bois-Reymond, Emil: Untersuchungen über tierische Flektrizität, I. Berlin 1848. 240

Dudley, Robert: Awaiting the Reply... Oil painting (1866). Metropolitan Museum of Art, New York. 138

Duhamel Du Monceau, Henri: Traité des arbres fruitiers, I. Paris 1768. 179

Duret, Claude: Histoire admirable des plantes et herbes esmerveillables... Paris 1605. 152 (left and right)

Ecker, Alexander: Icones physiologicae. Leipzig 1851. 236

Ehrenberg, Christian Gottfried: Die Infusionstierchen als vollkommene Organismen, Atlas. Leipzig 1838. 263

Elsheimer, Adam: The Flight into Egypt. Oil painting. Alte Pinakothek, Munich. 354

Erdl, Michael Pius: Die Entwickelung des Menschen und des Hühnchens im Ei. Leipzig 1845. 300 (Fig. bottom right), 301

Euler, Leonhard: Theoria motuum planetarum et cometarum. Berlin 1744. ETH. 347

Eustachius, Bartolomeo: Tabulae anatomicae (*c.* 1552). Amsterdam 1722. 289

Fabricius ab Aquapendente, Hieronymus: De formatione ovi et pulli. Padua 1621. 234

Faraday, Michael: Faraday working in his Chemical Laboratory. Watercolour by Harriet Moore, 1852. The Royal Institution, London. 54

– Lecture in the Royal Institution. Colour lithograph by Alexander Blaikley. The Royal Institution, London. 136

– Sketches from diaries. By kind permission of the Royal Institution, London. 137

Figuier, Louis: Les merveilles de l'industrie, II. Paris 1873–76. British Museum. 66

– Les merveilles de la science, I. Paris 1866. Universitätsbibl. Basel. 89, 130

Flamsteed, John: The Royal Observatory in Flamsteed's Time. Etching. Photo Science Museum, London. 344

Flammarion, Camille: La fin du monde. Paris 1893. Bibliothèque Nationale, Paris. 94

Flechsig, Paul: Gehirn und Seele. Leipzig 1896[2]. Universitätsbibl., Basel. 295

Fludd, Robert: Tractatus secundus de naturae simia seu technica macrocosmi historia... Oppenheim 1618. 298

Fol, Hermann: Recherches sur la fécondation. Paris 1879. 236 (top)

Fontana, Dom.: Della trasportazione dell Obelisco Vaticano. Rome 1590. 82

Fontenelle, Bernard le Bovier de: Entretiens sur la pluralité des mondes. Oeuvres diverses, I. The Hague 1728. Universitätsbibliothek, Basel. 346

Fouqé, Ferdinand: Santorin et ses éruptions. Paris 1879. 64 (bottom)

Fragonard, Alexandre-Evariste: Volta demonstrates his Pile to Napoleon. Private collection. Photo Wildenstein, Paris. 132/133

Fraunhofer, Joseph: Neue Modifikationen des Lichtes... Munich 1820. 115

– Solar spectrum coloured by himself. Deutsches Museum, Munich. 117

Frézier, Amédée-François: Traité des feux d'artifice pour le spectacle. The Hague 1741. Science Museum, London. 96

Friedrich, Caspar David: Man and Women watching the Moon. Oil painting, *c.* 1820. National Gallery of the Staatliche Museen, Berlin-Dahlem. 365

Fuchs, Leonhart: De historia stirpium commentarii insignes. Basel 1542. 153

Fürbringer, Max: Untersuchungen zur Morphologie und Systematik der Vögel. Jena 1888. 228 (top)

Gärtner, Joseph: De fructibus et seminibus plantarum. Stuttgart 1788–1791. 178 (top)

Galen: Frontispiece of an edition from the early 16th cent. Bettmann Archive, New York. 272

– s. Vesal

Galilei, Galileo: Opere, III. Padua 1744. 100 (right and top left)

– Robert Fleury: Galileo before the Holy Office. Oil painting, 1846. Louvre, Paris. 318/319

– Sidereus nuncius. Venice 1610. 321

– s. Gatti and Martelli

Gall, Franz Joseph: Anatomie et physiologie du système nerveux. Paris 1810–1819. 295 (Fig. 4 top and 2 bottom)

Galvani, Luigi: De viribus electricitatis in motu musculari. Modena 1792. ETH. 131

Garthe, C.: Foucaults Versuch als direkter Beweis der Achsendrehung der Erde... Cologne 1852. 320

Gatti, Annibale: Galileo and Milton. 1877. Photo Alinari, Florence. 314

Gau, F.C.: Neu entdeckte Denkmäler von Nubien... Stuttgart 1822. 13

Gauss on the Terrace of his Observatory in Göttingen. Lithograph by Eduard Ritmüller. Städt. Museum, Göttingen. 125

Genga, Bern.: Anatomia per uso ed intelligenza del disegno. Rome 1691. 271

Gesner, Conrad: Thierbuch. Zurich 1563. 211

Gilbert, William: De magnete... London 1600. 124

Goethe dictating to his Secretary John. Oil painting by Johann Joseph Schmeller, 1831. Thüringische Landesbibliothek, Weimar. 366

INDEX OF NAMES